Practical
Non-Destructive Testing

THIRD EDITION

Practical
Non-Destructive Testing

Baldev Raj

T. Jayakumar

M. Thavasimuthu

GEORGE GREEN LIBRARY OF
SCIENCE AND ENGINEERING

Alpha Science International Ltd.

Oxford, U.K.

Baldev Raj
T. Jayakumar
M. Thavasimuthu
Indira Gandhi Centre for Atomic Research
Kalpakkam, India

Copyright © 1996, 2002, 2007
Second Edition 2002
Third Edition 2007
Reprint 2008

ALPHA SCIENCE INTERNATIONAL LTD.

7200 The Quorum, Oxford Business Park North
Garsington Road, Oxford OX4 2JZ, U.K.

www.alphasci.com

ISBN 978-1-84265-375-3   1005590860

Printed in India

Foreword

The first edition of the "Practical Non-Destructive Testing" book was a leading edge and pioneering general reference for practical understanding of nondestructive testing technology. Both of the prior editions served needs that were not addressed elsewhere. This edition updates and expands the scope and adds new methods and applications. The addition of case studies enriches the content and ease in understanding practical principles, applications and use. Both past and new users should richly benefit from the sound knowledge and practical examples provided in this edition.

Practical application requires understanding the capabilities and advantages of each NDE method in order to select, compare and optimize detection capabilities. The Probability of Detection (POD) Section (Chapter 13) is an essential addition to understanding that NDE procedures are characterized by the unique capabilities for detection of flaws of different types and sizes to quantify capabilities, advantages and limitations. It is an aid to selecting and comparing the capabilities of each nondestructive testing method. POD emphasizes the importance of discipline and rigor in application to produce reliable detection results. It is integral to both assurance of structural integrity of new components, structures and systems; and to life-cycle (condition based) management of modern engineering structures.

The Total Quality Management (TQM) section provides added insight to methods of assuring the NDE methods applied will continue to perform at the required detection level. It highlights the importance and methods of materials and systems process control management and application.

Overall, the 3rd edition has been expanded and updated to provide a more comprehensive introduction to and reference to "Practical Nondestructive Testing" technology. Since introduction of the first edition in 1996, it has been widely accepted and used through-out the world.

I extend my hearty congratulations to the authors and to those who use and enjoy the benefits of the considerable knowledge and experience provided in this new edition.

Ward D. Rummel
D&W Enterprised, Ltd.
Littleton, Colorado, USA
10 December 2006

Preface to the Third Edition

'*Practical Non-Destructive Testing*' first published in 1996 has been written essentially to cover the principles, procedures, applications, limitations and codes and standards of widely used non-destructive testing (NDT) techniques, that meets the requirements of graduate students, engineers and practicing professionals. Subsequently, in the second edition of the book, a few more recently emerged techniques that found increasing practical applications have been added. These include neutron radiography, pulsed eddy current testing, low frequency eddy current testing, SQUID based eddy current testing and mechanical impedance analysis. Chapter 13 on 'Reliability in NDT' has been revised and expanded with a new title 'POD Concepts in NDT'. The latest concepts and developments in the area of POD were included in this chapter.

The revised second edition has been sold both nationally and internationally and the book has been well appreciated by the readers. However, a few readers felt that the book still does not contain adequate practical illustrations with responses to discontinuities for different techniques and also typical case studies of inspection as practical examples. Based on this feedback, we have now revised the book and added a few case studies with practical examples. A member of practical illustrations showing the discontinuity/defect indications have also been included in the third edition. These additions have been made in various chapters including Liquid Penetrant Testing, Magnetic Particle Testing, Eddy Current Testing, Radiographic Testing, Ultrasonic Testing, Acoustic Emission Testing, Infrared Thermography and In-situ Metallography. We have also added an additional section on 'Total Quality Management in Chapter 13 on 'PoD concepts in NDT', in view of its widespread acceptance and importance in enhancing the reliability of quality and its emphasis on continued improvement on a sustained basis.

The case studies / practical illustrations included in the third revision represent various industries such as nuclear, aeronautical, space, petrochemical and power industries and various materials such as austenitic stainless steel, ferritic steels and super alloys. The case studies also represent various types of flaws and defects associated with fabrication and in-service. These include welding defects, creep, fatigue, stress corrosion cracking and embrittlement. In the chapter on Eddy Current Testing, we have also included various types of eddy current probes, multi-frequency eddy current testing and remote field eddy current testing. In the chapter on Radiography, we have included microfocal radiography.

In the chapter on In-situ metallography, a few failure analysis case studies have been included.

We have also taken this opportunity to make corrections to the editorial mistakes in the second edition of the book. It is hoped that this third edition of the book is more comprehensive reflecting many practical illustrations and case studies, thus making it more interesting and attentive to the readers.

We would like to express our sincere thanks to Dr. Ward Rummel, Retired Chief Engineer, Quality Department, Lockheed Martin, Denver, USA and Currently President and Trustee, D&W Enterprises Limited, Littleton, Colorado, USA, for writing the Foreword for the third edition of the book.

We are also thankful to many colleagues from Indira Gandhi Centre for Atomic Research for their contributions to the third edition of the book.

AUTHORS

Preface to the First Edition

Non-destructive testing (NDT) of engineering materials, components and structures has steadily increased in recent years at an unprecedented rate because of the all-round thrust for improving material quality, component integrity and performance reliability. The demands for absolute safety and reliability in strategic industries like atomic energy, aerospace, defence etc. have also contributed to the growth in science and technology of NDT. Further more, there is an increasing emphasis in recent years on modern concepts like total quality management that are aimed to obtain almost defect free components. This is possible only through effective and reliable use of NDT methods.

Several effective quality assurance (QA) approaches are available for critical components in engineering structures. Pre-service QA approaches include improved design and manufacturing processes, selection of samples for destructive testing, proof testing of components, and non-destructive testing (NDT). The concept of component design strives towards greater efficiency and improved performance. Economic conditions demand stretching materials to limits of their performance. This can be achieved by employing materials with acceptable but minimum level of defects. An important aspect of the assessment of structural integrity, in power plants, petrochemical plants, nuclear plants etc. is that of nondestructive evaluation of flaws by using various NDT techniques which may remain in a fabricated component even after making it to the highest standards of quality. In-service QA approaches use NDT for on-line monitoring, periodic proof testing for requalification, for assessing continued use of component or for its timely replacement. As the plants come close to their design life, for economic reasons, it is the endeavour of the users to increase the life of various components after assessing their condition through NDT.

There are several NDT methods available for evaluation of components and structures. Each NDT method is based on a particular physical principle and has its own fields of application, advantages and disadvantages. In this book, the authors have made an attempt to discuss various NDT methods, including the five major methods, i.e. liquid penetrants, eddy currants, mangetic particles, radiography and ultrasonics in great detail. Relatively modern NDT methods such as acoustic emission, thermography etc. are also finding increasing applications in recent times for on-line monitoring of plant components. Hence, details on these techniques are also given in this book. In order to reduce the inspection costs and to achieve maximum productivity, analytical techniques such as reliability studies, statistical quality control etc. are employed. Therefore, the reader is also exposed to these concepts in this book. Another highlight of the book is an exclusive chapter on 'Selection of NDT Methods'. This chapter is written based on the vast experience of the authors. All in all, the book would be useful as a guide, and is primarily meant for professionals and technocrats in the engineering industry, who strive to increase plant's productivity, reduce shutdowns and extend life of plants. The book has been written in a simple form to ideally suit those who are new to the field of NDT but have strong necessity to utilise this technology for improving quality of component and/or plant performance.

Authors are greatful to many of their colleagues in the Division for PIE and NDT Development (DPEND), Indira Gandhi Centre for Atomic Research, Kalpakkam for their valuable contributions. Authors are also thankful to Mr. A.S. Ramesh of DPEND for readily volunteering to help in preparing the manuscript in the camera ready form, and to Mr. V. Chandraseker of DPEND for drawing the figures.

Authors are greatful to Dr Placid Rodriguez, Director, Indira Gandhi Centre for Atomic Research, Kalpakkam for his encouragement and support.

Authors also wish to record their deep appreciation to M/s Narosa Publishing House, New Delhi and in particular, Mr. N.K. Mehra, for excellent cooperation in publication of the book.

AUTHORS

Contents

Chapter 1

Non-Destructive Testing: An Introduction

An industrial product is designed to perform a certain function. The user buys a product with every expectation that it performs the assigned function well and gives trouble-free service for a stipulated period of time. Trouble free service given by any product may be termed as 'reliability'. The reliability of a machine or an assembly having a number of components depends upon the individual reliability factors of all the components. Most of the machines and systems in the modern day world, for example, power plants, chemical and other industrial plants, transport machines etc. are quite complex having thousands of components on which reliable operation and smooth performance depends. To ensure the reliability of such machines and the plant as a whole, it is important that each individual component is reliable and performs its function satisfactorily for an assigned period of time.

Reliability comes through improving the quality level of the components. The quality of products, components or parts depends upon many factors, important among them are the design, raw material properties and fabrication techniques. Quality is related to the presence of those defects and imperfections in the finished product which impair the performance level. Many defects are also generated during service. The nature of these defects differs according to the design, processing and fabrication and service conditions under which the components have to work. A knowledge of these defects with a view to detect and evaluate them and then minimising them in the product is essential to achieve improved or acceptable level of quality. An improvement in the product quality increases its reliability and in turn the safety of the machines and equipment, thus bringing economic returns to the user. There is, therefore, a need to have methods by which the defects in the products can be examined without affecting their performance.

Non-Destructive Testing (NDT), Non-Destructive Evaluation (NDE) and Non-Destructive Inspection (NDI) are the terms used in this connection to represent the techniques that are based on the application of physical principles employed for the purpose of determining the characteristics of materials or components or systems and for detecting and assessing the inhomogeneities and harmful defects without impairing the usefulness of such materials or components or systems.

NDT plays an important role not only in the quality control of the finished product but also during various stages of manufacturing. NDT is also used for condition monitoring of various items during operation to predict and assess the remaining life of the component while retaining its structural integrity. Table 1.1 describes the advantages and limitations of non-destructive testing over destructive testing. NDT enables optimum utilisation of components without sacrificing safety. The use of microprocessors for data acquisition and processing and automated devices for reliable testing have vastly improved the condition monitoring of complex components and plants. The operator dependency for routine inspection is reduced and thus the person can concentrate more on the technological aspects. The end result is the saving in time, cost and improvement in precision and reliability of the results obtained.

Table 1.1   Comparison of Destructive and Non-Destructive Tests

Destructive tests	*Non-destructive tests*
Advantages	**Limitations**
1. Measurements are direct and reliable.	Measurements are indirect and hence reliability is to be verified.
2. Usually quantitative measurements.	Usually qualitative measurements. Measurements can also be done quantitatively.
3. Correlation between test measurements and material properties is direct.	Skilled judgment and experience are required to interpret indications.
Limitations	**Advantages**
1. Tests are not made on the objects directly. Hence correlation between the sample specimen used and object needs to be proved.	Tests are made directly on the object. 100% testing on actual components is possible.
2. A single test may measure only one or a few of the properties.	Many NDT methods can be applied on the same part and hence many or all properties of interest can be measured.
3. Inservice testing is not possible.	Inservice testing is possible.
4. Measurement of properties over a cumulative period of time cannot readily be possible.	Repeated checks over a period of time are possible.
5. Preparation of the test specimen is costly.	Very little preparation is sufficient.
6. Time requirements are generally high.	Most test methods are rapid.

NDT methods range from the simple to the intricate. Visual inspection is the simplest of all. Surface imperfections invisible to the eye may be revealed by penetrant or magnetic methods. If serious surface defects are found, there is often little point in proceeding further to the more complicated examination of the interior by other methods like ultrasonics or radiography. The principal NDT methods are Visual or Optical inspection, Dye penetrant testing, Magnetic particle testing, Eddy Current testing, Radiographic testing and Ultrasonic testing.

The use of high technology in various industries, especially nuclear, defence and space has placed greater demands on the quality assurance (QA) in these industries. The specific requirements of these industries coupled with the desire for maintaining high performance standards have resulted in the development of new techniques and also the advancement of the principal techniques mentioned above. The emphasis has now shifted from detection of defects to sizing and characterisation of defects. Some of the new methods include Neutron

Radiography, Acoustic Emission, Thermography, Strain Sensing, Microwave Technique, Holography etc. Among these, Acoustic Emission and Thermography have grown to the state of applicability to plant components.

The choice of the specific method depends on many factors including availability, accessibility and suitability based on analysis and past experience. It may sometimes be necessary to use one method of NDT to confirm the findings of another. A guide to enable the choice of NDT methods for specific type of defects is given in the chapter 12 of this book.

The basic principles, applications, advantages and limitations of the important NDT methods normally used for inspection of plant components are discussed briefly in the following chapter. It is outside the scope of this book to provide detailed descriptions of the various methods. Further details on various methods may be obtained by perusing various references given at the end of each chapter.

Chapter 2

Visual Inspection

Visual inspection is probably the most widely used among all the non-destructive tests. It is simple, easy to apply, quickly carried out, and usually low in cost. Even though a component is to be inspected using other NDT methods, a good visual inspection should be carried out first. A simple visual test can reveal gross surface defects thus leading to an immediate rejection of the component and consequently saving much time and money, which would otherwise be spent on more complicated means of testing. It is often necessary to examine for the presence of finer defects. For this purpose, visual methods have been developed to a very high degree of precision. With the advent of microprocessors and computers, visual examination can be carried out very reliably and with minimum cost. Image processing, pattern recognition and automatic accept/reject choice are used when large number of components are to be assessed.

In this section, a brief discussion is made on various aids and their applications for visual inspection of plant components.

2.1 BASIC PRINCIPLE

The basic procedure used in visual NDT involves illumination of the test specimen with light, usually in the visible region. The specimen is then examined with eye or by light sensitive devices such as photocells. The equipment required for visual inspection is extremely simple, but adequate illumination is absolutely essential. The surface of the specimen should be adequately cleaned before being inspected.

2.2 THE EYE

The most valuable NDT tool is the human eye. The eye has excellent visual perception. The sensitivity of the human eye varies for light with different wavelengths. Under ordinary conditions, the eye is most sensitive to yellowgreen light, which has a wavelength of 5560 Å. The human eye will give satisfactory vision over a wide range of conditions. For this reason, eye can not be a good judge for distinguishing the differences in brightness or intensity, except under the most restricted conditions.

For visual inspection, adequate lighting i.e. about 800-1000 lux is of prime importance. The period of time during which a human inspector is permitted to work should be limited to not more than 2 hours on continuous basis to avoid errors due to decrease in visual reliability and discrimination.

2.2.1 Defects Which can be Detected by Unaided Visual Inspection

Visual inspection of a component by an experienced inspector can reveal the following information:

(a) the general condition of the component, (b) the presence or absence of oxide film or corrosive product on the surface, (c) the presence or absence of cracks, orientation of cracks and position of cracks relative to the various zones in the case of welds, (d) the surface porosity, unfilled craters, contour of the weld beads, and the probable orientation of the interface between the fused weld bead and the adjoining parent metal, (e) potential sources of mechanical weakness such as sharp notches or misalignment etc. and (f) the results of visual examination may be of great assistance to other tests.

2.3 OPTICAL AIDS USED FOR VISUAL INSPECTION

The use of optical instruments in visual inspection is beneficial and is recommended to (a) magnify defects that cannot be detected by the unaided eye and (b) permit visual checks of areas not accessible to the unaided eye. In performing visual/optical checks, it is of utmost importance to know the type of defects that may develop and to recognize the areas where such failures may occur. Magnifying devices and lighting aids should be used wherever appropriate. The general area should be checked for cleanliness, presence of foreign objects, corrosion and damage. In many cases, area to be inspected should be cleaned before examination.

2.3.1 Microscope

An optical microscope is a combination of lenses used to magnify the image of a small object. The object is placed close to the lens to obtain as high a magnification as possible. The distance from lens to object is adjusted until the object is at the depth of field of the lens and is in focus.

The simplest form of a microscope is a single converging lens, often referred to as a simple magnifier. Magnification (M) of a single lens is determined by the equation $M = 10/f$. In this equation, f is the focal length of the lens and 10 is a constant that represents the average minimum distance at which objects can be distinctly seen by the unaided eye. Using the equation $M = 10/f$, a lens with a focal length of 5″ has a magnification of two or is said to be a two-power lens (2×). The focal length of a simple magnifier and its working distance are approximately the same. The field of view is the area seen through the magnifier. The diameter of the field of view of a simple magnifier is less than its focal length. Selection of a magnifier with the proper field of view is important. For example, if a large object is to be examined, the time involved using a 20 power magnifier (with a field of view slightly greater than 9.5 mm) would be prohibitive. The proper procedure is to first use a low-power magnifier, marking questionable areas, and then examine the suspected areas in detail with a higher-powered magnifier.

Depth of field is the term used to indicate the distance a magnifier can be moved towards or away from a subject with the subject remaining in good focus (sharply defined). At other distances, the subject is out of focus and not sharply defined. Depth of field varies with the power of the lens and is comparatively greater in lower-power magnifiers, decreasing as the power of the lens increases.

Minute defects and details of fine structure on a surface can be detected more easily with the aid of microscope. The practical upper limit of the magnifying power of a simple microscope is in the region of 10×. Optical microscopes are used to evaluate with respect to shape and orientation of cracks. In the first case a low power microscope having a magnification of 2 to 20× is used, in the second case a magnification of 100 to 500× is used, and in the latter case a magnification of 1500 to 2000× is needed.

2.3.2 Borescope

As the name implies, a Borescope is an instrument designed to enable an observer to inspect the inside of a narrow tube, bore, or chamber. Borescope consists of precision built-in illumination system having a complex arrangement of prisms and plain lenses through which light is passed to the observer with maximum efficiency. The light source located in front or ahead of the object lens provides illumination for the part being examined. As the length of the borescope is increased, the image becomes less bright because of loss of light. Borescopes are available in numerous models from 2.5 to 19 mm in diameter and a few meters in length. Generally, the diameter of the borescope depends upon the diameter of the hole or bore to be inspected. The length of the borescope is governed by the distance between the available access and the distance to the inspection area. Optical systems are generally designed to provide direct, right-angle, retrospective and oblique vision. The choice of the inspection angle is determined by flaw type and location. In most borescopes, the observed visual area is approximately 25 mm in diameter at 25 mm distance from the object. The size of the visual field usually varies with the diameter, for a given magnification system.

2.3.3 Endoscope

The endoscope is much like a borescope except that it has a superior optical system and a high-intensity light source. Various viewing angles, as discussed in the case of Borescope, can be used. A unique feature of endoscope is that objects are constantly in focus from about 4 mm to infinity. Actually, when the tip is about 4 mm from the surface being inspected, a magnification factor of about 10× is achieved. The 'no-focussing' feature of the endoscope makes it much easier to use than a borescope, which needs to be focused at the inspection area. Endoscopes are available in diameters down to 1.7 mm and in lengths from 100 to 1500 mm.

2.3.4 Flexible Fibre-Optic Borescope (Flexiscope)

Flexible fibre-optic borescopes permit manipulation of the instrument around corners and through passages with several directional changes. Woven stainless steel sheathing protects the image relay bundle during repeated flexing and maneuvering. These devices are designed to provide sharp and clear images of parts and interior surfaces that are normally impossible to inspect. Remote end-tip deflection allows the viewer to thread the fiberoscope through complex and series of bends. The end tip is deflected by using a rotating control mechanism mounted on the handle. Most of the devices have a wide-angle objective lens that provides a 100 degree field of view and tip deflection of ± 90°. They all have a fibre-optic image bundle and are equipped with a focus control to bring the subject into sharp focus over a wide range of viewing distances. The working lengths are normally from 60 to 365 cm, with diameters from 3 to 12.5 mm.

2.3.5   Telescope

Telescope is used to obtain magnified images of objects at considerable distance from the eye. It is particularly useful for providing visual examination of the surface which is otherwise inaccessible. It consists, essentially, of two lenses (or lens systems) called the objective and eye piece. The telescope can be used in conjunction with a periscope for viewing a concealed surface. But, Closed Circuit Television (CCTV) is also used for the purpose.

2.3.6   Holography

Holography is the name given to the method of obtaining an accurate three-dimensional image of a given object. The process is carried out in two stages. First, a permanent record in the form of a two dimensional interference pattern is obtained on a photographic plate by means of a laser beam. The three dimensional image is then obtained from the two dimensional record, again using a laser. In this way, a picture having a high definition and free from aberrations can be obtained without the use of a camera.

Holography is used for the NDT of surfaces of highly complicated and precision components without the disadvantages of having to use a high-power microscope. In a simple operation, a hologram can provide a record of the image of an entire surface which can be readily compared with that of a standard defect free surface.

2.4   APPLICATIONS

(a) Inspection of plant systems/component for any leakage, abnormal operation etc.
(b) Misalignment of parts in the equipments.
(c) Corrosion, erosion, cracks, fracture etc.
(d) Defects in the new/repaired weldments such as gross surface cracks, lack of penetration, tear cracks, excess reinforcements, porosities, mismatch etc.
(e) Minute discontinuities with the help of optical aids in pumps, compressors, turbogenerator parts, instruments etc.

Chapter 3

Liquid Penetrant Testing

Penetrant inspection utilizes the natural accumulation of a fluid around a discontinuity to create a recognizable indication of a crack or other surface opening defect. Capillary action attracts the fluid to the discontinuity as compared to its surroundings. In order to locate the area of excess fluid (defect region), the background area must be of sufficient contrast thus leading to distinct detection of the defect on the surface.

3.1 PHYSICAL PRINCIPLES

Penetrant inspection depends mainly on the ability of liquid to wet the surface of a solid work piece or specimen and flow over that surface to form a continuous and reasonably uniform coating, thus penetrating into cavities that are open to the surface. The ability of a given liquid to flow over a surface and enter surface cavities mainly depends on the surface tension and capillary action. The cohesive force between the molecules of a liquid causes surface tension.

Capillary action is the phenomenon of rise or depression of liquid in narrow cavities. Viscosity, another factor, although has negligible effect on penetrating ability of liquid, affects the flowing ability of penetrant. Very viscous liquids are unsuitable as penetrants because they do not flow rapidly enough over the surface of a work piece; consequently they require excessive long periods of time to penetrate into fine flaws.

Visible light or ultraviolet light is required for inspection of penetrant indications. Initially, the only detection method used was the unaided observation by the eye of the inspector under visible light. The characteristics of the human eye strongly affect the perception of brightness of an indication. The nature of the light source strongly affects the perceived brightness of the coloured region being observed. Thus it is important to have proper lighting at the inspection area.

Fluorescence describes the release of light energy by some substances when they are excited by external radiation such as ultraviolet light. In penetrant inspection, when the particles in fluid are struck by the incident ultraviolet light, they are excited to a higher energy level. After being excited, each particle then, returns to the original unexcited level with the emission of light having a wave length longer than the original source. Thus the emitted light is in the visible spectrum. Because, the UV light is not normally seen by the human eye, it is also called black light. The advantages of this in penetrant inspection is that, regions holding greater amounts of the fluorescent penetrant appear very bright. When the inspection is performed in very subdued light, the regions clear of penetrant material will appear black. Due to this effect, the visibility of small indications is greatly enhanced.

A significant improvement in both the reliability and sensitivity of penetrant inspection occurred with the introduction of laser scanning devices that are able to automatically scan large areas. Lasers, being monochromatic light sources, excitation by laser shows defect indications distinctly both in form and colour. Use of laser scanners however is confined currently to laboratory testing and not yet become applicable to in-situ inspection of components in plants.

3.2 PROCEDURE FOR PENETRANT TESTING

Penetrant inspection is accomplished with the following sequence of operations (Fig. 3.1).

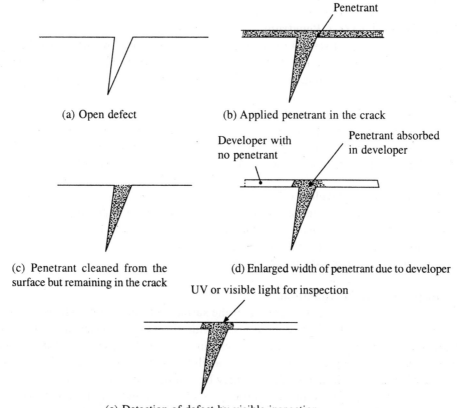

(a) Open defect

(b) Applied penetrant in the crack

(c) Penetrant cleaned from the surface but remaining in the crack

(d) Enlarged width of penetrant due to developer

(e) Detection of defect by visible inspection

Fig. 3.1   Sequence of operations in liquid penetrant inspection

3.2.1 Cleaning

One of the most important steps in the penetrant inspection procedure is the initial cleaning of the surface area to be inspected. The defect that is being sought must be open to the surface for the penetrant to enter. Scale, flakes, paint, dirt, grease and other chemicals that are not cleaned from the surface will tend to accumulate the penetrant. This leads to either masking of real indications or creation of defect indications where none exist. A satisfactory combination of solvents, brushes, rags, etchants, etc., must be chosen for a particular inspection problem. It is essential that the cleaned surface be adequately dried before the application of the penetrant since presence of any excess cleaning fluid would dilute the penetrant and diminish the brilliance of the indication.

3.2.2 Penetrant Application

The second step in the inspection process is the application of penetrant fluid to the cleaned surface. The fluid should spread freely and evenly over the surface and move into the crack. The dwel time, which is the amount of time required for the penetrant to move into the crack will vary depending on the crack size and shape characteristics and also the environmental conditions such as temperature and surface inclination. Application of penetrant may be achieved by dipping the component in a bath of penetrant liquid or by spraying or brushing. A minimum dwel time of about 20 to 30 min may be allowed after penetrant application. Larger periods may be necessary in certain circumstances.

3.2.3 Removal of Excess Penetrant

This is the most important step in the entire process. The desired result is that the surface is completely clear of penetrant. Yet, the crack/defect retains all of the penetrant that entered into it. Excess cleaning may remove the penetrant from the upper region of the defect with the result that the developer does not reach the penetrant and no defect is indicated. On the other hand, insufficient cleaning will leave a background of penetrant on the surface. Due to this, the defect will appear only slightly different from the background area. This difference in contrast may not be sufficient for the defect to be recognized. Thus, care must be exercised so that neither insufficient cleaning nor over cleaning is done.

3.2.4 Application of Developer

After removing the excess penetrant, a thin coating of developer is applied over the surface to draw the penetrant out of the crack and increase its visibility. Another important function of the developer is that it covers the surface with a colour that provides good visual contrast to the penetrant. This increases the visibility of the defect.

3.2.5 Inspection and Evaluation

The last step in the process is the scanning of the surface for indications. The scanning may be carried out under visible light conditions or with ultraviolet or laser incident light and the defect recognition may be made with the human eye or with automated optical scanners.

Each indication that appears should be evaluated. It may actually be unacceptable; it may be worse than it appears; it may be false; it may be real but non relevant; or it may actually be acceptable. Because penetrant inspection provides only indications corresponding to surface discontinuities, its severity cannot always be determined at first glance. A real indication is caused by an unacceptable flaw such as a crack. A false indication is an accumulation of penetrant caused by a drop of penetrant left on the work piece inadvertently. A non-relevant indication is the entrapment of penetrant caused at certain locations such as a press fit interface. After the inspection stage, acceptance/rejection of the component is made based on the applicable specifications and standards.

3.3 PENETRANT TESTING MATERIALS

A typical penetrant testing involves use of a variety of materials for cleaning and developing as well as the penetrant material itself. In general, the fluids involved in the penetrant process are either petroleum-or-water-based and the solvents or cleaners are selected according to the type of penetrant used.

3.3.1 Penetrants

The penetrant material consists of the indicating (tracer) dye plus the carrier (vehicle) fluid. The indicating dye may give a colour contrast with respect to the surroundings, as is the case for visible dye penetrant methods, or a brightness contrast for the fluorescent dye penetrants. For visible light penetrants, the dye is usually red in colour, while for fluorescent penetrants, the dye appears bright yellow-green under ultraviolet light.

One of the significant factors in the choice of penetrant material is the detection sensitivity. From the experimental results, it has been found that the highest sensitivity achievable is with the water washable and post-emulsifiable systems.

3.3.2 Cleaners and Emulsifiers

A cleaning fluid must act as a solvent for the material that is to be removed. For water-based penetrants, a simple water wash or rinse is suitable for the cleaning step. For petroleum-based penetrants, there are two alternate methods for cleaning the test piece. The most direct approach is to use an oil or chlorine-based solvent. Another method is to use an emulsifier that reacts with the oil-based penetrant to form a water-soluble substance, which then may be removed by water washing or rinsing.

Two types of emulsifiers, hydrophilic and lipophilic are available. Hydrophilic emulsifiers are composed of materials similar to common detergents, which react with the oil based penetrant in a way that removes the penetrant from the surface. Diffusion plays a minor role in the action of the hydrophilic emulsifiers. Lipophilic emulsifiers, on the other hand, are oil soluble and they diffuse into the penetrant, breaking down the structure so that the penetrant may be rinsed away with water. There are a number of methods used in the cleaning process such as wiping with a cloth, dipping in a tank, rinsing with a hose, or some combination of these. The choice of the cleaning process again depends on the many variables of the test, notably, size, shape and material of the component as well as the test environment. For in-situ/plant components applications, cleaning with cloth and solvent is most convenient. One of the most effective cleaning methods is the use of trichloroethylene vapour.

3.3.3 Developers

The developer material is used to enhance the conspicuity of the indication. For fluorescent penetrant, the developer background should appear black when illuminated by the ultraviolet light. The penetrant material concentrated around the defect will appear bright and appear distinct from the black background of the developer. The developer for visible dye penetrants normally creates a white background that contrasts the normal red appearance of the dye pulled out of the crack or pore.

The developer material may be one of the several types like dry powder, aqueous (wet) powder-suspension, solvent-suspendible, plastic-film, and water soluble. Application of the developer may be accomplished by several techniques such as spray, immersion, passing the part through a developer dust cloud chamber, fluidized bed and electrostatic means.

Solvent suspendible developer may be used along with both the visible light and fluorescent penetrants and is most suitable for in-situ applications on plant components. Aqueous or wet powder-suspension type developers are applied typically by immersion or spray immediately after the washing step and before the part is dried. Dry powder developer is applied directly to the part immediately after the penetrant removal process.

The highest sensitivity is obtained with solvent spray, plastic film spray, and water-soluble spray. The least sensitivity is obtained by the dry immersion and dust cloud methods.

3.3.4   Special Requirements
When using various chemicals or water penetrant materials on austenitic stainless steels, titanium, nickel-base or other high temperature alloys, it is needed to restrict the impurities such as sulphur, halogen, and alkali materials since these impurities may cause embrittlement or corrosion, particularly at elevated temperatures. Current standards indicate that impurity levels of sulphur and halogen exceeding 1% of any one suspect element may be considered excessive. However, even this level may be considered unacceptable in some cases, so the actual maximum acceptable impurity level must be decided by the user/designer. For example, halogens are required to be restricted to 25 ppm in all the chemicals used for testing austenitic stainless steels by dye penetrant methdods.

3.3.5   Test Blocks
Aluminium and steel blocks are used in quality control of penetrant testing materials. The test blocks are prepared to rigid specifications as stated in the codes.

Aluminium test blocks (75 × 100 × 8 mm) are prepared by heating at the center and water quenched so as to produce thermal shocks. Heating at the center of the block to 773K and then quenching in cold water produces cracks on the surface. Steel blocks are also used as test blocks and are prepared from AISI Type 301 or 302 stainless steel.

The blocks are used for checking the qualities of penetrants, emulsifiers and developers. Among them, the most important quality is the sensitivity of the penetrant, and is described in brief as given below. For checking the other properties such as water content and viscosity applicable codes may be referred to.

For checking the sensitivity, the suspected or faulty penetrant is applied on one half of the surface of the test block and the standard penetrant is applied to the remaining half of the surface. Operational procedure to be followed is as per the recommended procedure of the manufacturer. If the sensitivity of the tested penetrant is less than that of the standard penetrant, the penetrant being tested is considered inadequate in quality and discarded.

3.4   PENETRANT TESTING METHODS
The type of penetrant inspection method that is used depends on a number of factors. The three principal methods of penetrant inspection are discussed below:

3.4.1   Water Washable Method
In this method (Fig. 3.2), all of the materials used are water soluble. Following the initial cleaning and drying process, the penetrant applied shall be a water based fluid. Dwell time for various penetrant inspection methods is given in Table 3.1. After the dwell time, the rinse or penetrant removal step is different for various application methods. Use of large

volume of water would require facilities for adequate draining and disposal of the rinsed water.

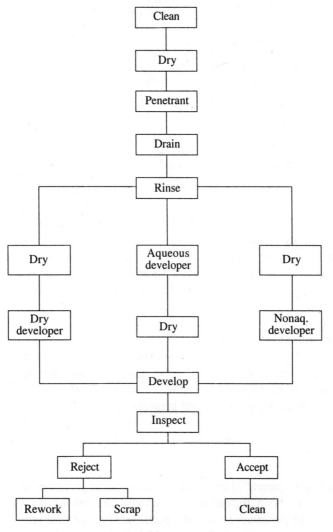

Fig. 3.2   Water washable penetrant method

Developer application follows the rinse step. When aqueous developers are used, there is no need for a drying step prior to the application of the developer. However, the part must be dried after the application. If non-aqueous developer is used, the part is dried before the developer application.

Development time begins immediately after application of the dry developer and as soon as wet developer coating dries on the surface of the part. The development step is complete whenever the movement of penetrant coming out of the defect has ceased. Typical development times are also given in Table 3.1.

3.4.2   Post-Emulsifiable Method

This method (Fig. 3.3) is a combination of solvent and water based inspections. The differences

Table 3.1   Recommended Dwell Times for Penetrant and Developer

Material	Form	Type of discontinuity	Dwell time (min.) for	
			Penetrant	Developer
Aluminium, magnesium, steel, titanium, various alloys	Castings, welds	Cold shuts, porosity, lack of fusion, cracks	5	7
	Wrought extrusions	Laps, cracks	10	7
Carbide tipped tools		Lack of fusion, porosity	5	7
Plastic, glass, ceramics	All forms	Cracks, porosity	5	7

between the post-emulsifiable penetrant process and the water-washable method are (a) the penetrant used and (b) the need for an emulsifier. If the solvent-based penetrant is used and followed by an emulsifier application, it allows the remainder of the process to follow the water-washable path. Both hydrophilic and lipophilic emulsifiers may be used in this method. The advantage of the post-emulsifiable system is that solvent penetrants that may be required for some parts may be removed by water.

3.4.3   Solvent Removable Method

This process (Fig. 3.4) is an oil-based inspection process. Penetrant removal must be accomplished by hand wiping the part with a rag dampend with solvent. Solvent technique is most often applied for the inspection of either a few small parts or for localized inspection such as in-situ inspection of pipe welds and pressure vessel welds and is most amenable to portability.

3.5   SENSITIVITY

Since the introduction of penetrant examination, various experiments have been conducted and methods have thus been formulated to measure the sensitivity. Sensitivity can be defined as the ability of penetrant to reveal a particular type of discontinuity in a material. This is related to fine or wide discontinuities which are deep or shallow in nature. Factors affecting sensitivity are the ability of the penetrant to enter the discontinuity and removal of the penetrant from the surface of the component without its significant removal from the defect. In addition, the penetrant must have the ability to come out of the discontinuity, with the aid of a developer, and to form an indication which is readily visible with good contrast with respect to the background.

Following is the list of various systems of penetrant, in the order of decreasing sensitivity (and decreasing cost):

(a) Post-emulsifiable fluorescent (b) Solvent-removable fluorescent (c) Water-washable fluorescent (d) Post-emulsifiable visible dye (e) Solvent-removable visible dye (f) Water-washable visible dye.

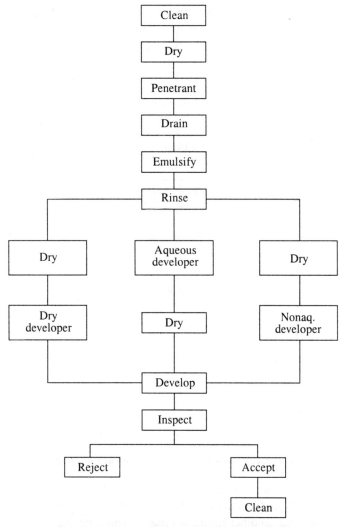

Fig. 3.3   Post emulsifiable penetrant method

It has been found that visible dye penetrant can detect cracks having width of approx. 5 μm whereas fluorescent penetrant can detect cracks having width in the range of 1 to 2 μm.

3.6   APPLICATIONS AND LIMITATIONS

In order to obtain optimum results from penetrant testing, a full understanding of the capabilities and limitations of the method should be appreciated. The method is capable of detecting discontinuities open to the surface of the material under test. These are usually cracks, laps, seams, porosity etc. in products like pressure vessels, pipes, weld joints etc. Penetrant method is very reliable in the detection of fatigue cracks which occur during the service life of a material. Penetrant method has a significant advantage over other NDT methods, with the possible exception of MPT. This is because of the fact that a part can be tested over its complete surface in a relatively short time, irrespective of shape, size and orientation of the

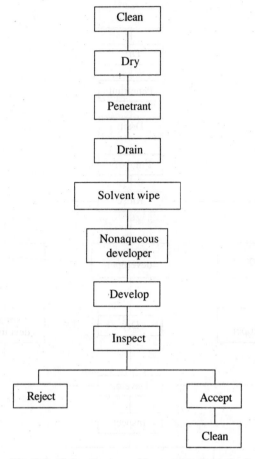

Fig. 3.4 Solvent removable penetrant method

defect. In the case of magnetic materials, MPT is preferred because it will also detect subsurface discontinuities, defects filled with oxide and defects covered by paint films. The liquid penetrant method has another limitation that it cannot be applied to porous materials.

3.7 STANDARD

1. IS 3658:1981   Code of practice for liquid penetrant flaw detection.

3.8 TYPICAL EXAMPLES

Typical examples showing the usefulness of liquid penetrant testing for revealing surface connected cracks are given here. Figure 3.5 shows the indications obtained in a heat treated male part of a die using liquid penetrant testing. For obtaining the indications, solvent removable visible dye penetrant with a dwell time of 30 minutes has been used. The heat treated die is made from EN-8 steel used for fabrication of containers. Two tight cracks (indicated by arrows) from the guide pin hole are clearly revealed by the liquid penetrant testing. The cracks were formed during heat treatment of the component. Figure 3.6 shows a collar crack extending into a part of a raiser used for casting purpose. The crack is very tight and the edge of the crack had a large depth indicated by the excess oozing out of penetrant. Figure 3.7 shows gross cracks including a branched one revealed by visible dye penetrant in a cut section of a boiler tube. The broadness of the LPT indication reveals that the crack is of sufficient depth. A dwell time of 15 minutes was used.

Fig. 3.5   Cracks in a heat treated male part of a die, revealed by LPT

Fig. 3.6   A collar crack extending into a part of a raiser, revealed by LPT

Fig. 3.7 Gross cracks including a branched one revealed by visible dye penetrant in a cut section of a boiler tube

Typical examples showing the usefulness of fluorescent liquid penetrant testing for revealing surface connected cracks are given here. Figure 3.8 shows the indications obtained by fluorescent liquid penetrant examination on the fillet radius of the leading edge of the dovetail slots in a aeroengine compressor disc. Two fine cracks have been found to emanate from the dovetail edges in the compressor disc can be observed (areas marked in the left figure). On the right is the magnified view of one of the cracks revealed by fluorescent liquid penetrant testing using solvent removable penetrant system and as observed under UV lighting. A dwell time of 30 minutes was used. The length of the two cracks was subsequently measured using a low power microscope and was found to be 4mm and 2mm.

 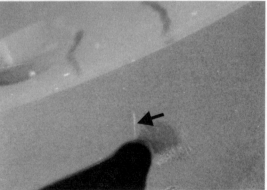

Fig. 3.8   Fluorescent dye penetrant examination of the fillet radii of the leading edges of the dovetail slots of a compressor disc of an aeroengine. One of the two fine cracks (indicated by arrows) emanating from the dovetail edges in the compressor disc is shown in the right figure (indicated by arrow)

Figure 3.9 shows another example of fluorescent liquid penetrant indications (arrows) of   300 micron and 600 micron flat bottom holes in a wheel axle of an undercarriage of a defence aircraft. These rounded indications were to serve as reference defects for UT examination. LPT was carried out using solvent removable fluorescent penetrant system. A dwell time of 15 minutes was given. The excessive bleed out has resulted in the magnification of the defect size by more than 10 times. The image is as-viewed through the digital camera with UV lighting. Figure 3.10 shows liquid penetrant indication from a tight crack in the wheel axle which was in service. Compared to the reference defect (flat bottom hole), the crack is inferred to be tight and very shallow (less than 300 microns in depth). Figure 3.11 shows the fluorescent indications of a few tight fatigue cracks revealed by fluorescent liquid penetrant testing in wheel axles of undercarriages of aircraft. The intermittent indications revealed in right image (two arrows) is an indirect pointer to the tightness of the crack while the sharpness of the indication indicates its shallowness.

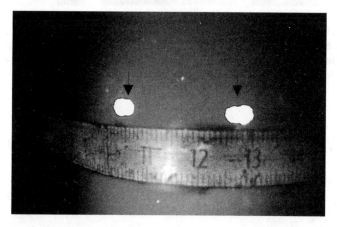

Fig. 3.9   **Fluorescent liquid penetrant indications (arrows) of 300 micron and 600 micron flat bottom holes in a wheel axle of an undercarriage of a defence aircraft**

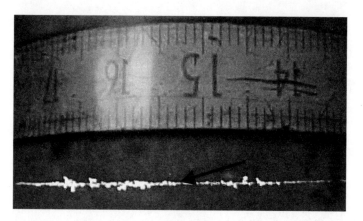

Fig. 3.10   **Fluorescent liquid penetrant indication from a tight crack in a wheel axle of an undercarriage of an aircraft**

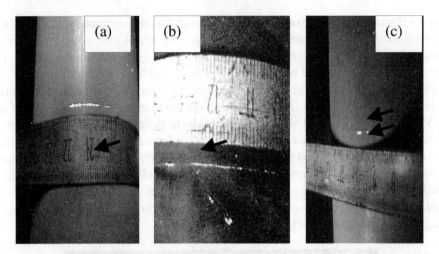

Fig. 3.11 **Tight fatigue cracks revealed by liquid penetrant testing in wheel axle of an undercarriage of an aircraft. The intermittent indications revealed in right image (two arrows) is an indirect pointer to the tightness of the crack while the sharpness of the indication indicates its shallowness**

Chapter 4

Magnetic Particle Testing

Magnetic particle testing (MPT) is used for the testing of materials (ferromagnetic materials) which can be easily magnetized. This method is capable of detecting flaws open-to-surface and just below the surface. Ferromagnetic materials include most of iron, nickel and cobalt alloys and many of the precipitation-hardening steels such as 17-4 PH. These materials lose their ferromagnetic properties above a characteristic temperature called the Curie point which is approximately 1033K for most ferromagnetic materials. The MPT equipment is cheap, robust and can be handled by semi-skilled personnel without requiring elaborate protection such as that needed for radiography.

4.1 MAGNETISM: BASIC DEFINITIONS AND PRINCIPLE OF MPT

The ability of a ferromagnetic material to attract other ferromagnetic materials is called magnetism and the pieces with this ability are called magnets. Magnets are classified as permanent or temporary. The latter type retains magnetic qualities only as long as a magnetizing force is being applied. Materials are usually classified into three categories: (a) diamagnetic—which are feebly repelled by a strong magnet, (b) paramagnetic—that can be magnetized but only weakly and (c) ferromagnetic—those which can be strongly magnetized and are suitable for magnetic particle inspection.

Ferromagnetic materials are not magnetized in direct proportion to the applied magnetizing force. There is a limit, called the saturation point, beyond which a part cannot be made more magnetic.

Magnetic lines of force existing in a magnetic field are called the magnetic flux. The unit of magnetic force is Maxwell.

Magnetizing force H is that force which tends to set up magnetic flux in a material.

Flux density B is the flux per unit area. The unit of flux measurement is Gauss.

Reluctance is the resistance of material to the establishment of a magnetic field. The reluctance of a material determines the magnitude of the flux produced. Reluctance can be compared to electrical resistance.

Permeability is the ease with which a material can be magnetized. It can be expressed numerically as B/H. A material with high permeability has low reluctance and vice versa.

By exposing an unmagnetized piece of material to magnetizing current, we can plot the flux density B of the field induced by the applied magnetizing force H, and the resultant curve is called the hysteresis loop (Fig. 4.1).

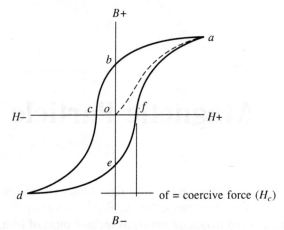

Fig. 4.1   Representative magnetisation (hysteresis) curve for a ferromagnetic material

4.1.1   Principle of MPT

When a specimen is magnetized, and magnetic lines of force (magnetic flux) are predominantly inside the ferromagnetic material. The magnetic field introduced into the specimen is composed of magnetic lines of force. Wherever there is a flaw which interrupts the flow of magnetic lines of force, some of these lines must exit and re-enter the specimen. These points of exit and re-entry form opposite magnetic poles. When minute magnetic particles are sprinkled onto the specimen, these particles are attracted by these magnetic poles to create a visual indication approximating the size and shape of the flaw. It is the abrupt change in permeability that causes this particle build-up.

The magnetic particles can be applied as powder or more commonly as liquid suspension, usually known as 'magnetic ink'. To be detected, linear flaws such as cracks must be favourably oriented in relation to the direction of the magnetic field. The colour of the magnetic particles should be in good contrast to the colour of the surface of the specimen for easy detection. For maximum sensitivity, the flux density should be oriented 90° to the discontinuity. However, it is generally possible to detect flaws which lie upto about ± 45° to the direction of flux lines. It is important to note that, because of the better sensitivity, when the discontinuity is at 90° to the lines of force, the magnetic flux should be induced in several different directions when the possible flaw orientations are not known.

4.2   MAGNETIZING TECHNIQUES

The essential requirements for any test is the application of magnetic field (flux flow) of adequate intensity along a known direction in the component. There are various techniques available for magnetizing a component. They are briefly described below.

4.2.1 Magnetization using a Magnet

The simplest possible way of magnetizing a component, like a bar, is to position it across the poles of a horse-shoe magnet (Fig. 4.2). The direction of flux is known and the intensity can be varied by using a strong or weak magnet, or by introducing a gap in the flux path with a thin piece of aluminum or other nonmagnetic material. Defects basically transverse to the test direction will be revealed.

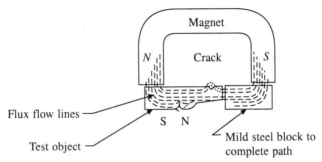

Fig. 4.2 Magnetization using horse shoe magnet

4.2.2 Magnetization Using an Electromagnet

A more refined method of producing magnetic flux flow is to use an electromagnet with a variable flux path, adjustable to suit the components (Fig. 4.3). In this method, the energizing direct current can be varied so as to provide a wide range of induced flux density. Components of varying cross section will obviously need equivalent variation in flux levels to give the same sensitivity. For components of simple form and reasonably regular section, this method is most satisfactory and gives high sensitivity.

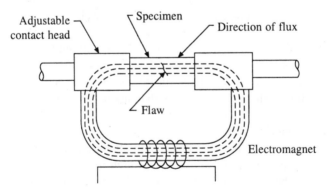

Fig. 4.3 Magnetization using an electromagnet

4.2.3 Contact Current Flow Method

By passing current through a component, a magnetic field is induced at right angles to the current flow (Fig. 4.4). This method locates defects at right angles to the applied magnetic direction.

For objects of extreme bulk, where the positioning of the object between machine poles would be difficult, it is quite practical to use heavy welding type cable to feed the power from the transformer to the object through C-clamps, prods or other means of coupling. Figure 4.5 shows magnetization with prods.

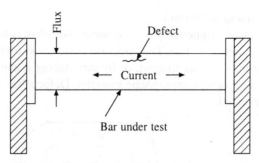

Fig. 4.4   Flux flow in a bar carrying current

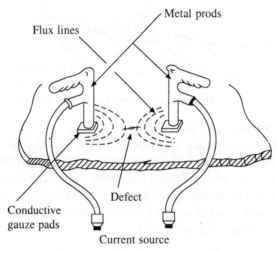

Fig. 4.5   Cables in use with prods

It should be realized that alternating current (rectified and unrectified) tends to travel on the surface of a component. Thus, the flux will stay on the surface and there will be very little flux flow inside a tube. Any defects on the internal surface will not be adequately revealed unless the tube will thickness is less than about 1.5 mm.

4.2.4   Using the Threading Bar
In the case of objects such as tubes, it is possible to obtain the same effects as in the case of direct current flow by placing a threading bar through the box and energizing it. The bar should not be of steel but of a good conductor such a copper or aluminum, and it can be hollow if the diameter is fairly large (Fig. 4.6). The resultant flux field in the surrounding steel object will be at right angles to the current flow and therefore will show defects basically parallel to the current direction. A big advantage is that the flux flows both on the inner surface of the tube as well as on the outer surface so that internal defects can be found. There is much less risk of burning with the threading bar than with current flow by direct contact.

4.2.5   The Coil
If a component is placed longitudinally within a coil carrying the current, flux will be generated in the component, giving 'North' and 'South' poles at its ends (Fig. 4.7). The

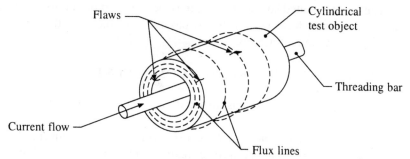

Fig. 4.6   Threading bar (central cable) flux flow in a tubular product

defects revealed will be oriented basically at right angles to the flux and therefore in the transverse direction to the length of the part.

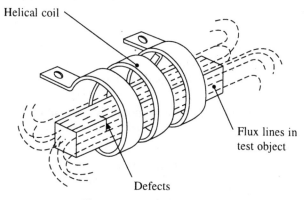

Fig. 4.7   Flux flow in a coil

4.2.6   Induced Current Flow

It is very difficult to detect radial defects in large rings because they have unfavourable shapes and do not respond well to the testing using the coil. The induced current flow method overcomes this by the use of a special transformer (Fig. 4.8). This transformer has

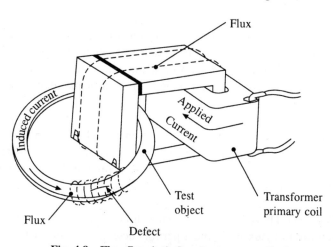

Fig. 4.8   Flux flow in induced current method

a core which can be demounted so that the ring may be threaded onto it to become a single turn secondary winding. Defects will be found basically in line with the circumferential current flow, i.e. circumferential defects.

4.3   PROCEDURE USED FOR TESTING A COMPONENT

The following stages are necessary to ensure satisfactory detection of defects:

(a) Surface preparation of component before testing: Normally, machined or plated surfaces do not require any preliminary surface treatment other than degreasing. Loose rust and scale should be removed from the component to prevent contamination of the ink. On painted parts, the paint should be removed locally, so as to provide adequate contact areas for the current flow. Other painted parts will only require degreasing unless the colour of the paint is the same as that of the particles in the ink to be used and is likely to reduce the contrast of the defect indications.

(b) Initial demagnetization: Components which have been machined on magnetic chucks or handled in the vicinity of any magnetic field could have been magnetized either wholly or partially. It is advisable to remove this residual magnetism to avoid false indications.

(c) Degreasing and cleaning: The component should be thoroughly cleaned before testing, because adhering grease and dirt can mask defects and also contaminate the ink. Degreasing may be carried out satisfactorily by means of spirit or trichloroethylene bath. When a component is to be tested in-situ, the cleaning is accomplished by a clean rag or cotton waste moistened with a suitable solvent, preferably spirit or paraffin.

(d) Magnetization of the component: Magnetization of the component may be carried out by following one of the methods specified in Section 3.3. It is necessary to choose suitable operating values of electrical parameters to obtain optimum magnetization of the part being inspected. Various types of electrical current sources are used to produce the magnetic field.

Electrical Current Sources

Direct current (DC): Direct current is used for detection of both surface and subsurface discontinuities. Using DC, it is possible to obtain full penetration of flux into the object permitting detection of subsurface discontinuities, which is a primary advantage. The disadvantages of using DC are: (i) requirement of battery maintenance, (ii) difficult to demagnetize and (iii) fixed voltage.

Alternating current (AC): AC is used for the detection of surface discontinuities. It provides maximum flux density on the surface for obtaining best sensitivity in detecting surface discontinuities. Particle mobility is better under AC. It is relatively easy to demagnetize. The shallow penetration of flux makes AC ineffective for subsurface discontinuities.

Half wave rectification (HWAC): HWAC provides higher flux density for the same average current. Full penetration of flux into object permits detection of subsurface discontinuities.

HWAC can be obtained from the same test equipment as AC by addition of a rectifier and a switch. It provides better particle mobility. It is relatively difficult to demagnetize.

The required current value for magnetizing a component can be calculated from the following relationships:

(i) Current flow method in bar, $\qquad H = \dfrac{I}{\pi d}$ $\hfill$ (4.1)

(ii) Current flow method using prod, $H = \dfrac{I}{\pi D}$ $\hfill$ (4.2)

(iii) Threading bar $\qquad\qquad\qquad H = \dfrac{I}{2\pi RN}$ $\hfill$ (4.3)

(iv) Bar inside the coil $\qquad\qquad\qquad I = \dfrac{6400\,R}{LN}$ $\hfill$ (4.4)

where H = magnetic field, I = current, d = diameter of the bar, D = distance between the centers of two prods, R = radius of the test surface, N = Number of turns and, L = specimen length.

There are two ways of magnetization of a component. (a) Continuous method and (b) Residual method. Continuous method of magnetization is used by applying the magnetic particles while the current is flowing. If the magnetic particles are applied after the magnetizing current is shut off, the technique is called residual method. The residual method is less sensitive than the continuous method. Both methods may be applied with wet or dry magnetic particles. Dry powders of black, red or grey colour or the wet methods using fluorescent or nonfluorescent suspensions are used for both continuous and residual methods.

(e) Application of magnetic particles: There are two classes of magnetic particles available depending upon the vehicle or carrying agent used. In the wet method, particles use a liquid vehicle and in the dry method, particles are carried by air.

The particles used in the wet method are suspended in oil or water, and are obtained from the manufacturer as a powder or heavy thick paste. The concentration of particles is about 2% by volume for optimum results. The particles must be carefully and completely dispersed in a liquid bath of proper consistency, colour, and flash point. Magnetic particles for the wet method are available in black or red colour and fluorescent.

Since the dry particles depend upon air to carry them to the surface of the part, care must be taken to apply them correctly. When using the dry powder method, it must be remembered that a light and even distribution of the magnetic powder is the best type of coating because a heavy coating will impede the particle movement towards the leakage field.

The magnetic properties and particle size are similar for all colours, making the particles equally efficient. The choice of colour is such that the powder will show up or give the best contrast of the parts being inspected. For best results, the particle mean size shall be $\simeq$ 6 μm and shape can be a mixture of roughly spherical and columnar.

(f) Viewing: The black or red paste or powder indications are viewed under proper illumination. The level of illumination can be 500 lux at the surface. Good daylight is the best. The fluorescent paste or powder particles must be viewed under 'black light' and the equipment or inspection area must be darkened with a booth or curtain to cut off normal light (room lighting must be reduced to around 10 lux) and must be equipped with an adequate black light source.

(g) Marking of defects: All relevant indication should be marked after allowing the ink to drain. For permanent record, apart from television recording and photography, the area under inspection can be covered with a transparent adhesive film. When the film is peeled off, it comes out with magnetic particles adhered corresponding to the indications.

(h) Demagnetization: All ferromagnetic materials retain some residual magnetism after magnetic particle inspection. Demagnetization can only be accomplished totally when a material is heated to approximately 1033 K. The basis of electrical demagnetization is the diminishing, reversing magnetizing force sufficient to overcome the original field. In general, two methods are used for demagnetization:

(i) The part is placed in the field of an AC coil and withdrawn slowly to about 1.2 to 2 m away. Small parts should be kept close to the I.D. of the coil.

(ii) Part is subjected to a reversing, diminishing DC or HWAC current. When separate demagnetizing units are required, for demagnetizing large numbers of small parts, the AC coil is used normally. Coils of this type are used in a number of sizes, since demagnetizing efficiency is higher when the parts nearly fill the coil opening. In the case of special inspection units, special demagnetizers are often built into the unit to suit the size and operating cycles required for the particular application.

The effectiveness of the demagnetizing sequence can be measured in one of the following ways:

(i) Magnetometer: A sensitive laboratory instrument usually not applicable to general inspection.

(ii) Field Indicator: A small pocket sized device which is quite accurate when properly calibrated. This instrument is generally used for MPT.

(iii) Compass: To be used only when a qualitative estimation is needed.

(iv) Tag Wire: A magnetic piece of wire hung such that it moves freely when placed in a magnetic field. This is used for very rough estimation only.

(i) Removal of ink from the component: Ink particles can be deleterious during later assembly of the component. A paraffin oil wash by hand brush is usually adequate for removing the ink.

4.4 EQUIPMENT USED FOR MPT

Magnetic particle testing equipment serves the following purposes. It provides (i) sufficient power of the right type, (ii) suitable contact and coils, (iii) convenient means for accomplishing proper magnetization with respect to field strength and direction, (iv) means of applying the magnetic particles, and (v) well lighted space for careful examination of the part for indications.

To suit the various needs, the following types of equipment are available.

(a) Simple equipment: For occasional testing of small castings or machine parts for detection of surface cracks, small and easily portable equipment is most convenient. For the inspection of welds, magnetic yokes are often adequate and very easy to use. They are able to give a strong field to that portion of the part that lies between the poles of the yoke.

Yokes are available for using with either AC or DC. In one model, permanent magnets are used. The latter permits inspections where no source of electric current is available, or where its use is not permissible because of the fire or explosion hazard in the area where inspection must be made. For longitudinal magnetization of shafts and spindles and similar articles, portable kits are furnished with a fixed coil covered with a heavy protective coating.

(b) Large portable equipment: Large portable equipment is used where higher power is required or heavier duty cycles make the small kits inadequate. One of the smallest of this series operates at 120 V AC and delivers up to 700 amperes, either AC or half wave DC. Dual prods for direct contact are provided. Flexible cable for making loops for longitudinal magnetization are included. Large units with output upto 6000 amperes, delivering either AC or half wave DC are used for testing castings, forgins or weldments, where such heavy currents are required.

(c) Stationary magnetizing equipment: A large variety of stationary, bench-type units is available, with various characteristics to fit different testing requirements. The smaller size equipment is used for small parts that can be easily transported and handled by hand. The larger ones are used for heavy parts such as long diesel engine crankshafts, where handling must be made by crane. Such units are made to deliver AC or DC with various types of current control.

(d) Large heavy duty DC equipment: Very versatile types of heavy duty stationary equipment are those direct current units designed for application of the "overall" method of magnetizing, for the inspection of very large and complicated castings. Rectified three-phase AC is delivered with current values running as high as 20,000 amperes. Such high currents are needed to magnetize, at one time, an entire casting which may weigh many tonnes. Another feature of these units is that they deliver currents, separately and in rapid succession, through three circuits, thus making it possible to locate cracks in all directions in one operation itself. The system is known as multidirectional magnetization. By means of electromechanical switching, demagnetization can be accomplished by utilizing one circuit in conjunction with reversing DC and a 30 point step-down switch.

4.5 SENSITIVITY

MPT methods are sensitive means of locating small and shallow surface cracks in ferromagnetic components. Many incipient fatigue cracks and fine grinding cracks having sizes less than 0.02 mm deep and surface openings of one tenth of that or less can be located using MPT. Detectability generally involves a relation between surface opening and depth. A surface scratch, which may be as wide at the surface as its depth, usually does not produce a magnetic pattern, although it may do so at high level of magnetization. Because of many variables, it is not possible to establish any exact values for this relationship, but in general a surface discontinuity whose depth is at least five times its opening (width) at the surface will be detected. Exceedingly wide cracks will not produce a particle pattern if the surface opening is too wide for the particles to bridge.

If the defects sought are usual cracks, comparatively low level of magnetic force will give sufficient build-up. However, to find minute cracks or subsurface flaws, the flux level should be high. Theoretically, a level just below saturation would give the most sensitive results. But this is impractical owing to the non-regular shapes of the components encountered. In practice, lower levels are quite adequate. An accepted standard is about 40% of saturation of the material being tested.

Sensitivity also depends on the type of current used. Various tests have conclusively proved the following information:

(a) Alternating current magnetization is most effective for surface defects.
(b) Alternating current magnetization is not effective for subsurface defects.
(c) Direct current (straight or half wave) must be used for subsurface defects.
(d) Half wave DC gives superior penetration as compared to straight DC.
(e) Half wave DC dry method gives the greatest penetration.

4.6 LIMITATIONS

There are certain limitations for using MPT methods. It can detect only surface opening and subsurface defects in ferromagnetic materials. The operator must know that thin coatings of paint and other nonmagnetic surface layers such as plating adversely affect sensitivity. For best results, the magnetic field must be in a direction that will intercept the discontinuity at 90°. Sometimes this requires two or more sequential inspection steps with different magnetization directions. Care is necessary to avoid local heating and burning of finished parts or surfaces at the points of electrode contact. Another limitation is the necessity for complete demagnetization of the part after completing the MPT.

4.7 STANDARDS

1. IS 3415:1987   Glossary of terms used in magnetic particle flaw detection.
2. IS 9709:1980   Code of practice for magnetic particle flaw detection.
3. IS 6994:1981   Code of practice for magnetic particle flaw detection of welds.
4. IS 6410:1971   Specification for magnetic flaw detection ink and powders.
5. IS 6752:1972   Code of practice for magnetic flaw detection of ferrous pipes and tubes.
6. IS 7749:1975   Recommended practice for magnetic particle testing and inspection of steel forgings.
7. IS 10543:1983   Dry powder magnetic particle testing.
8. IS 11655:1986   Stray flux testing of ferromagnetic seamless steel tubular products.
9. IS 12147:1987   Recommended practice for wet magnetic particle examination.

4.8 TYPICAL EXAMPLES

Typical examples showing the usefulness of magnetic particle testing for revealing surface and subsurface cracks are given here. Figure 4.9 shows a tight fatigue crack emanating from the fir tree root region of a steam turbine blade, revealed by fluorescent magnetic particle testing. Figure 4.10 shows a fatigue crack in a wheel axle of an undercarriage of a defence aircraft, revealed by fluorescent magnetic particle testing. The sharpness of the indication reveals the tightness of the fatigue crack.

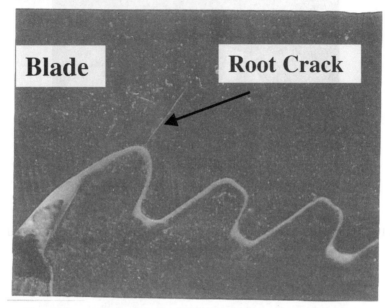

Fig. 4.9 **Tight fatigue crack in fir tree root region of a steam turbine blade, revealed by fluorescent magnetic particle testing**

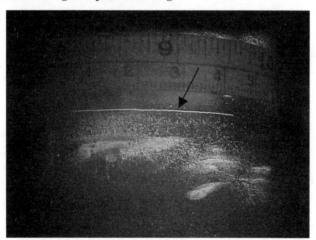

Fig. 4.10 **Fluorescent magnetic particle indication of a fatigue crack in a wheel axle of an undercarriage of an aircraft**

In magnetic particle testing, 'Ketos ring' is used to serve as an indicator of the magnetic field strength to ensure reliable detection of defects. A typical reference defect indications in the 'Ketos ring', revealed by magnetic particle testing is shown in Fig. 4.11. It can be seen that the field strength is adequate in the vertical directions as well as at 30 degree inclination. However, the absence of the indication in the horizontal direction reflects the inadequate magnetic field strength in the horizontal direction.

Fig. 4.11   The magnetic particle indications observed in a standard 'Ketos ring' indicating inadequate filed strength in the horizontal direction

Eddy Current Testing

Although the evolution of the basic eddy current theory can be traced back to the initial discovery of both electricity and magnetism by early man, the scientific development of eddy current theory started with the discovery of the law of electromagnetic induction by Faraday in 1832. Faraday's law states that when a magnetic field cuts a conductor or when a conductor cuts a magnetic field, an electrical current will flow through the conductor if a closed path is provided over which the current can circulate. From Oersted's discovery, a magnetic flux exists around a coil carrying current proportional to the number of turns in the coil and the current. Eddy currents are defined as oscillating electrical currents induced in a conductive material by an alternating magnetic field, due to electromagnetic induction. Eddy current testing (ECT) is used for sorting materials, measurement and control of dimensions of tubes, sheets and rods, coating thickness and for pre-service and in-service examination of heat exchanger tubes for detection of defects.

5.1 PRINCIPLES

In ECT, an alternating current (frequency 1 kHz-2 MHz) is made to flow in a coil (also called probe) which, in turn, produces an alternating magnetic field around it. This coil, when brought close to the electrically conducting surface of a metallic material to be inspected, induces an eddy current flow in the material due to electromagnetic induction (Fig. 5.1). These eddy currents are generally parallel to the coil winding. The presence of any defect or discontinuity in the material disturbs the eddy current flow. These eddy currents, in turn, generate an alternating magnetic field (in opposite direction) which may be detected either as a voltage across a second coil or by the perturbation of the impedance of the original coil.

The impedance change is affected, mainly, by electrical conductivity, magnetic permeability and geometry of the material, test frequency and the spacing between the coil and the material. This impedance change can be measured and correlated with the changes in the above mentioned parameters.

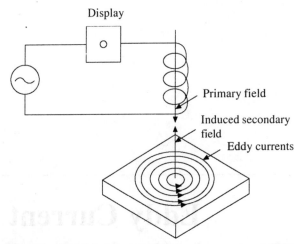

Fig. 5.1   Initial balance conditions of current and fields

Factors which affect the eddy current are:

Test parameters
   (i) Frequency
   (ii) Type and geometry of test coil(s)
   (iii) Fill factor

Test object
   (i) Electrical conductivity
   (ii) Magnetic permeability
   (iii) Dimensions
   (iv) Temperature

Effect of test frequency: The importance of test frequency is that it determines the depth of penetration of eddy currents in the material. The eddy current density decreases exponentially from the material surface but the rate of decrease depends on the test frequency, the electrical conductivity and the magnetic permeability of the test material. Figure 5.2 shows the eddy current and magnetic flux distribution with depth into a conductor. The test

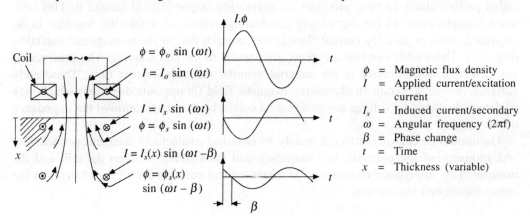

Fig. 5.2   Eddy currents and magnetic flux distribution along the depth into a conductor

frequency is the only parameter that can be varied by the inspector during inspection. Although higher frequencies are suitable for achieving higher inspection speeds and better sensitivity to defects, they mainly increase the noise due to lift-off or fill factor to such an extent that sometimes even masking the signals due to defects. Similarly lower frequencies yield reduced noise due to lift-off or fill factor but at the cost of sensitivity. In view of this, enough care should be taken while selecting the test frequency.

Depth of penetration and frequency: The depth of penetration of eddy currents in a material is a critical factor. For example, in the case of tube inspection, if the eddy currents do not penetrate the wall thickness of the tube, then it is possible to miss the defects. The depth of penetration of eddy currents can be found by the relation

$$\delta = \frac{500}{\sqrt{\sigma \mu f}} \qquad (5.1)$$

where δ = standard depth of penetration (mm), σ = conductivity (mhos/m), μ = relative permeability, f = inspection frequency (Hz).

The standard depth of penetration is generally taken to be that depth at which the eddy current field intensity drops to 37% of the intensity at the surface of the conductor (Fig. 5.2). As can be seen that higher the frequency, lower the depth of penetration. Thus a frequency must be chosen which permits penetration to the depth upto which defects are to be found. For general tube inspection, the frequency used is often the frequency at which the standard depth of penetration is equal to the wall thickness of the tube. This is given by the equation,

$$f = \frac{250}{\sigma r^2} \text{kHz} \qquad (5.2)$$

where t is the wall thickness of the tube in mm.

Equation 5.1 shows that higher the permeability, lower is the depth of penetration. Since relative permeabilities of ferromagnetic materials are of 500 to 2000, eddy currents in these materials are concentrated at the surface. Hence subsurface defects are not detectable in ferromagnetic materials. Also, small variations in permeability give rise to relatively high impedance change. Hence, conventional ECT fails to inspect ferromagnetic materials. A detailed discussion on the use of advanced techniques to solve these problems is given in a later section.

Effect of lift off: For a simple geometry like eddy current probe over a metallic plate, the distance between the probe and the plate being inspected is called life-off (in case of encircling or inside coils as used for inspecting rods or tubes, it is termed as 'fill factor'). As lift-off increases, the eddy current density in the material, in turn, the impedance change in the probe decreases. In view of this, for achieving better sensitivity, it is always desirable to set lift-off as minimum as possible. However, its adverse affects can be minimised by adopting special probe designs (like differential pickup coils) and procedures that would yield enhanced phase separation between the signals due to wanted and the unwanted, in the present case the lift-off. Also it is interesting to note that lift-off is a function of coil diameter. The bigger the diameter of the probe, the smaller the lift-off.

Although lift-off signals are not preferred during routine defect detection, they are of great help in determining thickness of non-conducting coatings like paints on non-ferromagnetic and ferromagnetic materials.

Effect of conductivity: The material in which eddy currents can be induced should be of conductive in nature. All materials have characteristic resistance to the flow of electric current depending on which they can be classified into three categories: insulators, semi-conductors and conductors. We will limit our discussion to conductors only since both insulators and semi-conductors with their high resistivity will permit virtually no flow of eddy currents in the test material. Conductivity is the reverse of resistivity and is the measure of how easily the current can flow through the material. Conductivity is measured most conveniently by referring to the International Annealed Copper Standard (IACS) sets the conductivity of copper as 100% and for other materials as its percentage. In general, conductivity of a material is affected by(i) chemical composition (ii) heat treatment and (iii) temperature. ECT can be used to detect changes in any one of these properties in isolation.

Effect of magnetic permeability: Magnetic permeability is the ratio of magnetic flux density to the magnetizing force of the coil. The magnetic permeability of a metal affects the ease with which magnetic lines will flow through it. In a material with a high permeability, a larger density of these lines will be created for a given source and the lines will tend to concentrate in the material. This has two effects; firstly a greater amount of magnetic energy can be stored in the coil which increases inductance and secondly plenty of eddy currents are generated which increases the 'lift off' effect. The tendency of the lines of force to concentrate in the material causes very little penetration.

Effect of geometry: The geometry of a component under test causes many difficulties in ECT. A curved piece of metal will have a different 'lift off' response compared to a flat one, and the edge effect can distort the eddy current field and produces a signal lag. Another feature of the geometry is on the actual thickness of the material under test. If the eddy currents penetrate the full thickness, there will be some effect when the thickness changes. Signals from thickness changes are used to detect the loss of metal due to corrosion.

5.2 INSTRUMENTATION FOR ECT

In most inspections, probe impedance (voltage) changes only slightly as the probe passes a defect, typically less than 1%. This small change is difficult to detect by measuring absolute impedance or voltage. Special instruments have been developed incorporating various methods of detecting and amplifying small impedance changes.

The main functions of an eddy current instrument are illustrated in the block diagram of Fig. 5.3. A sine wave oscillator generates sinusoidal current, at a specified frequency, that passes through the test coils. Since the impedance of two coils is never exactly equal, balancing is required to eliminate the voltage difference between them. Most eddy current instruments achieve this through an AC bridge or by subtracting a voltage equal to the unbalance voltage. In general, they can tolerate an impedance mismatch of 5%. Once balanced, the presence of a defect in the vicinity of one coil creates a small unbalanced signal which is then amplified, filtered and displayed on *X-Y* monitor (storage oscilloscope) after converting to DC signal. The coil output may vary in both amplitude and phase and the relative variation of the parameters may be important for evaluation of the material under test. There are many variations in the design of eddy current instruments. For understanding the functional details of the circuits, the references given at the end of the chapter may be consulted.

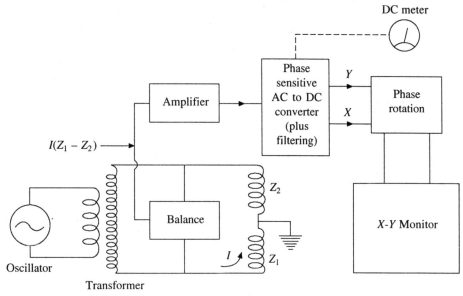

Fig. 5.3 Block diagram of eddy current test instrument

Simple ECT instruments usually operate at a fixed frequency and have an analog meter output, thus having limited applications. Modern ECT instruments utilize both amplitude and phase information of the eddy currents. Such instruments permit test frequency to be varied over a wide range enabling selection of suitable skin depth. ECT is a comparative test; signals from real defects are compared with those from calibrated artificial defects to establish type and depth of defects. The calibration and inspection results are normally recorded on dual channel chart recorders and on magnetic tapes. The data stored on magnetic tapes can be played back at a later stage for further evaluation or documentation. Recently, personal computer based eddy current instruments have been developed. These are very compact, light in weight and very efficient in acquiring, processing and storing eddy current data.

Coils: Coils are necessary in ECT to produce a sufficient magnetic field from limited current or a sufficient current from a limited magnetic field. A field from adjacent wires in a nearby coil add to provide a total magnetic field depending on the number of turns in the coils. This type of magnetic field from a coil is similar to that from a permanent magnet.

Eddy current generation: When the coil is brought in close proximity with the conductive material, the alternating magnetic field (primary field) will pass through the material. The coil can be placed onto the material, or encircle it or be inside a tube, or sideways to the object (Fig. 5.4) and eddy currents will be induced into the material. It can be shown that they normally have circular paths at right angles to the primary field, in other words, parallel to the coil winding (Fig. 5.1).

Eddy current detection: The eddy currents in the conducting material generate their own magnetic field (the secondary field) which in fact opposes and modifies the primary field. This in turn modifies the primary current usually in both phase and amplitude. If the current flowing through the primary field is shown on a display, then variations in it can be seen in presence of defects.

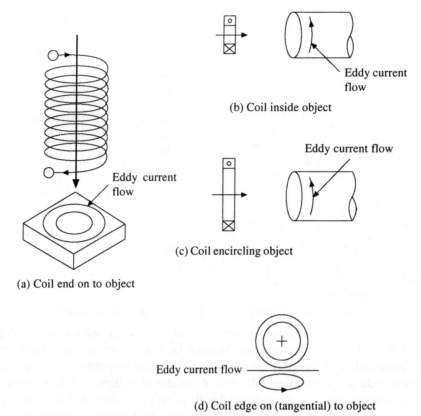

(b) Coil inside object

(c) Coil encircling object

(a) Coil end on to object

(d) Coil edge on (tangential) to object

Fig. 5.4   Eddy current flow with different coil arrangements

Coil arrangement: The same coil which is used for both generating the primary field and detecting the secondary field is called an absolute coil (Fig. 5.5). Often it is useful to have two coils in close proximity which are electrically arranged to be in opposition i.e. wound in opposite directions. This arrangement reduces the effects which affect both coils, for example lift off, material variations and temperature. Signals which affect each coil differently, for example a crack sensed by one coil at a time, are enhanced. This arrangement is called differential coil mode. Table 5.1 shows the relative advantages and disadvantages of two most widely used eddy current probe types; absolute and differential.

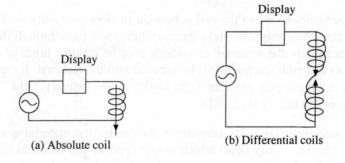

(a) Absolute coil

(b) Differential coils

Fig. 5.5   Coil variations

Table 5.1 Comparison of Absolute and Differential Probes

Absolute Probes	*Differential Probes*
Respond to both abrupt and gradual change in properties and dimensions.	More sensitive to abrupt localised changes.
Prone to drift due to temperature changes.	Immune to drift due to temperature changes.
Interpretation of signals is simple.	May yield signals difficult to interpret.
Can detect the length of defects.	Detects only the ends of long defects.
Sensitive to probe wobble.	Less sensitive to probe wobble.

Probe selection: The selection of a test coil (probe) is influenced by a number of factors, viz. (a) shape of test specimen (sheets, plates, tubes, rods, wires, etc.), (b) likely distribution of variables affecting eddy currents and type of information required-crack detection, conductivity variation, permeability variation etc.), (c) accessibility.

Probe size requirements: The probe size requirements for ECT of the tubes are determined by the 'fill factor', where

$$\text{Fill factor} = \frac{D_1^2}{D_2^2} \tag{5.3}$$

where D_1 is the diameter of the probe and D_2 is the ID of the tube.

Ideally the fill factor should be as close to 1.0 as possible. A fill factor of 1.0 can never be achieved in practice since the probe would not travel down the tube. As a rule of thumb, the optimum fill factor for tube testing is approx. 0.7. This allows reasonable sensitivity to be achieved whilst still maintaining adequate clearance when dirt or dents may be present in the tube.

Figure 5.6 shows different types of eddy current testing probes used for various applications. The details of the probes given in the Fig. 5.6 are as follows.

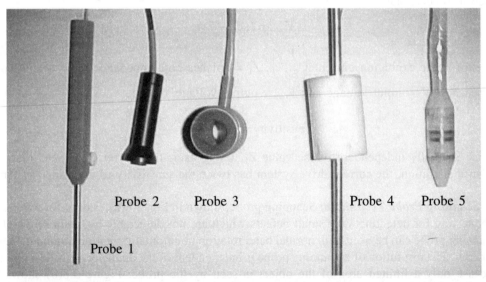

Probe 2   Probe 3   Probe 4   Probe 5

Probe 1

Fig. 5.6   Different types of eddy current testing probes used for various inspections

1. Focused pencil type absolute probe with adjustable probe holder for the inspection of components with limited accessibility
2. Spring loaded absolute probe for detecting surface and near surface defects in conducting non-ferromagnetic plates. A spring is used to apply a constant load on the probe which would avoid lift off variations and wobbling during probe movement and scanning.
3. Reflection type probe used for inspection of bolt holes without removing the bolts. As can be seen from the figure, the inner diameter of the probe should match the bolt head size for better defect detection.
4. A differential encircling probe used for inspection of small diameter tubes. One such example is the inspection of steam generator and heat exchanger tubes during the tube manufacturing stage, as part of quality control procedure. Another example is for inspection of fuel cladding tubes used in nuclear reactors. A stainless steel tube with a typical outer diameter of 5.31 mm and thickness of 0.35 mm, used in Indian fast breeder test reactor is shown in Fig. 5.6.
5. Differential bobbin type probe used for ISI of heat exchanger and steam generator tubes in chemical and power plants. Differential probes are normally used for eliminating slow varying thickness and temperature variations during testing.

5.3   TECHNIQUES

5.3.1   High Sensitivity Techniques

(a) Constant current drive ECT techniques: Enhanced sensitivity and better discrimination are possible with the use of constant current excitation of test coils. Additionally, use of this method can result in reducing nonlinear response inherent in the conventional balance bridge, virtually total discrimination against coil temperature changes, and ease of operation at high test frequency (1-30 MHz).

An eddy current coil system employing constant current drive is shown in Fig. 5.7. The analysis reveals that

$$V_{\text{out}} = I(Z_1 - Z_2) \tag{5.4}$$

where I = the excitation current $\left(\dfrac{V_i}{2Z_1}\right)$, Z_1 = balance coil impedance, Z_2 = search coil impedance, V_i = input voltage and V_{out} = output voltage.

$$\text{Sensitivity } (S) = \frac{dV_{\text{out}}}{dZ_2} \tag{5.5}$$

which is totally independent of the value Z_1. Using excitation current it is seen that, at balance condition, the current drive system has twice the sensitivity of the bridge system.

(b) Scanning Probe Technique: Scanning probe, shown in Fig. 5.8(a), is used for wire and tube testing for detecting very small defects which are not detectable by encircling coils. Scanning probe can be used with normal hand rotation or automatic rotation around the test material. The resolution of a scanning probe is independent of the diameter of the test object because only a limited area of the object is seen by the probe. Figure 5.8(b) shows a

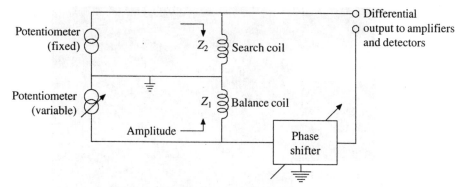

Fig. 5.7 Constant current ECT technique

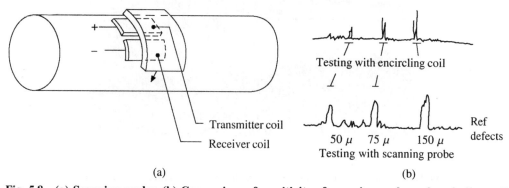

(a) (b)

Fig. 5.8 (a) Scanning probe; (b) Comparison of sensitivity of scanning probe and encircling coil

comparison of the test results obtained from encircling and scanning probe techniques. It can be seen that scanning probe performs better as far as sensitivity of testing is concerned.

(c) Detection of surface defects using absolute probe: An absolute probe is normally used for scanning the surface of plates and other rectangular shaped objects for the detection of surface opening and subsurface defects. Typical eddy current signals from a plate having notches of different size detected using an absolute surface probe has been shown in Fig. 5.9. Vertical (in phase) and horizontal (quadrature) components of eddy current signals, corresponding to 0.1mm, 0.2 mm and 0.3 mm deep, 0.1 mm width and 2 mm long notches in a 3 mm thick stainless steel plate using an absolute probe. Actual notches of 0.1 mm, 0.2 mm and 0.3 mm deep present in the stainless steel plate is also shown in the figure. The frequency of inspection is 50 kHz.

5.3.2 Inspection of Heat Exchanger Tubes by Single Frequency ECT System

One of the best applications of ECT is for in-service examination of heat exchangers. Specifically the heat exchangers are checked periodically during shutdown periods after they have entered into service. The purpose is to identify tube deterioration due to pitting, other corrosion or cracking such that failed or suspect tubes can be replaced or blanked avoiding failure during actual use.

In the case of heat exchanger tubes, the normally used configuration of the coil is differential and self comparison type where two coils are wound side by side on a bobbin

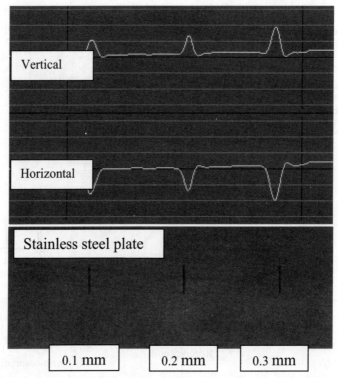

Fig. 5.9   **Typical EC response from a different size surface opening defects present in a stainless steel plate.**

and are very sensitive to localised defects. The two coils form the two arms of a Wheatstone bridge. The bridge is initially balanced by using instrument controls to compensate for minor variations between the two coils. The bridge unbalanced signal is amplified and split into its resistive and inductive parts, by **sample and hold circuits**. These signals can be displayed on X-Y scope.

While one of the coils senses a flaw, the bridge gets unbalanced. The signals are usually recorded on a magnetic tape recorder for real-time display latter. A two channel strip chart recorder is also used to facilitate analysis and also to serve as a 'hard copy' record.

In order to achieve reproducible results, a calibration standard is essential. In the case of in-service inspection of heat exchanger tubes, an identical tube of the same heat is taken as a standard tube and artificial defects are created in the tube by drilling holes to different depths. As per ASME Section XI, a through-wall hole, and flat bottom holes (FBH) of 80%, 60%, 40% and 20% of wall thickness drilled from outside and a circumferential groove of 10% on OD side and 20% wall thickness from inside are taken as reference defects (Fig. 5.10). The signals obtained from these artificial defects are used for calibration of the output of the instrument. The probe is pushed inside the tube and then while retracting the probe, the data are collected and analysed. When the probe approaches a flaw, the impedance of the leading coil changes and this causes an imbalance of the bridge giving an output signal to move the spot on the X-Y scope downward and to the right, in a curved path. The maximum deflection from the center occurs approximately when the leading coil is under the flaw. On continuing the probe movement, the flaw moves away from the

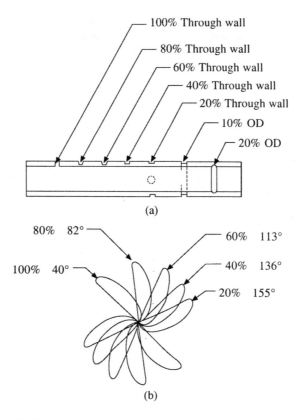

Fig. 5.10 (a) Typical ASME calibration tube and (b) Composite signal representation from the OD discontinuities of the ASME calibration tube at the proper frequency

leading coil and simultaneously, the trailing coil starts sensing it. When both the coils are equidistant from the flaw, the impedance of both the coils will be the same and the bridge output will again be zero, and the spot will return to origin completing a loop. After this the trailing coil passes the flaw and completes the upper part of the loop, completing a 'figure of eight' shape. The 'figure of eight' shape, which is the locus of the scope spot will remain fully visible if a storage oscilloscope is used. The phase angle for the 'figure of eight' shape with the X-axis will vary with depth of the defect and the size of the loop depends on the area of the defect. A calibration curve is drawn, as seen in Fig. 5.11, showing typical signals from different reference defects. Now on the actual job when an indication is obtained from a flaw, from the phase angle of the 'figure of eight', the depth of defect is found by comparing the calibration curve. For heat exchanger tubing, the depth of the defect is very much important as it is related to the integrity particularly the remaining life of the tubes.

5.3.3 Multifrequency ECT

Multifrequency mixing eddy current testing technique is applied to eliminate disturbing signals during eddy current testing. This technique is predominantly used for eliminating support plate signals during heat exchanger tube inspection. In this technique, two frequencies are simultaneously applied to an EC probe. The primary frequency is chosen to interrogate

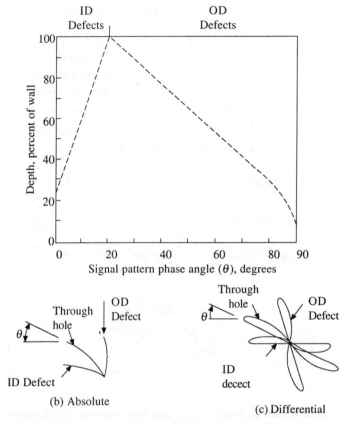

Fig. 5.11   Eddy current phase angle/defect depth calibration curve

the tube material and partially the support plate, based on the skin effect equation. The second frequency is normally chosen as the sub-harmonic of the primary, which would interrogate the tube material and fully the support plate. The support plate signals at these two frequencies are made to be same by suitably adjusting the gain and phase controls in the eddy current testing instrument. The arithmetic difference between these two signals would then be free from the influence of support plate. If defects are present under the support plate, the mixer will show only the signal due the defect and in this way support plate influence is completely eliminated. Figure 5.12(a) shows the influence of support plate on the signal from a through hole defect present under the support plate in dual frequency inspection. After proper mixing, the signal is found to be (shown as MX1) free from support plate influence and the phase of the signal is also maintained. Here D11 is the Impedance plane signals from 120 kHz which is the primary frequency. D21 is the Impedance plane signals from 60 kHz Second frequency. D31 is the Impedance plane signals from 100 kHz which is not used in this particular mixing because two frequencies arc sufficient for eliminating one variable namely the support plate. Hence, only D11 and D21 are considered for mixing operation. Time domain signal from one frequency (D11H) and vertical output of the mixer channels (MX1V) are also shown on the left side of the figure. The tube under inspection is an ASME calibration tube made of AISI type 304 stainless steel with 19 mm OD and 16.5 mm ID (Fig. 5.12(b)).

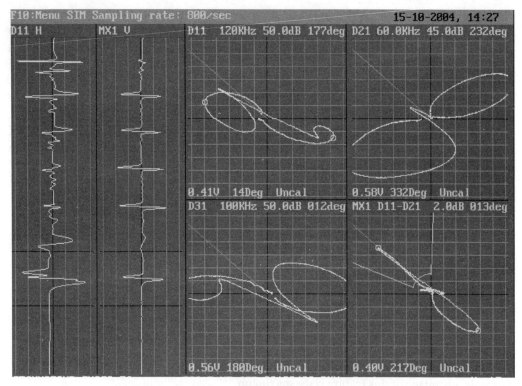

Fig.5.12(a) Eddy current signals due to a defect present under the support plate. Only the defect signal is seen in the mixer module and the support plate influence completely eliminated using dual frequency mixing technique

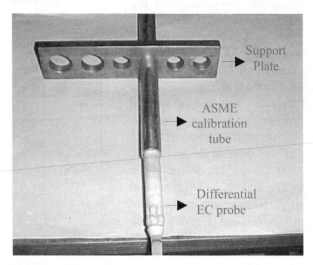

Fig. 5.12(b) Typical ASME calibration tube used for heat exchanger inspection with support plate and the differential probe bobbin probe

The multifrequency eddy current technique can be used to eliminate any number of disturbing variables during testing such as wobble and magnetic deposits. The general rule for the number of frequencies to be used is as follows. If we have N number of disturbing variables, we should use N+1 number of excitation frequencies and N number of mixing sequences to eliminate them. But large number of mixing operation would also result in poor signal to noise ratio which would again influence the detection sensitivity. Modern eddy current instruments use 4 frequencies and 3 mixer modules such that 3 disturbing variables during testing can be eliminated.

5.3.4 High Frequency ECT

In specialised applications for detecting fine surface cracks like fatigue cracks, the use of higher frequency is desired in order to reduce the penetration depth thus achieving high current density on the surface. To achieve this, electron spin precision resonance in ferromagnetic crystals such as Yttrium Iron Garnet (YIG) or Gallium doped YIG is employed. A spherical ferromagnetic crystal is placed in DC magnetic bias field and excited with a single coupling loop containing the DC magnetic bias in its plane, which produces the magnetic field with the frequency range 500-4000 MHz (Fig. 5.13). In microwave frequencies, the skin depth under ideal conditions is of the order of micrometers, much smaller than the dimensions of typical flaws. This means that the eddy currents do not flow deep into the material. The main advantage of this feature is the maximum concentration of eddy currents at the flaw and gives maximum detectable sensitivity. This technique is capable of providing the morphology of the defect in addition to its better detection sensitivity.

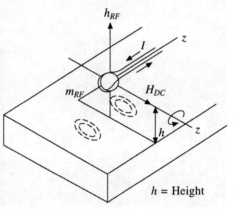

Fig. 5.13 Schematic sketch showing magnetic field and the eddy currents in high frequency

5.3.5 3D or Phased Array ECT

Conventional eddy current probes can not detect defects that are parallel to their windings (laminar or circumferential defects) because of limited interaction of eddy currents with the defects. The 3D system uses a substantially different bridge circuit where each of the three coils are driven with a unique phase of the inspection frequency (0, 120, 240 degrees). The magnetic field generated by this three coil configuration results in a constant magnitude rotating magnetic field (Fig. 5.14). The 3D system is not sensitive to any concentric variations such as an expansion transition zone, tube sheet or support plate. The current flow pattern in a 3D probe causes both circumferential and axial current

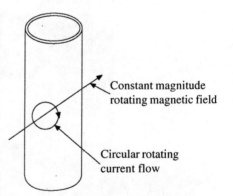

Fig. 5.14 Constant magnitude rotating magnetic field generated by a 3D probe

flow to occur at every point within the tube at some point in time. This makes the 3D ECT sensitive to circumferential and longitudinal defects and pits, whether these defects be at an expansion transition zone or elsewhere in the tube.

5.3.6   Inspection of Ferromagnetic Materials

Conventional ECT is not suitable for inspecting ferromagnetic materials such as carbon steel because of drastic attenuation of eddy currents and poor signal-to-noise ratio mainly due to permeability variations. The problem can be overcome by considering (a) saturation techniques or (b) remote field eddy current techniques.

Magnetic saturation can be achieved by adopting an electromagnet or a permanent magnet. While electromagnets are preferred for inspection during manufacturing stage, permanent magnets are preferred during in-service. In the permanent magnet ECT, a built-in magnet is used to magnetically saturate the tube wall and an eddy current coil to carry out inspection. The coil impedance change is therefore affected primarily by the combined probe fill factor and tube wall thickness changes, and other defects. If complete magnetic saturation of the tube wall is not obtained as in the case of thick walled ferritic tubing, the coil impedance change is predominantly affected by the permeability and probe fill factor changes. Thus, saturation of the ferromagnetic materials during ECT is essential. The technique is most suitable for tubing with thickness of about 0.9 mm. Figure 5.15 shows typical eddy current signals obtained from a high magnetically permeabile Monel-400 tube

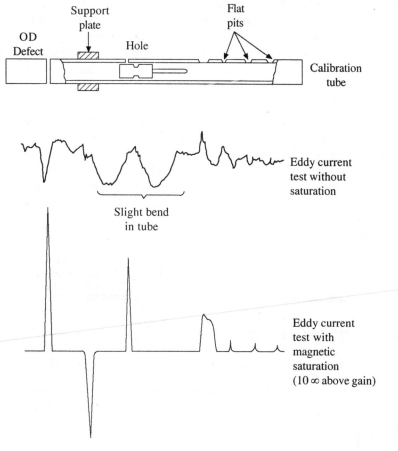

Fig. 5.15   Eddy current signals from a high magnetic permeability Monel 400 tube (test frequency 500 kHz)

with and without magnetic saturation. From the above figure, it is clear that saturation techniques are very effective in inspecting ferromagnetic materials.

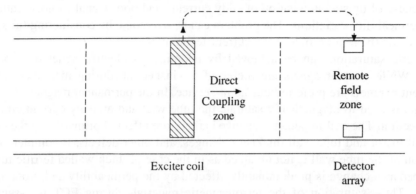

Fig. 5.16 **Schematic representation of the remote field concept showing double diffusion of the electromagnetic field through the tube wall**

In the case of remote field eddy current technique (RFECT), the probe uses a single internal sinusoidal exciter coil coaxial with the pipe and a circumferential array of detector coils mounted near the inner surface of the pipe wall. Unlike conventional eddy current tools, this detector array is located typically two to three tube diameters axially down the tube from the exciter as shown in Fig. 5.16. With this arrangement, the technique can detect internal and external defects in the tube wall with equal sensitivity. The schematic of the RFEC instrumentation setup shown in Fig. 5.17 consists of a function generator (sine wave excitation and reference square wave), low-distortion 20W power amplifier, special filters and a lock-in amplifier. The amplitude and phase lag (with respect to reference square wave of the exciter) of the receiver coil voltage are measured by a lock-in amplifier. The output of the lock-in amplifier is digitised using an ADC card and stored in the computer. Figure 5.18 shows typical remote field eddy current signals from 10%, 20% and 30% percentage wall loss grooves in a modified 9Cr-1Mo steel tube. Studies have indicated that the technique has detection capabilities of upto 10% wall thickness loss and thus has great promise for inspection of small diameter ferromagnetic tubings.

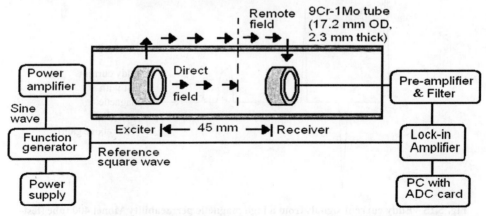

Fig. 5.17 **Schematic of RFEC instrumentation and the coupling of indirect field to the receiver coil**

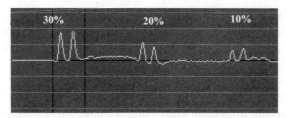

Fig. 5.18 **Remote field eddy current signals from 10%, 20% and 30% percentage wall loss grooves. Two peaks correspond to a single defect, one when the receiver is passing through defect and another when the exciter is passing through the defect**

5.4 SENSITIVITY

The sensitivity of defect detection depends upon the test material, its structure, the type of defect, the orientation of the defect, the depth of the defect, material quality and surface condition, i.e. surface roughness and surface layers such as scale. Furthermore, the detection sensitivity depends upon particular test technique, the type, magnitude and frequency of the excitation, and the type, size and performance of the sensors. In particular it should be noted that encircling coils see a large surface area of the material under test. Their sensitivity is, therefore, intrinsically less than a point probe system. In addition, the 'lift-off' effect is inescapable and the 'fit' of the coils round the test object is critical. The greater the mismatch between the diameter of the coil and the diameter of the object, the lower will be the sensitivity. Increasing the amplification of the measurement signal will partially overcome this problem but such amplification applies also to noise levels and the sensitivity is usually limited by this factor.

5.5 ADVANCED EDDY CURRENT TEST METHODS

For over four decades, eddy current testing has been one of the leading in-service inspection methods for detection of surface and subsurface defects. Significant improvements have been made to enhance the capabilities, reliability and user friendliness of the method. Modelling the effect of defects on eddy current response has also contributed significantly to the understanding of the key eddy current parameters as well as the reduction in the effect of noise and lift-off. Improved probes and instrumentation have been developed, and the effective use of low frequencies has enabled inspection of metallic layered structures for detection of defects in the second and third layers. The magneto-optic imaging (MOI) system is one of the spin-offs of the eddy current technique, and it is becoming an increasingly practical method for corrosion assessment of aircraft structures. Additionally, pulsed eddy current testing (PECT) and low frequency eddy current testing (LFECT) have recently emerged for specific applications. In this section, the principles and applications of MOI, PECT and LFECT are briefly described.

5.5.1 Magneto-optic/eddy current imaging (MOI)
In order to simplify the detection of defects and to visualize the eddy current response, the MOI technique has been developed. The MOI technique combines application of planar eddy current induction and magneto-optic imaging. MOI allows real time imaging of defects in components without removing surface coatings, if any. Since, the MOI system

employs an inductively coupled eddy current source, and because only magnetic fields are being sensed, there is no life-off correction. Therefore, paints and other coatings need not be removed prior to inspections. MOI system is a hand held portable instrument that requires minimal training. The speed and reliability of inspection are high.

(a) Principle of MOI: The development of MOI is based on the use of combination of principles of magneto-optic effect and eddy current induction. Faraday's law of induction states that a time varying magnetic field in the vicinity of an electrical conductor will induce a time varying electric field and thus a conduction current in the same conductor, which is the basis for the eddy current testing. The Faraday magneto-optic effect is defined as follows: When plane polarized light is transmitted through glass in a direction parallel to an applied magnetic field (M), the plane of polarization of linearly polarized light gets rotated by an angle (Fig. 5.19). The degree of rotation depends on the strength of the magnetic field and the value of the specific Faraday rotation of the glass or other material employed. In MOI, bismuth doped iron garnets with very large specific Faraday rotation, i.e., up to 30,000 degrees of rotation per centimeter of thickness is used instead of glass, thus increasing the sensitivity for detection of small variations in the magnetic fields, associated with fine defects in materials.

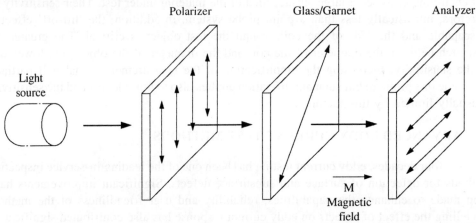

Fig. 5.19   Faraday magneto-optic effect

MOI uses a reflection mode geometry similar to that illustrated in Fig. 5.20. The reflection mode meets the twin requirements of near contact imaging: (1) The garnet film must be close to the sample otherwise the magnetic field variations become weak with distance away from surface and (2) The need to reduce surface light reflections from the garnet film. In the MOI system, the magnetic garnet film (sensor in Fig. 5.20) senses the magnetization of a test piece across a circular area of 100 mm diameter. To increase the sensitivity, two garnet films separated by a distance of 500 μm are used as it doubles the Faraday rotation of the incident light. The eddy current induction mechanism of the MOI induces eddy currents to flow linearly across the surface of the sample throughout the test region. Unlike in conventional eddy current technique which relies on currents flowing in coils to induce magnetic fields in the test piece, in MOI, the magnetic field with current is induced in a thin, planar foil (Induction foil in Fig. 5.20) placed near, and parallel to the surface of the test piece. With this arrangement, the induced eddy currents are not circular but planar and linear in nature, and hence these are referred to as 'sheet currents'.

In the vicinity of a defect having a dimension perpendicular to the induced eddy current flow, there will be an inhomogeneity in the eddy current density that will produce a stray magnetic field in the direction normal to the surface. When this stray field is added to the magnetic bias field introduced through the bias coils (Fig. 5.20) of the system, the Faraday rotation of polarized light transmitted through the area of the film will be in the opposite direction to that of light transmitted through a portion of the film where the stray magnetic field is absent. In other words, the polariser and the analyser are arranged in such a way (Fig. 5.20) that light is transmitted only when the Faraday rotation corresponds to defect free region with no stray magnetic field. Flawed areas of the sample are therefore discriminated from unflawed areas by detecting only the light that has been rotated corresponding to absence of stray magnetic field. Hence, flawed areas with fatigue cracks and corrosion, for example, are displayed black while unflawed areas are brighter. This output can be directly visualized through an eyepiece of the MOI system and can be filmed and displayed on a monitor or digitized for computer storage and signal processing.

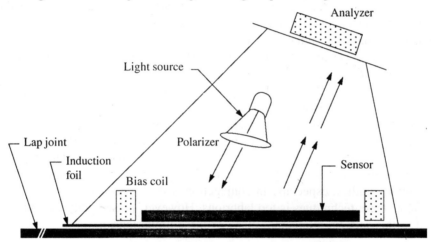

Fig. 5.20 Schematic setup of magneto-optic imaging

(b) Applications of MOI: The MOI system is designed to provide images of a relatively large area compared to that covered by conventional eddy current probe. Because of this, this method is more suitable for large, flat, convex, and relatively unobstructed areas. This also makes it ideal for examination of aircraft structures, viz. fuselage, wing and control surfaces. This technique has proved to be highly reliable and accurate in detection of fatigue cracks below the rivets and also for characterization of corrosion and other subsurface defects. Figure 5.21 shows a magneto optic image of fasteners without and with cracks in an airframe structure. The MOI system has also been employed for detection of inclusions that have different magnetic properties than the surrounding steel material.

5.5.2 Pulsed eddy current testing

(a) Introduction: Conventional eddy current techniques use single frequency sinusoidal excitation and measure the defect responses as impedance or voltage changes on an impedance plane display. To detect the defects, the magnitude and phase changes are interpreted. However, these methods are sensitive to a variety of parameters that hamper the complete

Fig. 5.21 Magneto-optic image showing fasteners with and without cracks in an airframe structure

characterization of the defects. Multiple frequency measurements can be combined to more accurately assess the integrity of the structures by reducing unwanted interfering signals that might otherwise mask the signals due to defects. Initial development led to the use of dual frequency eddy current testing where frequency-mixing functions allowed the quick application of the technique. This approach has been shown to be useful in reducing the effects of variations in plate separation when inspecting for second layer corrosion in lap splices of aircraft structures, for detection of defects under baffle plates in heat exchanger tubes etc.

The dual frequency method is advantageous when performing large area inspections by means of eddy current C-scans of specimens with corrosion under fasteners. Unfortunately, conventional multiple frequency methods can provide limited quantitative data. Swept frequency measurements using impedance analyzers perform well in quantitative corrosion characterization studies, especially in conjunction with theoretical models. However, the application of these techniques is too laborious. However, pulsed eddy current technique, discussed in this section, overcomes many of these limitations.

(b) Principle: In contrast to the conventional eddy current method that uses time-harmonic excitation of probes, pulsed eddy current (PEC) excites the probe's driving coil with a repetitive broadband pulse, such as a square wave. The advantages of pulsed excitation lie in its broadband nature; a spectrum of eddy current frequencies is applied simultaneously to the test specimen. The resulting transient current through the coil induces transient eddy currents in the test piece, which are associated with highly attenuating magnetic pulses propagating through the material. At each probe location, a series of voltage-time data pairs are produced as the induced field decays, analogous to ultrasonic inspection data. Since the produced pulses consist of a broad frequency spectrum, the reflected signal contains the depth information of the defect. Physically, the pulse is broadened and delayed as it travels deeper into the highly dispersive material. Therefore, defects close to the surface affect the eddy current response earlier in time than the defects located interior. Similar to the ultrasonic methods, the modes of presentation of PEC data can include A-, B- and C- scans. The excitation pulse, signal gain, and sensor configuration can be modified to suit specific applications.

Faraday's law states that eddy currents are induced in a conductor by a varying magnetic field. This magnetic field can be generated by passing a sinusoidally varying current through a coil. This is usually the situation in the conventional eddy current testing, discussed earlier. However, the current can be of other waveforms such as a train of pulses. Working on these lines, pulsed eddy current technique is based on send-receive principle, where the flow of eddy currents is monitored by observing the effect of their associated electromagnetic fields on the induced voltage of the receiver coil. The voltage pulse is analyzed by observing its amplitude with time. This pulsed eddy current response data can be analysed either in time domain or in the frequency domain or both. In time domain analysis, the peak amplitude is used to determine the size of the defect and the time of zero crossing is used to determine the depth of the flaw or in many cases the wall (thickness). The deeper the defect is located inside the test material, the longer the time to zero crossing. Time to zero crossing and phases at two different frequencies have also been used to determine the depth, length and height of flaws under rivets.

The pulsed eddy current technique, in a sense, is an extension to the multi frequency eddy current technique. The pulsed driving current produces an inherently wideband frequency spectrum, permitting extraction of more selective information that can not be obtained from the test specimen by single frequency method. This provides an opportunity for better discrimination of defect signals against interfering signals.

Eddy currents have advantage of penetrating into subsurface layers and therefore being sensitive to their condition, whether or not the layers are mechanically bonded. Pulsed eddy current technique is used for detection of hidden corrosion in layered structures such as aircraft lap-splices and corrosion under insulation in insulated components. The technique has the potential for distinguishing true metal loss and mere separation of the plates in lap-splices. A 10% loss of metal from the backside of a 4 mm thick plate of aluminum is the typical sensitivity that is achieved with PECT.

(c) Instrumentation: Pulsed eddy current system has special requirements in terms of excitation and detection. A large excitation coil is needed because of the predominantly low frequency components. Two types of systems are used for this technique: one is based on step function excitation at constant voltage of a single absolute coil and the other is based on a two-port reflection type probe. In the two-port system, an outer drive coil is excited with a constant voltage step function and the e.m.f. induced in a second coaxial coil is monitored. For detection, induction coils have less sensitivity because of their weak response to slow rate of change of magnetic field. A better solution is to use magnetic field transducers, such as magnetostrictive and Hall effect devices.

Typical block diagram of a pulsed eddy current instrument is shown in Fig. 5.22. The instrument is normally PC based with a 1 MHz 16 bit A/D converter card, a probe, electronic circuits for driving the probe and pre-conditioning the signal before digitization. Typical two-port pitch-catch probe consists of two coaxial air-core coils. The probe is excited with a 5V, 1kHz TTL square wave and the current in the coils is monitored by digitizing the voltage across a 1 Ohm resistor in series with the coil. A preamplifier provides a gain of 10 dB to the signal from the current-monitoring resistor prior to digitization. The system has a bandwidth of at least 200 kHz and most of the signal is centered at about 20 kHz. The high speed of the A/D card is important to achieve high bandwidth for making the measurements that give adequate resolution.

The high dynamic range is required because of the necessity to measure small change in the impedance caused by a defect as compared to high background signal. To make these

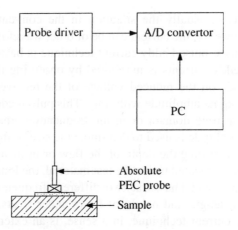

Fig. 5.22   Block diagram of pulsed eddy-current (PEC) instrument

small signals visible, the reference signal corresponding to a defect free region is subtracted from the incoming signal and this subtracted signal is used for display. Average of 100 to 500 signals is used to obtain a stable, relatively noise free display. Typical experimental results along with theoretical comparison for detection of 10 to 30% thinning at the bottom of top plate and top of bottom plate in a lap joint consisting of 1 mm thick 2024 aluminum plates are shown in Fig. 5.23. There is a good agreement between the theoretical and experimental values. The subtle differences in the patterns for the signals due to metal loss in top plate and bottom plate include: much less shift in time to the peak signal with increasing metal loss, and the time shift increases with increasing metal loss in the later case. This is attributed to the fact that the metal/air interface in the later case remains stationary, with the second interface (air/metal) receding with increasing loss of metal.

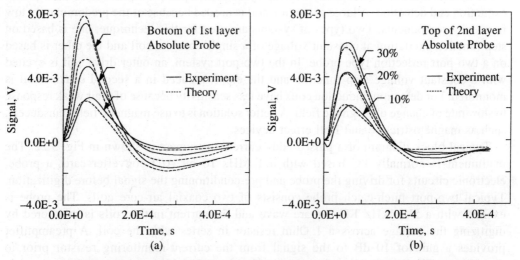

Fig. 5.23   Comparison of theory and experiment for pulsed eddy current measurements of flat-bottomed holes in simulated lap joints composed of 1 mm thick 2024 aluminum plates. (a) 10%, 20% and 30% loss of metal at the bottom of the first layer (b) 10%, 20% and 30% loss of metal at the top of the second layer

Pulsed eddy current technique can also be employed for testing materials with high electrical conductivity, such as copper, where single frequency techniques generally fail. This technique also enables detection of flaws, near the surface and at depth, simultaneously, without the need to change the probe and the operating frequency.

Pulsed eddy current technique is also used for inspection of corrosion under insulation (CUI) in insulated pipelines. M/s. Rontgen Technische Dienst bv., The Netherlands, has developed a system INCOTEST (Insulated Component Test) for inspection of thermally insulated carbon steel components. The method, originated in the USA, is based on worldwide patents held by M/s. ARCO, USA. The technique measures the wall thickness without the need to have contact with the steel component itself, thus avoiding labor-intensive and expensive insulation removal. An eddy current sensor of a design with extremely tight tolerances is placed on top of the thermal insulation. This sensor consists of a transmitter coil and a receiver coil, again within narrow tolerances, to achieve a quasi-focusing effect, thus giving a smallest possible sensing area, called 'footprint'.

The current through the transmitter coil is pulsed. First, the transmitter coil is excited, the current flows and a magnetic field is built-up in the material. Then the current is switched off and the magnetic field vanishes. As a result, eddy currents are induced in the near surface region (skin) of the material. These eddy currents then diffuse into the wall and decay with a certain rate. Once they arrive at the far surface (back wall), the eddy currents decay more rapidly. Using the receiver coil, this time of arrival at the back-wall is sensed. At places with wall loss, the arrival time will be earlier than at places with no wall loss. From this time of arrival, the system calculates the average wall thickness. A change in the wall thickness indicates the presence of corrosion/erosion. Each measurement takes several seconds depending on the thickness of the material/component.

The system can measure wall thickness through insulation up to 100 mm thickness, and in favourable circumstances even up to 150 mm (including chicken wire as reinforcement and aluminum or steel sheathing). The system is also suited to detect erosion (at the inside surface). The measurement area (foot print) depends on the thickness of the insulation (sensor lift off) and type of sheathing. Typically, with 50 mm of insulation, a corroded area having a diameter of 80 mm can be detected. The system can be used for wall thickness measurement in the range of 6 to 65 mm and pipes of more than 75 mm diameter. The measurement time is about 2 to 5 seconds for 6 to 12 mm wall thickness and 7 to 40 seconds for 12 to 65 mm thickness.

Although this system is originally developed for large stand-off applications, it can also be used for 'semi-contact/non-contact' measurements. The method is suitable for measuring through non-conductive and non-magnetic coatings and thick layers of deposit. It is possible to measure the wall thickness of a pipe through 20 mm Neoprene coating or through a 6 mm thick Monel cladding. Because the method is tolerant to bad surface conditions, it can be applied on dirty and very rough surfaces, for example encrusted boiler tubes. By protecting the sensor from extreme heat, the system can be used on hot components with temperature up to 773K.

'Passive' pulsed eddy current inspection is being considered for detection of non-metallic inclusions such as silicon dioxides and aluminum oxides in sheet metal. Normally inclusions are clustered, and one can be in the form of elongated stringers due to the rolling and drawing processes used in making the sheet metal. Attempts are being made to develop NDE techniques capable of on-line detection of such clustered and elongated inclusions in sheet metals moving at speeds of 300 to 1500 meters per minute during rolling process. Earlier studies showed that eddy current technique can be employed for detection of such inclusion clusters if the speed of movement of sheet is low, i.e. about 60 meters per minute. For overcoming this limitation, a new approach is attempted. In this approach, rather than inducing currents into the metal while measuring the coil impedance, the motion of the metal sheet is used to induce current as it passes over a fixed magnetic field. The voltage developed across a sense coil is monitored to detect changes in the induced current caused by resistivity changes in the metal. This method is called 'passive' pulsed eddy current testing.

Figure 5.24 shows how a coil and magnet are placed with respect to the moving sheet metal. Figure 5.25 shows the magnetic field seen at a reference location along a moving metal sheet at one instant in time. The width (in time) of the magnetic pulse is the ratio of the magnet width to the metal speed. The typical pulse time is expected to be about 1 millisecond. This technique is equivalent to holding the metal while moving the magnet, or equivalently, pushing a coil with 1 millisecond current pulses. The voltage measured across the coil remains zero until a flaw (or resistivity change) moves into the magnetic field and alters the induced current distribution. The voltage induced would be proportional to the volume of the inclusions.

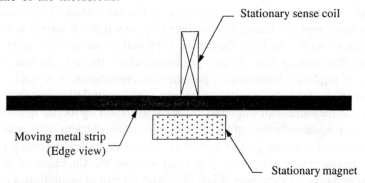

Fig. 5.24   Experimental setup showing sheet metal moving between fixed magnet and sense coil

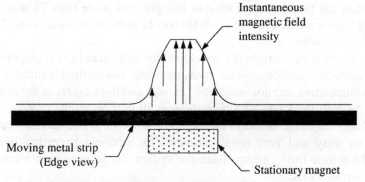

Fig. 5.25   Snapshot of magnetic field applied to metal strip

Preliminary results from laboratory studies carried out under simulated conditions indicated that surface breaking inclusions could be detected in a 0.25 mm thick steel disc moving at high speed (Figs. 5.26(a) and (b)). The investigators point out that without metallographic comparison, it is difficult to quantify the effectiveness of this technique in measuring the inclusion content or sizing capabilities. The images in Fig. 5.26 imply that this method can detect more inclusions in sheet with inclusions seen breaking the surface than a sheet without surface-breaking inclusions. However, Fig. 5.26(b) does not imply that there are no inclusions present and also the sheet tested to obtain Fig. 5.26(a) could have had inclusions beneath the surface.

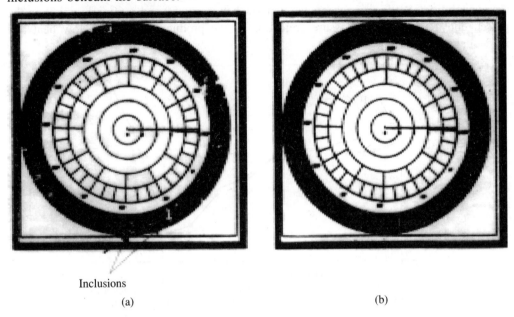

Inclusions

(a)   (b)

Fig. 5.26   (a) Radial scan of thin steel disk with inclusions seen at surface;
(b) Radial scan of thin steel disk without inclusions seen at surface

Pulsed eddy current technique has also been considered for assessing heat treating or thermal forming processes. The surface hardness measurements to qualify the process/product can not recognize the alterations in the process that do not cause variation in the surface hardness but do alter the subsurface microstructure. For example, it has been found that in induction heat treating operations (including post heat oil quenching), it is possible to reduce the quench time to far below process specification without significantly altering the surface hardness, although subsurface microstructure may not meet the specification. Such unacceptable variations can be detected using pulsed eddy current measurements by employing field excitation with a broad frequency spectrum from DC to hundreds of kilohertz. This allows one to detect small changes in the electromagnetic properties of a product both at surface and subsurface regions.

Two process variables are found to decide the surface hardness and the subsurface microstructure in induction hardening process. These are total applied heat and quench time. Pulsed eddy current technique for assessing the induction hardened intake and exhaust valves of the automobile engines is discussed below. Through simulated studies, it has been first established that the pulsed eddy current output is found to linearly increase with increase in the hardness. Subsequently, variations in the surface hardness and subsurface microstructure have been simulated in a set of specimens by varying the applied heat and the quench time. Figure 5.27 shows the influence of these process variables on the eddy current output and the hardness. For the conditions of normal quench time (15 seconds) and variable heat, the pulsed eddy current response tracks the Rockwell C hardness, as indicated by the first simulated studies. For the case of fixed normal heat input, but with variable quench time, the Rockwell C hardness shows little or no change with respect to changing quench time, indicating its failure to detect the improper quench time employed. However, the pulsed eddy current response shows a significant change with respect to the change in the quench time. Setting an acceptance window between + 50 and + 60 (arb. units) on the pulsed eddy current output assures rejection of the products made with low heat and inadequate quenching.

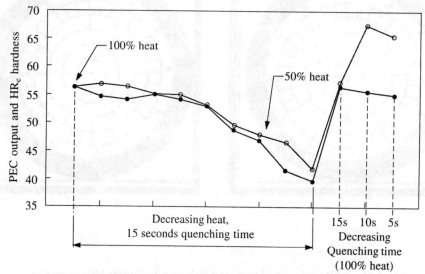

Fig. 5.27   **Variation in pulsed eddy current output (O) and hardness (□) with input heat and quenching time**

5.5.3 Low frequency eddy current testing

Low frequency eddy current testing (LFECT) technique has been primarily developed for detection of corrosion under insulation on piping and vessels. Corrosion under insulation (CUI) on piping and vessels represents one of the major maintenance problems and inspection challenges in the petrochemical industry. The corrosion on the outside of the component is usually the result of water entrapment in the thermal insulation. If undetected, this could eventually lead to leaks in the pipes and vessels. It would be highly cost effective to use appropriate NDT technique to detect CUI without removing the insulation. The LFECT technique is also gaining popularity for other applications such as inspection of multi layer structures and welds of pipes with small diameter and high thickness.

(a) Detection of corrosion under insulation: The CUI problems are found to be (1) severe in carbon steel components and moderately severe in those made of stainless steel, (2) the problem is severe in pipes less than 300 mm diameter and (3) CUI occurs in the case of a variety of insulations including asbestos, calcium silicate, fiberglass, mineral fibre, mineral wool, flexible rubber, polyisocyanurate, polyurethane and other foams.

Real time portable X-ray devices have been developed to view CUI using a tangential X-ray beam. However, this method is very slow to use in routine inspection. One relatively new technique for detection of CUI is the pulsed eddy current testing technique discussed in the earlier section. The pulsed eddy current technique is not a scanning technique; the probe head must be left in place for a few seconds to tens of seconds depending on the wall thickness of the component being inspected. However, the LFECT technique has the capability for rapid scanning in comparison to pulsed eddy current testing. The method is very sensitive to localized damage, such as cracks, or pits, and can detect severe wall thinning. The primary limitation of this technique is its limited lift-off capabilities, which restricts the insulation thickness to a few tens of centimeters.

LFECT technique uses frequencies less than 50 Hz to penetrate up to 50 mm of insulation in addition to the metallic weather cover (overcap) on the component. The technique has the capability for detection of CUI in areas as small as 50 mm diameter. Smaller areas of CUI can be detected with thinner insulation.

LFECT technique relies on specialized eddy current probes and modified instrumentation in order to provide high intensity, stable eddy currents at very low frequencies. Special probes with dual elements and built-in position encoder to give location information have been developed. The LFECT systems have the following capabilities:

- For piping with up to 50 mm of insulation and smooth metallic weather covers, detection of CUI in areas as small as 20 cm^2 with a 25% loss of wall.
- The system is capable of discriminating between CUI and other indications that provide spurious signals associated with weather cover overcaps and straps, carbon steel insulation retaining wires, heating lines, access plugs and weld joints.

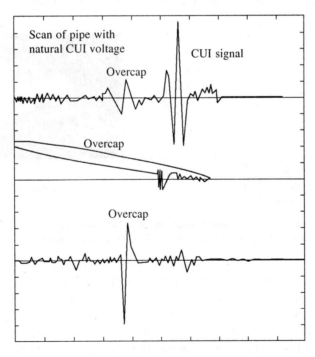

Fig. 5.28 System response to CUI damage on 350 mm pipe through 50 mm of insulation and weather cover

Figure 5.28 shows the response of a LFECT system, i.e. trace of voltage (Y-axis) vs. time or position (X-axis) from a pipe section covered with 50 mm insulation and an aluminum cover (overcap). The signal corresponding to the CUI (later confirmed by removing the insulation) along with the signal due to the overcap is seen in the top trace. The bottom trace, which is generated simultaneously along with the top trace, contains no signal from the CUI due to the selection of phase angle for the display. The signal due to the overcap is also shown in the impedance plane display as given in the middle portion of Fig. 5.28.

(b) Other applications of LFECT: LFECT has been employed by Fraunhofer Institute for NDT, Germany, for assessment of stainless steel internal cladding of reactor pressure vessels in Germany. The technique has been used to determine the thickness of the cladding and to detect sub-clad flaws. The technique can also be used to detect thinning due to corrosion and cracks in multi-layered structures. One important application is for detecting or estimating corrosion on the hidden side of aircraft skin panels and detection of fatigue cracks beneath external repair doublers. Reflections of ultrasound at layer boundaries would not allow application of ultrasonic technique. Low frequency eddy current testing can be used for estimating corrosion in underlying structure because the eddy currents will penetrate into the second layer of material even in presence of air gap. Detection of small changes in the low frequency field caused by deeply buried defects, is however, a major challenge. This challenge is met by using newly developed Giant Magnetic Resistance (GMR) based sensors. The use of the GMR device, combined with appropriate shielding and flux focusing has enabled the detection of fatigue cracks buried up to 1 centimeter in aluminum alloy plates.

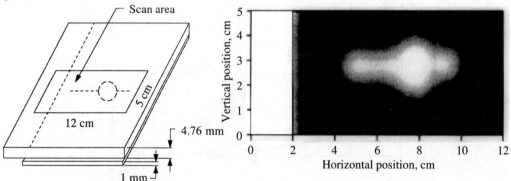

Fig. 5.29 **Low frequency eddy current C-scan image of a double layer aluminum alloy specimen with fatigue cracks grown from either side of a drilled center hole**

The GMR devices have several advantages. The devices are small, low cost, highly sensitive, and require minimal instrumentation. Commercial GMR sensors are based upon electron scattering in antiferromagnetically coupled multi-layers. In the absence of an applied field, the resistivity of the device is high due to scattering between oppositely polarized electrons. An external field aligns the magnetic moments of the ferromagnetic layers, eliminating this scattering mechanism and thereby reducing the resistivity of the material. This mechanism is sensitive only to the magnitude of the field but not to its direction. The sensors have sensitivities between 10^{-9} and 10^{-12} Tesla. As an example of application of GMR probe, imaging of a fatigue crack in an aluminum alloy is given here. Figure 5.29 shows the geometry of the specimen with fatigue crack along with the C-scan image of the scanned area of the specimen obtained by GMR probe. The specimen is a two layered aluminum alloy lay-up. The top layer was formed of an unflawed 4.76 mm thick plate. The lower layer was a 1 mm thick plate with fatigue cracks grown from either side of a drilled center hole. The sample was scanned from the unflawed side. The two fatigue cracks originating from the center hole could be seen clearly in Fig. 5.29.

Attempts are also being made to apply LFECT together with GMR sensors for detection of ID surface-breaking cracks in girth welds of austenitic pipes of small diameter but wall thickness up to 15 mm. Developments are also underway for use of LFECT in place of magnetic particle technique for inspection of ferritic weldments.

5.5.4 SQUID based eddy current testing

Superconducting quantum interference devices (SQUID) generally work at cryogenic temperatures, where coolant is required. Below a certain temperature, superconductors will have a zero resistance in conducting a DC current and a superconductor ring will enclose only specific levels of magnetic flux related to quantum theory. SQUID has very high magnetic field sensitivity, which is nearly independent of frequency. The advantages of SQUID are especially evident where a low excitation frequency is required. A typical comparison between conventional eddy current systems and the SQUID-based system shows an improvement in the signal to noise ratio of up to three orders of magnitude for cracks at a depth larger than 13 mm. The high dynamic range, of typically 140 dB/šHz or more allows the detection of small field changes in the presence of large background fields produced, for example, by edge effects or inhomogeneities in conductivity. The other advantages of SQUIDs include broad dynamic range (> 80 dB) and their intrinsically quantitative nature.

SQUIDs that operate at room temperature have also been developed. An instrument, based on high transition temperature (high-T_c) SQUID, that is able to carry out inspections for detection of cracks and corrosion through layers of aluminum with combined thickness of 50 mm has been successfully built. Although SQUID based eddy current testing has promising capabilities, it is still not yet an option for general industry today because the cost involved is still very high.

As discussed in this chapter, several advanced eddy current testing techniques have shown promise for various applications. Together with advances in digital computing power and signal processing techniques, these advanced eddy current testing techniques can provide reliable methodologies for detection of subsurface flaws, and development of methods to reconstruct the images of the flaws.

5.6 APPLICATIONS

Eddy current testing is used for evaluation of a wide range of products in the industry. ECT can be applied to round, flat and irregularly shaped conductive objects.

(a) Conductivity (varies with material characteristics)
(b) Hardness (conductivity changes as the hardness changes)
(c) Strength (conductivity value is related to the stress characteristics of the object)
(d) Heat treatment (variation in heat treatment causes variations in conductivity)
(e) Dimensions (dimensional changes cause charges in lift-off or fill factor between the object and the coil)

(f) Discontinuities (cracks, inclusions, etc. cause change in output impedance)

(g) Coating thickness (differences in conductivity exist between a conductive coating and article. Nonconductive coating varies the lift-off between the coil and the conductive surface of the object).

ECT has been successfully employed for on line testing of wires, rods and tubes. A wide range of diameters of different materials are being inspected as part of quality control, using ECT. The use of microprocessors has lent itself to automated analysis of the results and on-line testing, leading to increased reliability, extended flexibility, enhanced production and cost saving in a number of industries.

5.7 LIMITATIONS

Like other NDT technique, ECT has certain limitations. The major limitation of ECT is that only electrically conductive materials can be inspected. Since too many parameters affect the eddy current probe impedance, ECT is not effective when more that one variable are present. Another limitation of ECT is that it can inspect, with reasonable sensitivity, metallic components of thickness up to 6 mm only. The EC signal is more closely related to volume of the material lost than to the wall thickness lost. Hence, evaluations should be made cautiously. For critical applications, results may need to be verified by an alternate technique. Equipment is costly as compared with MPT.

5.8 STANDARDS

1. Doc: Glossary of terms used in electromagnetic (eddy current) testing
   MTD21(3534)   (in print).
2. IS 6398: 1984   Code of practice for eddy current testing of seamless ferrous pipes and tubes.
3. IS 11612: 1986 Code of practice for eddy current testing of nonferrous seamless pipes and tubes.
4. ASTM E309–87 Eddy current examination of steel tubular products using magnetic saturation.
5. ASTM E371–88 Electromagnetic (Eddy current) examination of Nickel and Nickel alloy tubular products.
6. ASTM E426–88 Electromagnetic (Eddy current) examination of seamless and welded tubular products, austenitic stainless steel and similar alloys.
7. ASTM E243–85 Electromagnetic examination of seamless copper and copper alloy tubes.
8. ASTM E690–85 In-situ electromagnetic eddy current examination of non-magnetic heat exchanger tubes.

Radiography

The historic discovery of X-rays by W.C. Roentgen in 1895 and radioactivity by Becquerel in 1896 and their subsequent and logical application to the examination of material objects provided the starting point for the development and advancement of industrial radiography. This technique is one of the most widely used NDT methods for the detection of internal defects such as porosity and voids. With proper orientation of the X-ray beam, planar defects can also be detected with radiography. It is also suitable for detecting changes in material composition, thickness measurements, and locating unwanted or defective components hidden from view in an assembled part. The basic advantage of the use of ionising radiation in NDT arises from the fact that the objects which can be examined can range in size and shapes from microminiature electronic parts to mammoth missiles or power plant structures. Further, the method can be used on a variety of materials. No prior preparation of the specimen surface is necessary, unlike with other NDT methods. The main disadvantage of radiography is the hazards due to exposure to radiation for the operators, which can produce biological damage to body tissues. Consequently, strict control of human exposure to radiation is necessary. In this chapter, an overview is made on the basic principles of radiography and the various techniques used for inspection of engineering components.

6.1 BASIC PRINCIPLE

The purpose of radiography is to show the presence and nature of defects or other structural discontinuities in the interior of the materials under examination. The principle of radiographic examination is shown in Fig. 6.1. This technique makes use of the ability of short wavelength electromagnetic radiations, such as X-rays or gamma rays, to penetrate objects. In general, the shorter the wavelength, the greater is the penetrating power. The radiation that enters through the material, some being absorbed in the material itself and amount of absorption is a function of the density and thickness of the material. Should there be a cavity or discontinuity in the interior of the material, the beam of radiation will have less material to pass through than in solid material. Consequently, there will be a variation in the absorption of the rays by the material in the defective area. The variation, if measured or recorded on a film sensitive to X- or gamma radiation, produces an image that will indicate the presence of the defect. The image is an X-ray shadow of the interior of the material. Thus, radiography is essentially based on the principle of shadow projection and such a shadow picture is called a radiograph. Variations in the darkness may be interpreted to provide information concerning the internal structure of the material. The basic setup essentially consists of a source of radiation, the object to be radiographed and a detector which is normally a sheet of photographic film.

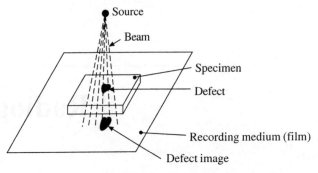

Fig. 6.1   Principle of radiographic examination

6.2   ELECTROMAGNETIC RADIATION SOURCES

6.2.1   X-Ray Source

In the widely used conventional X-radiography, the source of radiation is an X-ray tube. The X-ray tube consists of a glass bulb under vacuum, enclosing a positive electrode or 'anode' and a negative electrode or 'cathode'. The cathode comprises a filament which, when brought to incandescence by a current of a few amperes emits electrons. Under the effect of electrical tension set up between the anode and the cathode, these electrons from the cathode are attracted to the anode. This stream of electrons is concentrated in a beam by a cylinder or a focusing cup. The anti-cathode is a slip of metal with high melting point recessed into the anode at the place where it is struck by the beam of electrons. It is by impinging on the anti-cathode that fast moving electrons give rise to X-rays. Figure 6.2 shows the layout of a typical X-ray tube built by Collidge in 1913 which also used a heated filament to produce electrons. The development of electronics has led to the availability of constant potential

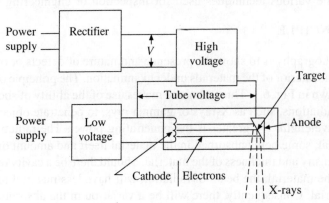

Fig. 6.2   Schematic setup of X-ray tube and circuit

units which give stable operating conditions. The replacement of the glass tubes by metal ceramic ones has led to an extended tube life. X-ray machines are characterised by the operating voltage and current which determine the penetrability and intensity of the radiation produced. Modern X-ray generators are available up to 450 kV and 15 mA. X-ray equipment with dual focal spot sizes and ultra-small focal spot and portable (~ 15 kg) equipment with an output voltage of 200 kV and 3 mA current are also available. Highly automated self propelled X-ray mini-crawlers which travel within pipelines are used to take radiographs of pipelines/welds from inside.

The area of the anti-cathode which is struck by the electron flux is called the "focal spot" or "TARGET". It is essential that this area should be sufficiently large, in order to avoid local overheating which might damage the anti-cathode and to allow rapid dissipation of heat. The projection of the focal spot on a surface perpendicular to the axis of the beam of X-rays is termed as the "optical focus" or "focus". This focus has to be as small as possible in order to achieve maximum sharpness in the radiographic image. The size of the focal spot is measured by the pinhole imaging technique. Here, a pinhole made in a suitably thick material with high density (lead) and having dimension one order less than the expected focal spot size is used. The pinhole is aligned parallel to the tube axis and perpendicular to X-ray beam and a radiographic image of the focal spot is obtained. By scanning this image using a microdensitometer, the focal spot size is obtained.

6.2.2 Production of X-Rays

X-rays are produced when fast moving electrons are suddenly brought to rest by colliding with matter. Electrons may also lose energy by ionisation and excitation of the target atoms. However, these do not result in X-ray production. The accelerated electrons therefore lose their kinetic energy very rapidly at the surface of the metal plate, and energy conversion consequently occurs. The kinetic energy of the accelerated electrons can be converted in three different ways.

(i) A very small fraction, i.e. less than 1%, is converted into X-radiation. The conversion factor f can be estimated by an approximate empirical relation

$$f = 1.1 \times 10^{-9} ZV$$

where Z is the atomic number of the target and V the energy of electron in volts. For tungsten ($Z = 74$) target, the fraction of X-ray energy converted into X-rays at 120 kV is 0.98%.

(ii) Approximately 99% of energy of electrons is converted into heat by increasing the thermal vibration of the atoms of the target, the temperature of which may consequently rise considerably.

(iii) Some of the electrons have sufficient energy to eject orbital electrons from the atoms of the target material which are ionised. The secondary electrons produced in this way may escape from the surface of the target and subsequently be recaptured by it producing further heat or secondary radiation.

The two most important distinguishing features of a beam of X-rays are its INTENSITY and QUALITY. The first term of course refers to how much radiation i.e. quantity of radiation. The second term quality refers to the kind of radiation i.e. how penetrating the radiation is.

6.2.3 High Energy X-Ray Source

Examination of thicker sections is carried out using high energy X-rays whose energy value is 1 MeV or more. Using high energy X-rays, possibilities of large distance to thickness ratios with correspondingly low geometrical distortion, short exposure times and high production rate can be achieved. Also, small focal spot size and reduced amount of high angle scattered X-rays reaching the film result in radiographs with good contrast, excellent penetrameter sensitivity and good resolution. A number of machines such as synchrotron, betatron and Van De Graff type electrostatic generators are available of which, electron Linear Accelerator (Linac) is the most popular.

6.2.4 Gamma Ray Sources

In contra-distinction to X-ray machines which emit a broad band of wavelengths, gamma ray sources emit one or few discrete wavelengths. Radiography with gamma rays has the advantages of simplicity of the apparatus used, compactness of radiation source, and independence from outside power. This facilitates the examination of pipe, pressure vessels and other assemblies in which the access to interior is difficult. Gamma rays are electromagnetic radiation emitted from an unstable nucleus. Each isotope with unstable nucleus will have characteristic nuclear energy levels and intensities for the emitted radiation. The gamma ray energy levels remain constant for a particular isotope but the intensity decays with time as indicated by the half life.

Where a variety of radioisotopes are produced in a nuclear reactor, only a select few have been utilised for the purposes of radiography. The rest of the other isotopes produced have been found to be unsuitable for a variety of reasons such as shorter half life, low intensity and high cost of production. The four most popular radiographic sources are: Cobalt 60 (Co-60), Iridium 192 (Ir-192), Caesium 137 (Cs-137) and Thulium 170 (Th-170). Table 6.1 lists important characteristics of four isotopes most commonly used for radiography.

Table 6.1 Characteristics of Gamma Ray Isotopes

Characteristics	Cobalt-60	Iridium-192	Caesium-137	Thulium-170
Half life	5.27 yrs	74.3 days	30.1 yrs	129 days
Energy (MeV)	1.33–1.17	0.3–0.6	0.66	0.08–0.05
Rhm/Ci	1.35	0.55	0.34	0.003
Typical source				
curies	10	30	75	50
size (dia. mm)	2.5	2.5	10	2.5
Steel thickness which can be radiographed	200 mm	75 mm	40–100 mm	10 mm

All the above radioisotopes, except Caesium-137 are produced by (n, γ) reaction. Caesium-137 is separated out from the fission products of the irradiated reactor fuel. Cobalt-60 and Iridium-192 are available in high specific activities and thus tiny sources of these radioisotopes giving intense radiation have found popular use. Specific activity is defined as activity in curies per gram of material.

6.2.5 Properties of X- and Gamma Rays

X-rays and gamma rays are electromagnetic radiations similar to light waves except that their wavelength is much shorter. Some of their properties are given below.

1. They move in straight lines and at the speed of light.
2. They cannot be deflected by means of lens or prism although their path can be bent (diffracted) by a crystalline grid.
3. They pass through matter. The degree of penetration depends on the kind of matter and the energy of radiation.
4. They are ionising radiation, that is to say they liberate electrons in matter.
5. They can impair and destroy living cells.
6. Many substances fluoresce when they absorb X-radiation notable among them are calcium tungstate, zincsulphide, lead-barium sulphate and some cadmium compounds.

6.3 RADIATION ATTENUATION IN THE SPECIMEN

X-ray or gamma radiation when pass through the specimen get attenuated and reduced in the intensity. The important modes of this absorption are: (i) Photoelectric effect, (ii) Rayleigh scattering, (iii) Compton scattering and (iv) Pair production. The radiation attenuation in the specimen of thickness x can be calculated by using the following expression:

$$I = I_0 B e^{-\mu x} \tag{6.1}$$

where I = intensity of radiation emerging out of the specimen, I_0 = intensity of radiation when value of $x = 0$, μ = linear absorption coefficient per mm thickness, B = build up factor.

For practical purposes in radiographic testing, half value layers (HVL) or tenth value layers (TVL) as given in Table 6.2 can also be used for calculation of radiation attenuation.

Table 6.2   HVL and TVL of Steel and Lead (Thickness in mm)

Material		Cobalt-60	Caesium-137	Iridium-192	Thulium-170
Lead	HVL	12.5	6.35	4.8	–
	TVL	41.2	21.3	16.25	–
Steel	HVL	21.1	17.0	15.5	1.8
	TVL	70.0	57.0	51.0	6.1

6.4   EFFECT OF RADIATION ON FILM

6.4.1 Film Ionisation

The radiation source required to produce a certain blackening on the film depends on the energy of radiation. Low energy radiation needs smaller dose to ensure a certain film density as compared with hard radiation. Various isotopic sources with different radiation energy will cause different film ionisation. For example,

Cobalt-60 = 1   Iridium-192 = 2.35
Caesium-137 = 5.5   Thulium-170 = 4-4.5

6.4.2 Inherent Unsharpness

The inherent unsharpness is the result of the interaction of high energy radiation with emulsion on the film. During the interaction, the electrons are dislodged from the silver halide emulsion after gaining excess energy in the form of kinetic energy. The electrons with high kinetic energy tend to fly off causing ionisation in the adjacent silver halide grains. Thus the boundaries of the exposed areas will show an unsharpness of the image which is called inherent unsharpness or film unsharpness (U_i). Inherent unsharpness value is about 0.1 mm without lead screen and it is 0.2 mm when a film is used with a lead screen.

6.5   RADIOGRAPHIC IMAGING

The appearance of a distinguishable image on a radiograph is dependent on several factors, the most important of which is the difference in radiation intensity at various locations in the image plane. The difference in intensity, then must be a function of the abnormality within the part being inspected.

6.5.1   Geometrical Factors

True focal spot for sources used in conventional radiography is not point source but rather is of a few *millimetres* in size. Due to the finite source size, the image projected on to the film is enlarged leading to geometric unsharpness (Fig. 6.3). Geometric unsharpness (U_g) is given by

$$U_g = \frac{ft}{L_0} \qquad (6.2)$$

where F = focal spot size, t = distance from the object to the receiving plane, L_0 = distance from the source to the object.

General rules as given below should be practised for optimum results:

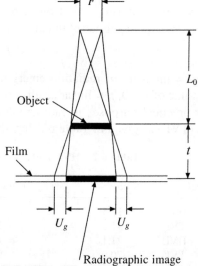

Fig. 6.3   **Geometric unsharpness in radiographic examination**

(i)   Source or focal spot size should be as small as practicable. Ideal source will be a point source.

(ii) Source to object distance should be as large as possible.

(iii) The film should be in close contact with object.

(iv) Source location should be such that radiation passes through the object thickness.

6.5.2   Radiographic Film

Radiographic film is similar to photographic film in that there is a central carrier called the film base that is made of thin sheet of polyester type material. This is normally transparent and serves only as the carrier for the chemically reactive material that forms the emulsion. Emulsion consisting of a silver halide recording medium with a binder (gelatin) is applied to both sides of the base. Additionally, a protective layer may be applied over the emulsion. The silver halide is a granular material and its grain size has a significant effect on the exposure as well as the resolution ability of the film for defect detail. When radiation strikes the emulsion a change takes place in the emulsion. This change is referred to as the "latent image" (latent simply means 'not available', or hidden). Upon processing, the grains that have been exposed will be darkened. The silver halide is removed from the unexposed grains during film processing leaving a transparent area. Thus the darkness or density of the film is directly a function of the exposure of the grains on the film to the radiation.

The film speed is another important film parameter. A film is called high speed film when its grains would begin reacting to the exposure considerably sooner than other films. Realizing that exposure is the product of time and intensity, the effect of film speed is rather significant. For a constant intensity, for e.g., the grains of high speed film would produce the required density before the grains of slow speed film. It is to be noted that, the faster speed films have larger grains and, therefore may not be able to produce the minute detail. Grain size in a film affects quality and time of exposure. Slow films have extra-fine grain or fine grain and give better quality even though the exposure time is longer.

Of the many films available, the films that are referred in many standards and their classification are given in the Table 6.3.

Table 6.3   Various Class of Films and Their Characteristics

Class	Film	Characteristics
Class I	Kodak RR, Kodak M, Structurix D 2	Extra fine grain high contrast, slow speed
Class II	Kodak AA, Structurix D4, Structurix D 7	Fine grain, high contrast, medium speed
Class III	Kodak Kodirex X, Structurix D 10	High speed
Class IV	They are screen type films used in conjunction with fluorescent screens. These films are not recommended in industrial radiography.	

6.5.3   Intensifying Screens

Use of thin screens/foils made out of heavier metals has been found to produce intensification when exposed them along with films to X or gamma radiations of 70 kV and above. The screens help to cut down the exposure time by utilising more effectively the radiations reaching the film. The intensification effect is primarily due to the liberation of photo-electrons from the screen/foil. For exposure using X or gamma radiation, following pairs of lead screens are recommended for optimum results:

Cobalt-60	Front	0.1-0.2 mm
	Rear	0.2-0.5 mm
Iridium-192	Front	0.1-0.15 mm
Caesium-137	Rear	0.2 mm
Thulium-70	Front	0.02 mm

The intensification factor with the above screens is generally 2 to 2.5. Fluorescent screens, though give much higher intensification factor (approximately 5 to 6 or even more), are not recommended for use in radiography because of high screen unsharpness. The fluorometallic screens have been reported to have twin advantages of speed and low screen unsharpness.

6.5.4 Film Density

All radiographs must have a readable density (blackening of the film). This is one of the first checks made on a radiograph before attempting to interpret it. The radiograph, when exposed and developed, will have various shades of density, depending upon how much exposure it received. The variables that affect density in a radiograph are kV, milliampere/source strength, distances, development procedure, film speed, and time.

A measure of the amount of exposure seen by the developed film is the light transmission density or optical density or film density D which is given by

$$D = \log_{10} \frac{I_0}{I_t} \qquad (6.3)$$

where I_0 = light intensity which strikes the film, I_t = transmitted light intensity. To check the density in a radiograph, a densitometer is used. Most specifications call for a film density of 1.5 to 3.3.

6.5.5 Radiographic Sensitivity

The important consideration that must be made in making a radiograph is the amount of exposure that will penetrate in a given material. The radiographers should select an exposure that will produce just enough X-rays to penetrate the material to be radiographed. In other words use as low an exposure as possible to penetrate the material. Most standards recommend X-ray voltage settings and radioisotope sources to be used for various material thicknesses. This is one of the many variables the inspector must check and understand in radiographic inspection.

Radiographic sensitivity is the ability of the technique to reveal the smallest discontinuity on the radiograph. The term sensitivity is used in the sense that smaller the value better is the detection capability. The sensitivity can be expressed either in absolute value or in percentage with respect to the thickness of the specimen.

Contrast sensitivity: Amount of radiation exposure affects the contrast sensitivity. Contrast sensitivity may be defined as the film density. In other words, it is the ease with which an image can be seen against the radiograph's background. Without contrast sensitivity, material defects in the radiograph cannot be seen. If there is less material in one area, the film will record that area darker than the surrounding area. This will be shown on the radiograph an area with different film density (difference in blackness) which is the contrast. It is obvious that optimum contrast is required. Lowering the contrast sensitivity leads to failure to locate the defects that would normally be found.

Detail sensitivity: When proper contrast is produced on a radiograph, all the defects that the radiographic test can locate will be seen. In addition, 'detail sensitivity' is needed to identify the various types of defects. In radiographic inspection, 'detail sensitivity' is determined by the sharpness with which image detail of the penetrameter is shown.

The variables that control detail sensitivity in a radiograph are the focal spot, anode size or target area of the tube, the focal-to-film distance, and the type of film. The smaller the focal spot the better is the 'detail sensitivity'. Equipment manufacturer/radioactive source supplier specifies the focal spot/source size in mm.

In radiographic film, maximum definition occurs when the film accurately reproduces the edge of the discontinuity on the film. In actuality, the change in density on the film caused by the edge of the object occurs over some finite distance. The width of this gradient is known as the film unsharpness. Various types of unsharpnesses that contribute to the definition of the image are:

(i) Geometrical unsharpness (U_g)
(ii) Movement unsharpness (U_m)
(iii) Inherent or film unsharpness (U_i)
(iv) Scattering unsharpness (U_s)
(v) Film and processing factor.

The geometrical unsharpness U_g is a major factor which can be controlled under a certain exposure set up. Movement unsharpness can be considered negligible when source, object and the film are stationary during the exposure. The inherent unsharpness U_i is fixed once the radiation energy is selected for the test. Scattered radiation produced within the object reduces contrast whereas scatter radiation generated from the edge of the specimen lowers the definition. Total unsharpness can be calculated using the following relationship.

$$U = \sqrt{U_g^2 + U_i^2 + U_s^2} \tag{5.4}$$

6.5.6 Penetrameter

A 'penetrameter' also known as 'Image Quality Indicator' (IQI) is a gauge used to establish radiographic technique or quality level. To accomplish this, IQI must be made of material radiographically similar to the material being radiographed. The identifying numbers in the penetrameter are in thousands of an inch (for ASTM) or from a table (for ASME). The proper size penetrameter must be used in the material. The penetrameter letter/symbol on the radiograph indicates what type of material the penetrameter is made of.

The entire outer edge or outline of the penetrameter must be visible on the radiograph; if it is not, the radiograph does not have contrast sensitivity. The proper hole must be visible; if not, the radiograph does not have detail sensitivity. These two factors-contrast sensitivity and detail sensitivity-indicate the quality level for an established radiographic technique. The penetrameter will be placed on top of the material on the source side. A variety of penetrameter designs have been suggested, however some of the most common ones have been described below. Number of penetrameters to be used for a specific job and their locations are specified in the codes/standards.

Step type: This type of penetrameter is essentially a step wedge having 4 or 5 steps. The thickness of these steps increases either in geometric or arithmetic progression. In the following list of standards, step type penetrameters are used and the thickness of which increases in geometric progression.

1. Bureau of Indian Standard (BIS)- BIS 3657
2. AFNOR- French IQI - A04-304
3. IIW and ISO (similar to AFNOR)

Wire type: Among the wire type penetrameters, DIN wire type penetrameters are most common. These are available in two types:

(i) DIN 54109: This type of penetrameter consists of a series of equidistance parallel wires whose diameter increases in geometric progression. Three indicators form the series.

(ii) DIN 54110: This type of penetrameter consists of 4 indicators each having series of equidistance parallel wires, the diameter of which increases in arithmetic progression. BIS has also prescribed wire type penetrameters in BIS-3657.

Plaque type: All the American penetrameters are plaque type, also called strip type. The penetrameter has three holes drilled on a strip having thickness of usually 2% of the specimen.

6.5.7   Determining Radiographic Exposure

Obtaining a satisfactory radiograph is recognized to involve both material and geometric considerations as well as the knowledge of the source and film characteristics. These factors are summarized in exposure charts and are available with the X-ray machine manufacture and gamma ray source suppliers. Alternately, the exposure time can be calculated using the following expression.

$$\text{Exposure time in minutes} = \frac{fd^2\,2^{\left(\frac{x}{\text{HVL}}\right)}}{C(\text{RHM})100^2} \times 60$$

where f = film factor i.e. radiation dose in Roentgens to produce a certain film density. This can be obtained from the characteristic curve of the film, x = thickness of the specimen in cm, HVL = half value layer, d = source to film distance (SFD) in cm, C = source strength in curies, RHM = radiation output in Roentgen per hour by one curie at 1 m.

6.6   INSPECTION TECHNIQUES

With the various techniques available, the choice of appropriate one is made on the basis of geometry, size, sensitivity requirements, in-situ space availability etc. The techniques followed for various engineering components for radiographic inspection are given below.

6.6.1   Single Wall Single Image Technique

This technique is used when both the sides of the specimen are accessible. This is used for plates, cylinders, shells and large diameter pipes. This technique is illustrated in Fig. 6.4. The source is kept outside and the film inside or vice versa and the weld is exposed part by part (a smaller length of weld).

Panoramic technique: In this technique, the radiation source is kept in the centre of the pipe and the film is fixed around the weld on the outer surface of the pipe. The total circumferential weld length is exposed at a time. This technique reduces the examination time considerably. It can be effectively employed only when the source to film distance is sufficient enough to ensure the proper sensitivity. The required IQI, as per the governing code, can be placed either on source or film side as the case may be.

6.6.2   Double wall penetration technique

The double wall penetration technique can be effectively adopted, in three different methods, based on the prevailing pipe diameter and site restrictions. They are:

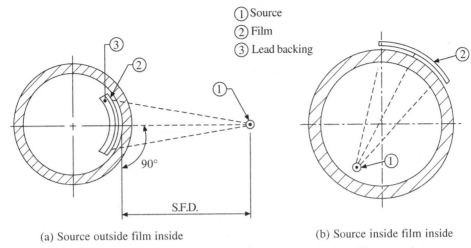

① Source
② Film
③ Lead backing

(a) Source outside film inside   (b) Source inside film inside

Fig. 6.4   Radiographic examination of pipes with single wall penetration

(a) Double wall single image, (b) Double wall double image and (c) Double wall superimposing image

The techniques are shown in Fig. 6.5. These techniques are used where the inside surface of the pipe is not accessible. The source of radiation and the film are kept outside. The radiation penetrates both the walls of the pipe.

(a) *Double wall single image:* The radiation source generally is kept on the pipe or very near to the OD, and just near the weld so that the source side weld is not falling on the film side weld (Fig. 6.5(a)). This technique is employed for the pipes with diameter more than 90 mm OD. The IQI is placed on the film side. Here film side weld only can be interpreted. As the interpretable weld length is being small, this technique requires a number of exposures to cover the entire weld length, depending upon the pipe diameter.

(b) *Double wall double image*: This technique is specially suited for the smaller diameter pipes upto 90 mm OD. The radiation source is kept at a distance (SFD) with an offset from the axis of the weld, to avoid the superimposing of the source side weld over the film side weld and to obtain an elliptical image on the film (Fig. 6.5 (b)). The IQI is positioned on the source side. In this, both the source and the film side welds can be interpreted from the image. This requires minimum of two exposures, perpendicular to each other, to cover the entire circumference of the weld.

(c) *Superimposing technique*: This technique is attempted whenever the required offset to obtain double image could not be possible due to site restrictions for the pipes with diameter upto 90 mm OD. The source is kept at a distance (SFD) without offset (Fig. 6.5(c)), thereby the source side weld is superimposed on the film side weld on the film. The IQI is positioned on the source side. This requires minimum of 3 exposures each at 120° apart, to cover the entire length of the weld.

6.6.3 Latitude technique

Latitude of a film is closely associated with contrast. It is the range of thickness of a material

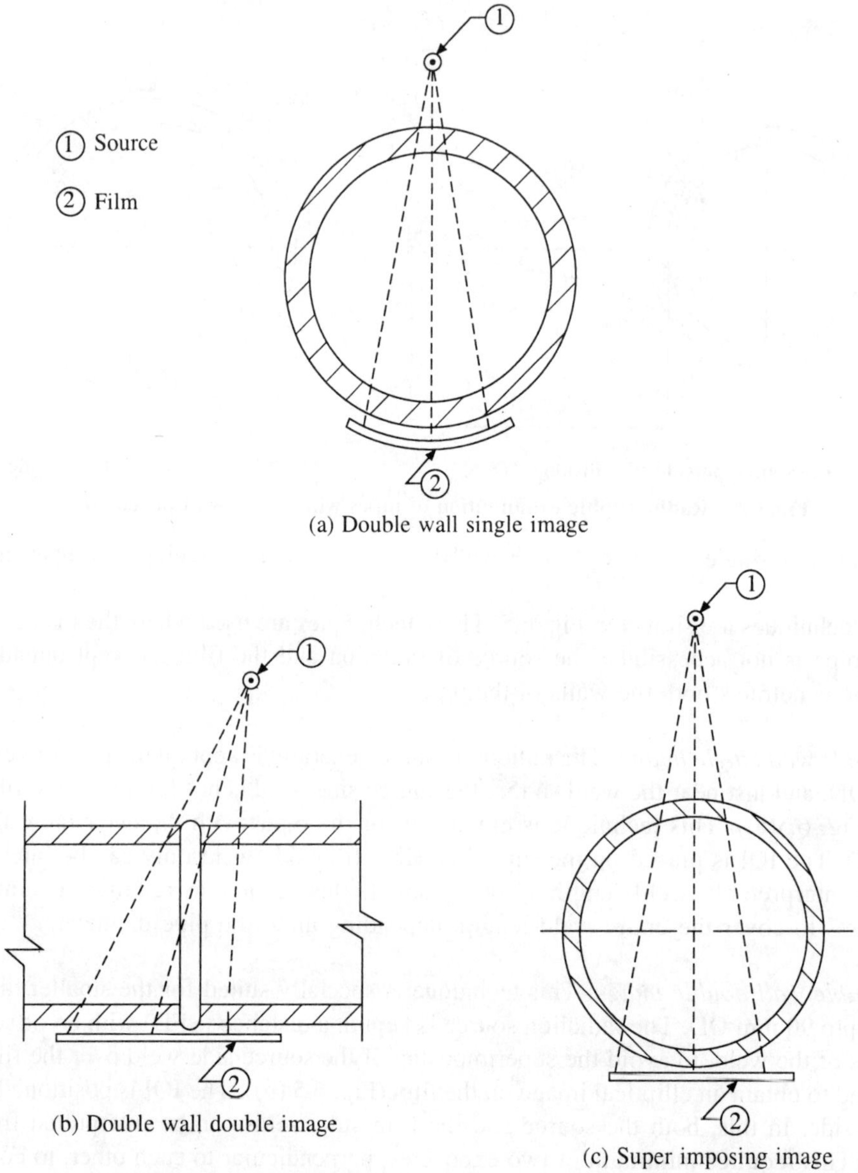

① Source

② Film

(a) Double wall single image

(b) Double wall double image

(c) Super imposing image

Fig. 6.5   Radiographic examination of pipes with double wall penetration

that can be recorded on the radiograph within the useful range of film density. A high contrast film has less latitude and conversely a low contrast film has higher latitude. There is a limitation on the specimen thickness range that can be inspected satisfactorily in a single radiograph. One method of extending this thickness range and thereby reducing the number of exposures required for a particular specimen involves the simultaneous exposure of two films of different speeds. When two films of different speeds are used to image the same subject in one exposure, the latitudes of the films are summed to expand the total latitude for the exposure. The technique is called double film technique.

Double film technique: With proper selection of films and exposure conditions, the thicker sections will be recorded on the faster film and the thinner sections on the slower film (Fig. 6.6). The double film technique can be used with or without lead screens. A centre screen, between the two films may also be used to advantage. Using the above factors, manipulation can be done to get a better latitude.

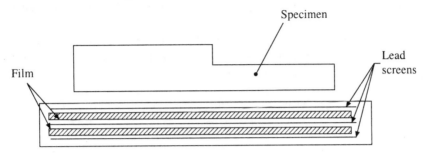

Fig. 6.6   Double film technique

6.6.4   Special techniques

In a complex part, it is often required to consider certain areas individually and prepare a separate technique for each area. Some pipe lines are designed to have the configurations of core pipe and an envelope pipe to meet the intended purposes. Double envelope welds can be tested by using multiwall penetration technique.

Multiwall penetration technique: This technique can be divided into two: (a) Multiwall single image technique and (b) Multiwall double image technique. In these techniques, the radiation beam penetrates all the four walls. Due to the geometry of the joint, the interpretable weld length in a single exposure is much reduced in both the techniques compared to the techniques normally employed for the same diameter pipe.

(a) Multiwall single image technique
This technique (Fig. 6.7) is used for double envelope pipe of more than 90 mm OD and the

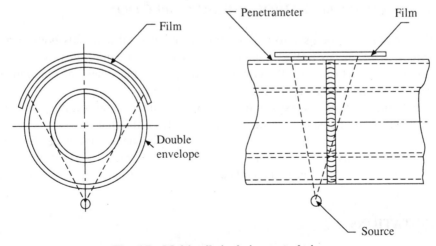

Fig. 6.7   Multiwall single image technique

interpretable length is ascertained by the radiographic weld density. Hence a number of exposures are required to cover the entire length of the weld.

(b) Multiwall double image technique
This technique (Fig. 6.8) is used for double envelope pipe of 90 mm OD or less. Usually four exposures are taken for each weld joint. Proper care should be taken to keep the film normal to the radiation beam without wrapping the film on the pipe. The annular gap is estimated from the film by taking care of the enlargement of the image of the core and the envelope pipes. Minimum of three exposures are to be taken each at 120° apart to assess the annular gap in various directions.

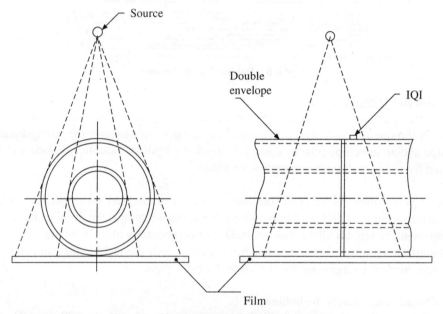

Fig. 6.8   Multiwall double image technique

6.7   APPLICATIONS OF RADIOGRAPHIC INSPECTION

(a) Radiography can be used to inspect most types of solid materials both ferrous and nonferrous alloys as well as nonmetallic materials and composites.
(b) It can be used to inspect the condition and proper placement of components, for liquid level measurement in sealed components, etc.
(c) The method is used extensively for castings, weldments and forgings when there is a critical need to ensure that the object is free from internal flaws.
(d) Radiography is well suited to the inspection of semiconductor devices for detection of cracks, broken wires, unsoldered connections, foreign material and misplaced components, whereas other methods are limited in ability to inspect semiconductor devices.

6.8   LIMITATIONS

Like other NDT methods, radiographic inspection method has certain limitations. Certain types of flaws are difficult to detected. For example, cracks cannot be detected unless they are parallel to the radiation beam. Tight cracks in thick sections usually cannot be detected at all, even when properly oriented. Minute discontinuities such as inclusions in wrought material, flakes, microporosity and microfissures cannot be detected unless they are sufficiently large in size. Laminations are nearly impossible to detect with radiography, because of their unfavourable orientations.

The defect or discontinuity must be parallel to the radiation beam, or sufficiently large, to register on the radiograph. A defect usually must be at least 2% of the thickness of the material before it can register on a radiograph with sufficient contrast, thus to be detected.

Certain areas in many items cannot be radiographed because of the geometric considerations involved. Often it is difficult, if not impossible, to position the film and source of radiation so as to obtain a radiograph of the area desired.

Compared to other NDT methods of inspection, radiography is expensive. When portable X-ray or gamma ray source is used, capital costs can be relatively low. Inspection of thick sections is a time consuming process. Radioactive sources also limit the thickness that can be inspected, primarily because high activity sources require heavy shielding for protection of personnel. Protection of personnel for not only those engaged in radiographic work but also those in the vicinity of radiographic inspection site is of major importance. Safety requirements impose both economic and operational constrains on the use of radiography for inspection.

6.9 TYPICAL EXAMPLES

Figure 6.9 shows the digitised radiographic image of a portion of an aluminum casting impeller. Radiography was carried out using a 420 kV industrial X-ray unit. The thickness of this impeller casting varied from about 2 mm to 25 mm. The casting was zoned into three different areas covering 2 – 6 mm, 6 – 15 mm and 15 – 25 mm and the radiography carried out accordingly. This is the radiograph of the thinner portion showing microshrinkage cavities (1 in figure) and inclusions (2 in figure). The voltage applied for taking the radiography was 100 kV and the exposure was 12 mA-minutes. The focus to film distance (FFD) used is 1000 mm and the film used is Agfa D2. Figure 6.10 shows the digitised image of another region of the impeller casting showing inclusions (arrow in figure) embedded with gas cavities (dark areas within the inclusions in the figure). The voltage applied is 100 kV and the exposure used is 12 mA-minutes. The FFD used is 1000 mm and

Fig. 6.9 Digitised X-ray radiographic image of a thinner portion of an aluminium casting impeller. Microshrinkage cavities (1) and inclusions (2) can be seen in the radiograph

the film used is Agfa D2. Figure 6.11 shows the digitised X-ray radiographic image of the thicker portion (25 mm) of the casting revealing excessive shrinkage cavities (arrow in figure). The voltage applied is 110 kV and the exposure used is 12 mA-mins. The FFD used is 1000 mm and the film used is NDT 55. Figure 6.12 shows the digitised X-ray radiographic image of the thicker portion of the casting with a thickness of 25 mm. Gas cavities (1 in the figure) and the 2T hole in the penetrameter (2 in the figure) can be seen. The voltage applied is 110 kV and the exposure used is 12 mA-minutes. The FFD used is 1000 mm and the film used is NDT 55. Figures 6.13(a, b and c) show radiographic images of casting defects, viz. hot tears, crack and unfused chaplet.

Figure 6.14 shows the digitised gamma radiographic image of a weld in an air receiver. The weld was radiographed using Ir-192 isotopic source by single wall single image technique.   The wall thickness of the "V" groove butt weld is 10 mm. A source to object distance of 400 mm was used. The exposure given is 80 Curie minutes. The film used is NDT-65. Slag line, indicated by arrow can be seen in the radiograph.

Fig. 6.10   **Digitised X-ray radiographic image of a region of thinner portion of the aluminium impeller casting, showing inclusions (arrow) embedded with gas cavities (dark areas within the inclusions)**

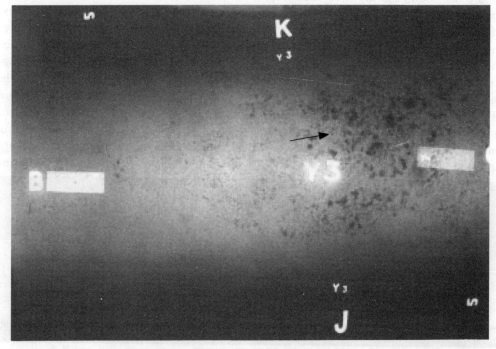

Fig. 6.11   **Digitised X-ray radiographic image of the thicker portion (25 mm) of the casting showing excessive shrinkage cavities (arrow)**

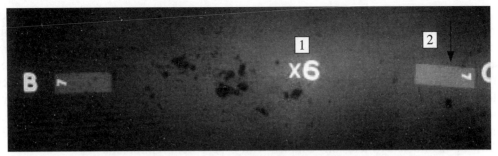

Fig. 6.12 Digitised radiographic image of the thicker portion of the casting with a thickness of 25 mm. Gas cavities (1) and the 2T hole in the penetrameter can be seen

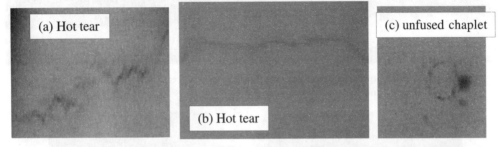

Fig. 6.13 Radiographic images of casting defects, viz. hot tears, crack and unfused chaplet

Fig. 6.14 Digitised gamma radiographic image of a weld in an air receiver. Slag line, indicated by arrow, can be seen in the radiograph

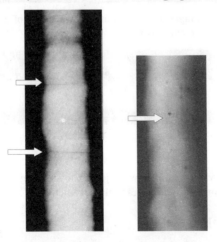

Fig. 6.15 Radiographic images of a weld showing (a) Transverse cracks and (b) Scattered porosity

Figure 6.15 shows the radiographic images of a weld joint showing transverse cracks (a) and porosity (b). Figure 6.16 shows the radiographic images of a weld joint showing excess reinforcement and concavity. Figure 6.17 shows radiographic images of a weld joint showing lack of penetration (left arrow) and undercuts (right arrow). The 8 mm thick SS 316 weld pad was radiographed using 200 kV industrial X-ray unit. A source to object distance of 700 mm was used. The voltage used was 120 kV and the exposure was 12 mA-mins. The film used was Agfa D2. A few wires of the wire penetrameters can also be seen in the radiograph. Figure 6.18 shows another radiographic image of the same weld pad, showing high density inclusions coupled with excess weld reinforcement.

Fig. 6.16   Radiographic images of a weld joint showing excess reinforcement (right arrow) and concavity (left arrow)

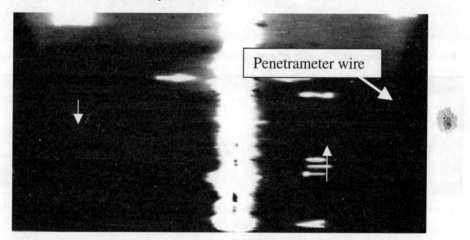

Fig. 6.17   Radiographic images of a weld joint showing lack of penetration (left arrow) and undercuts (right arrow).

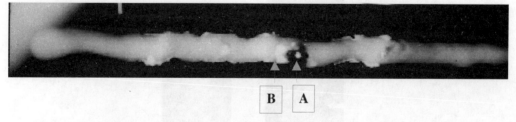

Fig. 6.18   Radiography images of a weld joint showing high density lead inclusions (A and B) coupled with excess reinforcement.

6.10   REAL TIME RADIOGRAPHY

Real time radiography uses X- or gamma radiation, as does conventional radiography, to produce a visible volumetric image of an object. A major difference is in viewing the image. During film radiography, the image is viewed in a static mode; during real-time radiography, the image is interpreted generally at the same time as the radiation passes through the object (dynamic mode). Another difference of real-time image is that a positive image is normally presented, whereas the X-ray film gives a negative image.

The term fluoroscopy is synonymous with real-time radiography and electronic radiography. Basic equipment for conventional fluoroscopy consists of a source of radiation, a fluoroscopic conversion screen, mirrors, and a viewing port. To get the basic real-time image, an object is placed between the source of radiation and a fluoroscopic screen that converts the transmitted radiation to visible light. A specially coated mirror then reflects the visible image to a viewing port that lets the interpreter view the object. Because low light levels are produced during conventional direct-viewing fluoroscopy, a device called image intensifier is used to provide brightness of 100 or more times the intensity of the fluoroscopic screen.

The image intensifier is a large glass enclosed electron tube. The function of the image intensifier is to convert radiation to light, light to electron for intensification and electron back to light for viewing. To make the conversions, the tube contains an input phosphor, a photocathode, accelerating and focusing electrodes, and a final output phosphor. Like the fluoroscopic screen, the input phosphor converts the radiation passing through the object to a light image. *Photocathodes* emit electrons when excited by the input phosphor light. Conversion is necessary because waves in the electromagnetic spectrum cannot be accelerated, whereas electrons can be. The acceleration of the electrons produces a brighter image when they are converted back to light by the output phosphor.

Real time radiography has the advantages of high speed and low cost of inspection. Real-time radiographic concept can be applied in the case of microfocal radiography. In real-time microfocal radiography, zooming or projection magnification of the object is carried out by dynamically positioning the object with the manipulators between the X-ray tube and image receptor. Higher the magnification, more the details one can see. Automatic defect recognition (ADR) is another application of real-time radiography. ADR is applied to parts which can be inspected for the presence or absence of certain components/materials for or the presence or absence of bonding agents such as solder or brazing. ADR may also be used at very high speed for objects that can be scanned and interrogated by intensity statistics, pixel statistics or similar window techniques for voids, inclusions or other anomalies with good contrast against the surrounding material.

Fluoroscopic units have the disadvantage of lower sensitivity due to higher unsharpness of the screens.

The use of microfocal units in conjunction with image intensifying system greatly enhances the versatility and sensitivity of the real-time radiographic setup. The inherent unsharpness of the fluorescent screens would be compensated by the focal spot size (<100 μm) of the microfocal units.

It has been reported that, real-time radiography has been applied to the inspection of laser welds or electron beam welds in thin pipes having thickness of about 1 mm and porosities in the range of 0.025-0.1 mm were detected. Approximately 1 second is required to complete the image.

A typical setup of real time radioscopy system consisting of a 200 kV Eresco industrial X-ray unit mounted on a "C" arm is shown in Fig. 6.19. The object is placed on the object manipulator which has provisions for x,y,z and q motions. The detector also mounted on the "C" arm so that the motion of X-ray source and detector is synchronised. The detector is a real time image intensifier unit the output of which can be directly connected to the TV monitor to observe the radioscopic images online.

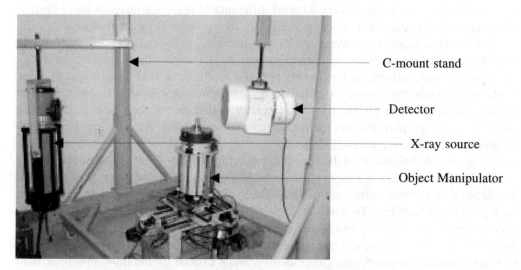

C-mount stand

Detector

X-ray source

Object Manipulator

Fig. 6.19   Setup of real time radioscopy system with a 200 kV Eresco industrial X-ray unit mounted on a "C" arm and a image intensifier based detector

Figure 6.20 shows a digitised radioscopic image of a welder's qualification stainless steel weld pad of 10mm thickness obtained using the real time radiography system. The weld pad has been inspected using 140 kV and 5 mA current. In order to enhance the detection sensitivity and resolution, image processing including edge enhancement has been adapted on the digitised image. The processed image shows lack of penetration and porosity in the weld.

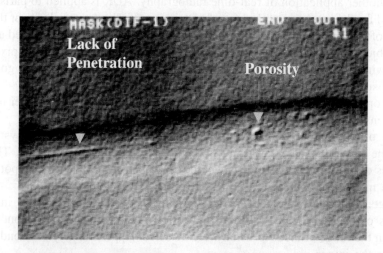

Fig. 6.20   Real time image of weld after image processing and edge enhancement indicating lack of penetration and porosity

6.11 MICROFOCAL RADIOGRAPHY

As indicated in section 6.5, in conventional radiography units, the size of the focal spot ranges from 1 to 5 mm. In order to keep the geometric unsharpness (U_g) as low as possible, the film is placed in intimate contact with the object (minimizing OFD) and the source to object distance is increased. However, the SOD cannot be increased beyond a limit, since this would make the exposure times impractical. An alternative method is to reduce the focal spot. X-ray equipment in which the size of the focal spot is between 0.1–1 mm, is commonly referred to as minifocus unit while X-ray equipment in which the focal spot size is less than 0.1 mm or 100 micrometers is referred to as microfocus unit. This small focal spot is achieved by focussing the electron beam on to the target. Present day microfocus units have focal spots in the range of 5–15 micrometers. The fundamental physical processes such as the electron scattering in the target makes it difficult to achieve focal spots better than 5 micrometers.

6.11.1 Advantages and limitations of microfocal radiography

Once the focal spot size is reduced, a number of advantages can be identified. These include:

(a) *Projection magnification*: The object need not be in contact with the film during exposure as in conventional radiography. Thus one can obtain enlarged primary radiographs with magnifications greater than 2X (Fig. 6.21). Magnification reduces the number of features that is masked by the background image noise thus enhancing the detection sensitivity of microdefects.

(b) *Improved radiographic contrast* : It is well known that in conventional radiography, scattered radiation especially generated from within the object reduces radiographic contrast to the maximum. Once the object is placed away from the film, the amount of scattered radiation reaching it is drastically reduced. Thus, microfocal radiographs have much better contrast as compared to conventional radiographs.

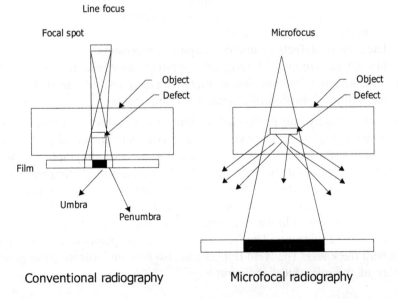

Fig. 6.21   Comparison of conventional and Microfocal radiography setups

(c) *Possibility of object manipulation :* Since the object and the film can be separated without sacrificing image definition, real time radiography of dynamic / temporally changing events is possible. Further the object can be rotated / translated within the radiation beam making stereo and micro tomography possible. These techniques allow better detection of planar defects and greater resolution of detail within the section thickness.

The limitations of the microfocal radiograph include the following:

Projection magnification has its inherent disadvantages: (a) Since the object is placed closed to the source, a smaller volume of the object is inspected at any one time. This means more number of exposures and more number of films. (b) Since the electrons are focussed on to the target, the heat is concentrated in a very small and localised spot. Hence, the target cannot be loaded to a great extent which limits the tube current. However, both of these are not very serious limitations.

Over the years, microfocus systems have continually improved. While the initial systems had limitations with respect to voltage and current (maximum of 160 kV and current of few 100 micro amperes only), present day systems have a voltage range of 5- 225 kV. Current of the order of milliamperes is possible. Presently both sealed and demountable systems are available in the market. One of the advantages of demountable systems is the use of rod anodes. A variety of rod anodes such as forward throw, backward throw, radial panoramic are available which can be used for specific applications. The diameter of the rod anodes can be as small as 6 – 8 mm making it possible to have high sensitivity radiography of small diameter pipes by single wall single image technique.

6.11.2   Applications

The main areas of application of microfocal radiography can be classified as:

  (a) those where conventional radiography cannot be applied due to problems of access such as evaluation of tube to tubesheet welds of steam generator, mode couplers etc.
  (b) those where conventional radiography can be applied but cannot resolve the fine defects necessary to be detected example
     (i) detection of microdefects such as voids, microcracks and inhomogenous distribution of material in ceramics and
     (ii) detection of defects in microelectronic components
  (c) for real time and computed tomography applications where microfocal radiography is an essential requirement due to higher unsharpness of the real time systems, example online evaluation of automotive components.

Microfocal radiography unit positioned in front of a tubesheet of a reheater of a steam generator is shown in Fig. 6.22. The rod anode is inserted into the tubesheet for radiography of the tube to tube sheet weld. Fig. 6.23 shows a microfocal radiograph of a tube to tube sheet weld. The tube with a OD of 17.2 mm and wall thickness of 2.3 mm was radiographed using a panoramic backward throw probe by single wall single image technique. Microporosities can be observed in the radiograph. The wire penetrameters can also be seen clearly. Four wires observed in the radiograph have diameters of 62 microns, 50 microns and 40 microns and 32 microns. The 32 micron wire corresponds to a sensitivity level of 1.4 % of the wall thickness. The weld ripples can also be seen indicating the good contrast and sensitivity of the microfocal radiograph.

Fig. 6.22 **Microfocal Radiography unit positioned in front of the tube sheet of a reheater of a steam generator.**

Fig. 6.23 **Microfocal radiograph of a tube to tubesheet weld**

6.12 SAFETY IN INDUSTRIAL RADIOGRAPHY

An important aspect to be considered in the radiographic inspection is the hazards involved and the safety of biological effects of ionizing radiation. There are two main aspects of safety: monitoring radiation dosage and protection of personnel.

6.12.1 Radiation Units

Radiation is measured in terms of the ionizing effect that it has on a given quantity of atoms. The Roentgen (R) is a unit derived on this basis. However, effects of radiation on the human body depend on both the intensity and the type of radiation involved.

Radioactivity is expressed in a unit called the Becquerel (Bq) = 1 disintegration per second (1 dps). The older unit of activity is Curie which corresponds to $3.7 \infty 10^{10}$ dps. Exposure is a quantity expressing the amount of ionisation caused in air by X- or gamma radiation. The exposure was originally expressed in a unit called Roentgen which referred to that quantity of radiation which produces one e.s.u. of charge in one c.c. of air.

Dose is a measure of energy imparted by any ionizing radiation in any medium like tissue. Absorbed dose is expressed in a unit called Gray (Gy). One Gy is equal to one joule per kg. Absorbed dose was formerly expressed in a unit called the rad. 1 Gray = 100 rad.

Equal absorbed doses from different radiations do not necessarily have equal biological effects. Dose equivalent is equal to the absorbed dose x a factor that takes into account the way a particular radiation distributes energy in tissues. For gamma rays, X rays and beta particles, the factor is set at one and the Gray and Sievert are numerically equal. For alpha particles, the factor is 20, so that 1 Gray of alpha radiation corresponds to DE of 20 Sieverts. Formerly this unit was called rem and 1 Sievert = 100 rems.

6.12.2   Limits for Radiation Exposure

Based on various studies, International Commission of Radiological Protection (ICRP-60) has recommended the following requirements:

(a) No practice shall be adopted unless its introduction produces a positive net benefit.

(b) All exposures shall be kept as low as reasonably achievable.

(c) The effective dose equivalent (whole body) to individuals working in radiation area (radiation workers) shall not exceed 2 rems (20 msv) in any one year and for the general public is 0.2 rem (2 msv) in a year. The above occupational limits are for adults (age > 18). No person under the age of 16 shall be assigned work involving ionizing radiation.

6.12.3   Methods for Exposure Control

There are three basic ways to control the exposure when working with radiography sources:

(a) *Time*: Don't stay near a radiation source any longer than you have to. Time of handling can be low by proper training, adopting fast work technique, mock up practices and efficient administrative control.

(b) *Distance*: Stay as far away as possible from the source. As the radiation intensity decreases with distance following the inverse square law, equipment design and operating procedure must take into account this factor.

(c) *Shielding*: Yet another important way to reduce the dose is to place a shielding material between the source and the operator. Denser the shielding material, more effective it will be in bringing down the dose from X-rays and gamma rays. The commonly used shielding materials in the radiographic installations/equipment are steel, lead, concrete and depleted uranium.

6.12.4   Radiation Monitoring

Another important aspect of hazard control is the radiation monitoring which consists of two components (a) area monitoring and (b) personnel monitoring.

Area monitoring for radiation levels can be carried out by installed monitors or portable surveymeters. The detectors normally used in the portable survey meters are, ionization chambers, Gieger Muller (GM) counters and scintillation detectors. The most frequently used radiation monitor in radiography work is the GM survey meter having a range of 0.1 mR/h to 20 mR/h. Ionization chambers have a range of 5 to 500 mR/h.

The objective of personnel monitoring is the measurement of radiation dose received by individual during the period of work. The most commonly used monitoring devices are (i) direct reading or pen type dosimeters (ii) film badge and (iii) TLD (*thermoluminescent*) dosimeters. These monitors are integrating type since they indicate total radiation dose received over a period.

6.13   STANDARDS

1. IS 2478:1987   Glossary of terms relating to industrial radiography.
2. IS 2953:1985   Glossary of terms used for interpretation of welds and castings radiographs.

3. IS 1182: 1983   Recommended practice for radiographic examination of fusion welded butt joints in steel plates.

4. IS 2595:1978   Code of practice for radiographic testing.

5. IS 2598:1968   Safety code for industrial radiographic practice.

6. IS 3657:1978   Radiographic image quality indicators (first revision).

7. IS 4853:1982   Recommended practice for radiographic inspection of fusion welded butt joints in steel pipes.

8. IS 7810:1975   Code of practice for the radiographic examination of resistance spot welds of aluminium and its alloys.

6.14   NEUTRON RADIOGRAPHY

Neutron radiography (NR) is a valuable NDT technique that is identical in principle to the conventional radiography but complementary with respect to the nature of the information obtained. The history of neutron radiography with thermal neutrons can be traced shortly after the discovery of neutron by Chadwick, in 1932. Thewlis and Derbyshire produced the first reactor based neutron radiographs in 1956, using a reactor beam of the 8 MW BEPO reactor at Harwell. Commercial interest in neutron radiography began in mid 1960's and today this technique, apart from its applications in nuclear industry, finds extensive applications in aerospace and other industries.

6.14.1   Principles of Neutron Radiography

Neutron radiography extends the ability to image the internal structure of a specimen beyond what can be accomplished with photon (X-ray & Gamma) radiation. Similarities as well as obvious differences exist when neutron radiography is compared to photon radiography. Similarities include the ability to produce a visual record of changes in density, thickness and composition of a specimen. It is the differences between the techniques, which provide the advantages of neutron radiography over photon radiography.

The basic principle underlying in this technique is due to the penetrating nature of neutron radiation and its differential absorption by the material to obtain details of the internal structure. Just as in conventional radiography, in neutron radiography also the object to be examined is placed in a colimated neutron beam. Neutrons on passing through the object are differentially absorbed. This absorption depends on the atomic number, thickness of the materials, homogeneity and composition. The geometric pattern of the transmitted neutron intensity is recorded using a suitable detector and visualized. Figure 6.24 gives the schematic sketch of the above description. Graphical representation of the mass absorption coefficient of the elements for thermal neutron and X-radiation is shown in Fig. 6.25. From this figure, it can be seen that the mass absorption coefficients for neutrons abruptly change and present a random picture when plotted against regularly increasing atomic number of absorber. On the other hand, the X-ray mass absorption coefficients increase with atomic number in a regular fashion. The differences in absorption coefficients between the neutrons and X-rays suggest a number of possible applications for NR, such as:

(a) Examination of dense materials like uranium, lead etc.
(b) Detection of light materials enveloped in denser materials
(c) Differentiating between isotopes of same elements and

(d) Examination of radioactive material due to availability of image detection methods, which are not sensitive to the associated gamma rays.

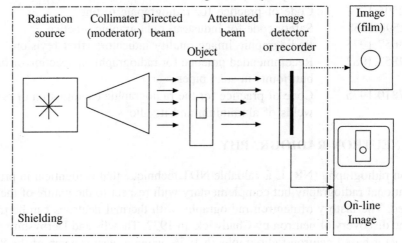

Fig. 6.24   Schematic sketch for neutron radiography

6.14.2   Neutron Sources

The neutron sources available for radiography fall conventionally into three classes namely: nuclear reactors, particle accelerators and radioisotopes in descending order of source intensity, engineering and operating complexity and cost. A majority of practical neutron radiography has been done using nuclear reactors as the source. This is because reactors are prolific sources of neutrons even when operating at low or medium power levels.

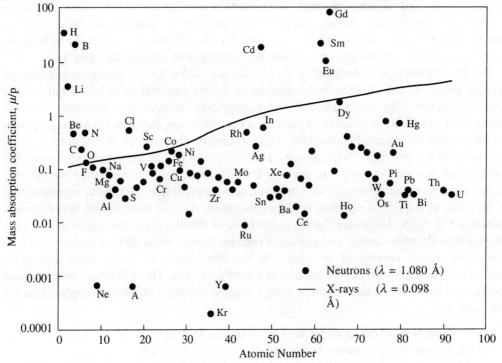

Fig. 6.25   Ariation of mass absorption coefficients with atomic number for X-rays and thermal neutrons

In the case of accelerators, nuclear reactions are used to produce neutrons from accelerated charged particles. Free neutrons can be produced by positive ion bombardment of selected materials with acceleration potential in the range of 100 keV to a few MeV. Some specific reactions for positive ion bombardment are H3 (D, n) He4, H2(D, n) He3, Li7(P, n) Be7 and B9 (D, n) B10. The most widely used accelerator source is the linear accelerator also called as LINAC. LINAC offers the possibility of both X-ray production and neutron production just by interchanging the targets.

Isotopic sources can also be used as neutron sources. Many isotopic neutron sources make use of either the (α, n) reaction or (γ, n) reaction for neutron production. These sources have the desirable features of being reliable and semi portable. Some of the isotopic sources are Sb-Be, Am-Be and Cf-252. Californium 252 is the most widely used isotopic source for neutron radiography. However, thermal neutron intensities that can be achieved from such isotopic sources tend to be lower especially when compared to an operating nuclear reactor or an accelerator based system. Also isotopic sources have considerable gamma background making them not so suitable for direct radiography. The length to diameter ratio of the collimators is also quite low. Thus the radiographs produced by such sources have low sensitivity and resolution.

6.14.3   Moderator and Collimator

Practically all neutron radiography work is performed using thermal neutrons. Whether it is a reactor, or accelerator or isotopic source, the primary neutrons are high energy neutrons. Their average energy is moderated to thermal range using a moderator such as water or other hydrogenous materials.

For neutron radiography, a useful beam of neutrons is required. The extraction of the neutron beam from the reactor core is achieved through the insertion of probe (beam) tube or collimator into the moderator. This permits only those neutrons having a direction to that of the tube axis to pass through. The divergent type collimator is widely used since a uniform beam can be projected over a large inspection area. The important geometric factors for a neutron collimator are the total length (L) from inlet aperture to detector and effective dimensions of the inlet collimator (D). This is usually expressed as L/D ratio. Higher this ratio, better would be the resolution.

6.14.4   Neutron Detection

Neutrons are not directly ionizing radiation and hence have no effect on the conventional films used in industrial radiography. Hence, the detection system for neutrons consists of a latent image recorded in close contact with a thin sheet of material (referred to as converter screen), which absorbs the neutrons and converts them into a form of secondary radiation to which the image recorder responds. The converter screens are often metallic foils. The emissions from these foils can be either charged particles or electromagnetic radiation, which produce the image on the film/screen. The technique used for imaging can be classified as direct and indirect. Apart from the industrial X-ray film, there are also etchable plastic films, image intensifiers and imaging plates for displaying the image.

(a) Direct technique: A foil of gadolinium is used before the film ((Fig. 6.26(a)). Gadolinium atoms in the foil absorb a neutron and promptly emit other radiation such as electron. Alternatively, a scintillator screen containing a mixture of lithium-6 and zinc sulphide can

be used. On absorbing a neutron, a lithium atom emits an alpha particle and this then strikes the zinc sulphide screen, which in turn emits a light photon. As the above processes are continuous reactions, this type of foil and scintillator screen can be used with low neutron fluxes and long integrating exposures. Also, as the film is in contact with the converter during the neutron exposure all of the forward emitted radiations takes part in the exposure of the film. Thus, the direct technique is fast, the scintillator screens being 30 to 100 times faster than metal foils.

(b) Indirect technique: This is also referred to as transfer technique. This method relies on the build up of radioactivity in the foil produced by neutron absorption. In this way an activation image is formed in the foil and this is subsequently transferred to a photographic film in contact and allowing the decay radiations from the foil to produce the latent image on the film (Fig. 6.26(b)). This method is useful for nuclear applications since the process of activation and film exposure are two independent processes. However, the technique is much slower compared to direct one.

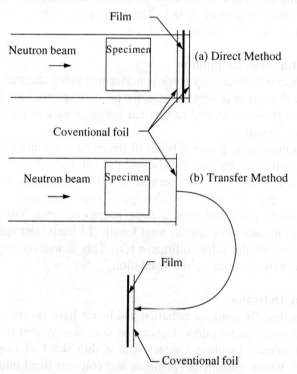

Fig. 6.26   Detection techniques for neutrons

(c) Track-etch technique: For neutron radiography of radioactive objects, nitrocellulose film is used as a neutron detector. This is a dielectric material which can detect charged particles by the radiation damage caused in it. The charged particles are produced by an α emitting converter. The radiation damage is made visible by etching this film in hot sodium hydroxide solution. Higher definition and very good spatial resolution can be obtained by this technique.

6.14.5 Applications of Neutron Radiography

In the nuclear field, neutron radiography has been used extensively for post irradiation metallurgical examination of nuclear fuel elements, control rods, irradiation rigs, for differentiation of isotopes like U235 from U238 etc. Figure 6.27 is a typical neutron radiograph of a fuel pin of a Pressurised Heavy Water Reactor. The pellet to pellet gap can be clearly seen. In the non-nuclear field, this technique is widely used for the inspection of pyrotechnic (explosive) devices, cooling passages in turbine blades, foreign materials in electronic relays and packages, adhesives in metallic honeycomb structures, ceramic component values and presence or absence of rubber seals, gaskets etc. in complex assemblies. One of the recent applications is the study of multiphase flow measurements in thermal hydraulics using real time image intensifier based systems. Neutron radiography is the only technique that makes possible visualization of the flow and also quantitative measurement of void fraction.

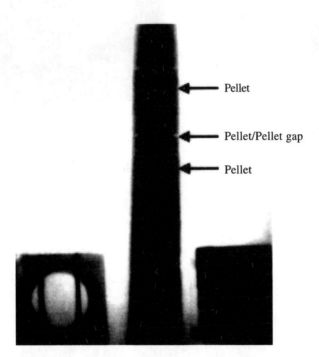

Pellet

Pellet/Pellet gap

Pellet

Fig. 6.27 Typical NR of fuel pin. The pellet to pellet gap can be seen clearly

Neutron radiography is applied in aerospace industry to detect hidden corrosion damage in multi layered structures made of aluminium alloys. In the space programme, pyro devices are also used in various launch vehicles and satellites. The pyro devices contain low density explosive charges encased in metal casing. Neutron radiography is used (a) to ensure presence and proper loading of pyro charges such as RDX, NC and PETN, (b) to ensure presence of "O" rings in assemblies, (c) to assess the condition of potting compound (epoxy) and (d) to identify the interface between the pyro charges and also between the charge and the metal. Figure 6.28 shows the typical neutron radiograph of two widely used pyro devices—bolt cutter and explosive manifold. The pyro charge is revealed by neutron radiography. In defence industry, neutron radiography is used to detect manufacturing defects in shielded metal detonator cords (SMDC), detonating charges, exploding bride wire assembly charge in lead cases, ammunition items etc.

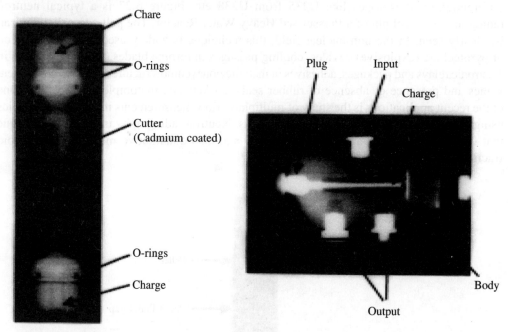

Fig. 6.28   Typical NR of two pyro devices: (a) Bolt cutter and (b) Explosive manifold

Chapter 7

Ultrasonic Testing

Ultrasonic testing is a versatile NDT method which is applicable to most materials, metallic or non-metallic. By this method, surface and internal discontinuities such as laps, seams, voids, cracks, blow holes, inclusions and lack of bond can be accurately evaluated from one side. Ultrasonic testing utilizes high frequency acoustic waves generated by piezoelectric transducers. Frequencies from 1 to 10 Mega Hertz (MHz) are typically used, although lower or higher ranges are sometimes required for certain applications. The resultant acoustic wavelengths in the test material (depend on the ultrasonic wave velocity) are of the order of one to ten millimetres. A highly directional sound beam is transmitted to the test piece through a suitable couplant, usually grease or oil like material. While various types of instrumentation and display modes are feasible, the most widely employed is the pulse-echo technique, with A-scan mode.

Since acoustic waves propagate effectively through most structural materials, but are dissipated or reflected by inhomogeneities or discontinuities, measurement of the transmitted and reflected energies may be related to the integrity, which is a function of the material inhomogeneity and defect parameters. Ultrasonic test method provides quantitative information regarding thickness of the component, depth of an indicated discontinuity, size of the discontinuity etc.

7.1 BASIC PROPERTIES OF SOUND BEAM

7.1.1 Sound Waves

All sound waves, whether audible or ultrasonic, are mechanical vibrations involving movement of the medium in which they are travelling. Because of the relative movement of the particles in the medium, the physical properties of the particles in the medium have to be taken into consideration. A sound wave may be transmitted through any material which behaves in an elastic manner. Ultrasonic waves are classified on the basis of the mode of vibration of the particles of the medium with respect to the direction of propagation of the waves, namely longitudinal, transverse, and surface waves.

(a) Longitudinal waves

The most common form of sound transmission is by longitudinal wave. In this form of wave mode, the oscillations occur in the longitudinal direction. Since compressional and dilational forces are active in it, it is also called compressional or dilational or pressure wave. In this type of ultrasonic wave, alternate compression and rarefaction zones are produced by the vibration of particles parallel to the direction of the propagation of the wave. Figure 7.1(a) represents schematically a longitudinal ultrasonic wave.

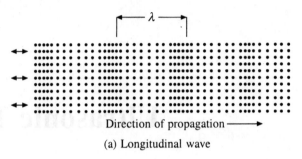

(a) Longitudinal wave

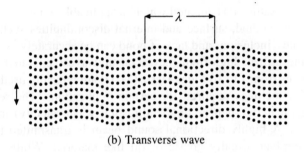

(b) Transverse wave

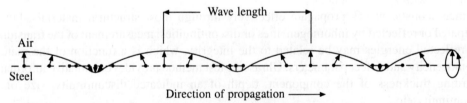

(c) Surface wave on steel on the right, oscillation ellipse of a particle and sense of rotation

Fig. 7.1   Schematic representation of various modes of wave propagation

Because of its easy generation and reception, this type of ultrasonic waves is most widely used in ultrasonic testing. Almost all of the ultrasonic energy used for the testing of materials originates in this mode and then is converted to the other modes for special test applications. This type of wave can propagate in solids, liquids and gases.

(b) Transverse or shear waves
In this type of wave, the direction of particle displacement is at right angles or transverse to the direction of propagation. It is schematically represented in Fig. 7.1(b). For such a wave to travel through a material, it is necessary that each particle of the material is strongly bound to its neighbours so that as one particle moves, it pulls its neighbour with it, thus

causing the ultrasonic energy to propagate through the material with a velocity which is about half that of longitudinal velocity.

For all practical purposes, transverse waves can only propagate in solids. This is because the distance between molecules or atoms, i.e. the mean-free path is so large in liquids and gases that the attraction between them is not sufficient to allow one of them to move the other more than a fraction of its own movement and so the waves are rapidly attenuated. Transmission of these waves through a material can be easily illustrated by the motion of a rope as it is shaken. Each particle in the rope moves only up and down yet the waves move along the rope from the excitation point.

(c) Surface or Rayleigh waves

Surface waves were first described by Lord Rayleigh. This type of waves can travel only along a surface bounded on one side by strong elastic forces of the solid and on the other by nearly nonexistent elastic forces between gas molecules. Surface waves therefore are essentially nonexistent in a solid immersed in liquid, unless the liquid covers the solid surface only as a very thin layer. The waves have a velocity of approximately 90% that of shear waves in the same material and they can propagate only in a region no thicker than about one wavelength beneath the surface of the material. At this depth, the wave energy is about 4% of the energy at the surface and the amplitude of vibration decreases sharply to a negligible value at greater depths. In surface waves, particle vibration generally follows an elliptical orbit as shown in Fig. 7.1(c). Surface waves are not useful for testing purposes because the attenuation they suffer for a given material is lower than that for an equivalent shear or longitudinal waves. However, they can bend around corners and thus be used for testing complicated shapes. Only surface or near surface cracks or defects can be detected.

In plates of thickness approximately equal to one wave length, surface waves cannot exist and the ultrasonic energy travels in the form of 'Plate' or 'Lamb' waves. They occur in two different basic modes, viz. symmetrical or dilational waves, and asymmetrical or bending waves. Unlike the longitudinal, shear and surface waves, Lamb wave velocity depends not only on the material through which the wave is travelling but also on the frequency, incident angle and thickness.

7.1.2 Velocity of Ultrasonic Waves

The velocity of sound wave in a material is determined by the relation,

$$V = f\lambda \tag{7.1}$$

where f is the frequency, λ the wavelength and V the wave velocity.

The equation is valid for all kinds of waves. For example, the most commonly used frequency of 2MHz in the case of longitudinal waves in steel corresponds to a wave length of approximately 3 mm. This gives an idea of the dimension of a flaw which can be detected reliably when using this frequency. Usually a defect which can be detected using a particular frequency is of the order of half of the wave length in that medium.

The velocity of propagation of longitudinal, transverse and surface waves depends on the density of the material. In a given material, it is independent of the frequency of the waves and the material dimensions. Velocities of longitudinal, transverse and surface waves are given by the following equations:

$$V_i = \sqrt{\frac{E\,(1-\mu)}{\rho\,(1+\mu)\,(1-2\mu)}} \qquad (7.2)$$

$$V_i = \sqrt{\frac{E}{\rho 2\,(1+\mu)}} = \sqrt{\frac{G}{\rho}} \qquad (7.3)$$

$$V_s = 0.9\,V_t \qquad (7.4)$$

where V_l = velocity of longitudinal wave, V_t = velocity of transverse wave, V_s = velocity of surface wave, E = Young's modulus of elasticity, G = modulus of rigidity, ρ = density of the material, μ = Poison's ratio.

7.1.3   Acoustic Impedance

The resistance offered to the propagation of an ultrasonic wave by a material is known as the acoustic impedance (Z), and is determined by,

$$Z = \rho\,V \qquad (7.5)$$

where ρ is the density of the material and V the sound velocity in the material

7.1.4   Behaviour of Ultrasonic Waves

Analysis of a wave in an extended substance is possible only theoretically because in practice every substance terminates somewhere i.e., it has a boundary. At the boundary, the propagation of the wave is disturbed. If the material concerned borders on an empty space, no wave can go beyond this boundary because the transmission of such a wave always requires the presence of particles of a material. At such a free boundary, the wave will therefore return in one form or another. If another material is behind the boundary and adheres to the first material so that energy can be transmitted, the wave can be propagated in it, although usually in a more or less changed direction, intensity and mode.

(a) Reflection and transmission at normal incidence
When ultrasonic waves are incident at right angles to the boundary (i.e. normal incidence) of two media of different acoustic impedance, then some of the energy is reflected and the balance is transmitted across the boundary. The amount of ultrasonic energy that is reflected or transmitted depends on the difference between the acoustic impedance of the two media. The amount of ultrasonic energy which is reflected and transmitted can be computed from the equations

$$R = \frac{(Z_2 - Z_1)^2}{(Z_2 + Z_1)^2} \qquad (7.6)$$

$$T = \frac{4 Z_2 Z_1}{(Z_2 + Z_1)^2} \qquad (7.7)$$

also,

$$T = 1 - R \qquad (7.8)$$

where R = reflection coefficient, T = transmission coefficient, Z_1 = acoustic impedance of medium 1 and Z_2 = acoustic impedance of medium 2.

For a water-steel interface, it can be seen therefore, that about 88% of the incident energy is reflected back into the water, leaving 12% to be transmitted into the steel. This figure will be further reduced by other factors such as change of mode, absorption and scattering.

Compared to liquid and solid materials, gases have a very low acoustic impedance. From the intensity relationship, it can be seen that for steel-air or air-steel interface, the coefficient of reflection is almost equal to one. Hence only sound phenomena in liquid or solid materials are considered, boundaries with air can be regarded as boundaries with vacuum. The fact that when sound energy travelling from a liquid or solid medium is incident on the boundary with air or vacuum, almost the entire energy is reflected back, is used as the basic principle of ultrasonic testing.

(b) Reflection and transmission at oblique incidence
When a sound wave is incident upon a boundary between two media of differing impedance, at an angle other than the normal, reflection and refraction take place. The angles of reflection and refraction depend upon the relative velocities in the respective media. Snell's law determines the directions of the reflected and refracted waves. Mathematically, Snell's law is expressed as:

$$\frac{\sin \alpha}{\sin \beta} = \frac{V_1}{V_2} \tag{7.9}$$

where α is the angle of incidence/reflection, β the angle of refraction, and V_1 and V_2 and the velocities of sound in medium 1 and 2, respectively.

7.2 ULTRASONIC TRANSDUCERS

Ultrasonic waves can be generated and detected in a number of ways. The one which is most commonly used in NDT is described here. Quartz and some other crystals have a lattice structure such that if a plate is cut out of the crystal with a certain orientation with respect to the crystallographic axes, and subjected it to an electric field in the right direction, it will change its dimensions: it will contract or expand according it to the polarity of the field. Conversely, when a similar deformation of the plate is brought about by an external mechanical force, electric charges appear on its opposite surfaces. This phenomenon is known as piezoelectric effect. The materials which exhibit this property are known as piezoelectric materials.

Among the various naturally occurring piezoelectric materials, quartz is the most important one, because it combines reasonably good piezoelectric properties with excellent mechanical and dielectric strength and stability. X-cut quartz plate is used for generating and receiving longitudinal waves. Y-cut plate is used for generating transverse and surface waves in solids. Quartz transducers can be operated at high temperatures up to 773K. A multitude of materials exhibiting piezoelectric properties are now available, each material having characteristics which suit to particular applications. Besides naturally occurring crystals like quartz, chemical compounds, such as lithium sulphate, lead niobate etc., and specially produced polycrystalline ceramics such as Barium titanate and lead zirconate titanate (PZT) are used for ultrasonic flaw detection. These transducer materials are mechanically less resistant. Lithium sulphate is the most sensitive but barium titanate is the best transmitter. Because of its higher acoustic impedance, the matching of barium titanate is always unsatisfactory and its sensitivity cannot be fully exploited. Lead metaniobate and lithium sulphate are far superior in this respect. Again because of their low acoustic impedance and high intrinsic internal damping, they are most suited to produce short pulses as is required in pulse-echo technique.

The transducers (piezoelectric crystals) can not be used on their own, but have to be mounted as suitable probes. The role of the probe is to protect the operator from electric shock, to protect the transducer from mechanical damage, and to make the transducer more suitable for the job. Various types of probes (Fig. 7.2) are made for different applications. Normal beam transducers are used for testing by using waves at normal incidence. For under-water testing, the probe, especially the cable, must be waterproof. For good performance, the transducer impedance should be matched to that of the water. For very short range operation, a twin probe is needed with separate transmitter and receiver probes built into one housing and acoustically isolated from each another. There is an acoustic delay rod, also called as stand-off, in front of both.

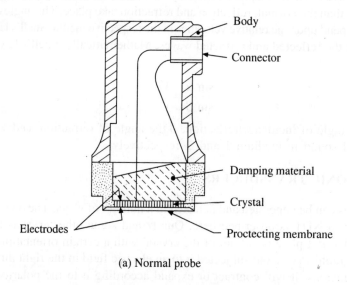

(a) Normal probe

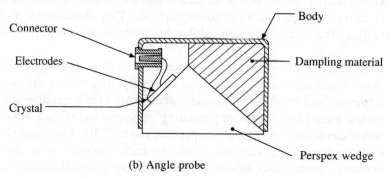

(b) Angle probe

Fig. 7.2   Types of ultrasonic probes

7.2.1   Characteristics of Ultrasonic Beam

The region in which ultrasonic waves are propagated is known as sound beam. In the sound beam, the region close to the transducer face where there is maxima and minima in intensity (large fluctuations in the intensity) of the beam is known as the near field. Flaws appearing in the near field must be carefully interpreted because a flaw occurring in this region can produce multiple indications and the amplitude of the reflected signal from the flaw can vary considerably.

The near field length N can be calculated from the equation

$$N = \frac{D^2}{4\lambda} \tag{7.10}$$

or
$$N = 1.3a_{\text{eff}}^2 \quad \text{(in case of angle beam)} \tag{7.11}$$

where D is the diameter of the transducer, λ the wavelength of sound in the material and a_{eff} the effective area of the transducer element.

The region beyond the near field is known as the far field. The intensity in the far field along the axial distance from the transducer beyond three near field lengths, decreases inversely with the square of the distance. There is always some spreading of the ultrasonic beam in the far field as the wave travels from the transducer. The greatest concentration of ultrasonic energy is in the centre (axis) of the beam; however, the intensity decreases at points away from the axis. For a circular transducer, the angle of beam spread can be calculated from the equation

$$\theta = \sin^{-1}\frac{1.22\lambda}{D} \tag{7.12}$$

where θ is the half angle beam spread.

7.2.2 Attenuation

When sound waves pass through materials, the sound pressure is essentially weakened by two physical processes: scattering and absorption. Scattering results from the fact that the material is not strictly homogeneous and may contain inhomogeneities like inclusions or pores. There are also materials, which by their nature are inhomogeneous e.g. cast iron, brass etc. Even when only a single type of crystal is present, the material may still be inhomogeneous for ultrasonic waves if it is anisotropic. In a material with very coarse grains as compared to the wavelength, the scatter can be visualised as due to the repeated reflections of sound waves at grain boundaries. In the case of grain sizes of 1/1000th to 1/100th of the wave length, scatter is for all practical purposes negligible. It increases very rapidly, however to make itself felt at sizes from 1/10th to the full value of the wavelength and increases to such an extent that testing may become impossible if the material concerned is anisotropic. The second cause of the attenuation, viz., absorption is a direct conversion of sound energy into heat, for which several processes like internal friction, elastic and magnetic hysteresis, heat conduction etc. are responsible. Absorption usually increases with the increase in frequency.

Both losses set limitations on the testing of materials, but in slightly different ways. Pure absorption weakens the transmitted energy or the echo from the flaw and the back wall. To counteract this effect, the transmitter voltage and the amplification can be increased, or the lower absorption at lower frequencies can be exploited. Much more concern, however, is the scattering because, in the echo method it not only reduces the height of the echo from both the flaw and the backwall but in addition produces numerous echoes with different transit time, the so called 'grass' in which the true echoes may get lost. This disturbance, as it can be seen clearly, cannot be counteracted by stepping up the initial sound energy. This is because, consequent to this, the 'grass' effect also increases simultaneously. The only remedy is to use lower frequencies, which sets a limit on the detectability of small flaws.

Attenuation taking place in the material can be calculated using the following relationship:

$$A = A_0 e^{-\alpha r} \tag{7.13}$$

where A_0 is the incident amplitude, A the value of amplitude after travelling a distance 'r' and α the attenuation coefficient.

The equation can be written as

$$\alpha = \frac{1}{r} \ln \frac{A_0}{A} \tag{7.14}$$

where the value of α is measured in nepers per mm.

7.3   INSPECTION METHODS

Ultrasonic testing is performed using one of the following procedures: (1) normal beam pulse-echo; (2) normal beam through-transmission; (3) angle beam pulse-echo; (4) angle beam through-transmission. Pulse-echo technique is most widely used for inspection of components.

7.3.1   Normal Incident Pulse-Echo Inspection

The ultrasonic energy is coupled to the component being inspected through a couplant (usually oil or grease or glycerine) that transmits the ultrasound between the face of the transducer and the surface of the component. When ultrasonic energy travels through a test sample and strikes a discontinuity, part of the energy will be reflected back and the remaining part propagates in the material in the forward direction. Also a refracted beam from the discontinuity is available for interpretation. Ultrasonic energy that is reflected and returned to the probe is the source of the defect indication shown on the instrument screen (Fig. 7.3). The sound energy that travelled completely through the test piece will be reflected at the end, giving the large back wall echo indication. Once excited in the material, the ultrasonic pulse will continue to reflect from the parallel surfaces, creating a multiple echo display when the

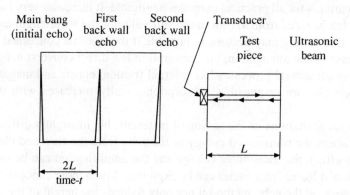

Fig. 7.3   Pulse-echo inspection of bar of length *L*

time base is sufficiently large. As there is continuous attenuation of the sound energy in the material, the amplitude of the echoes decreases.

7.3.2 Normal incident Through-Transmission Testing

Many a time, pulse-echo technique may not provide required test information. This may occur when a flaw or other anomaly does not provide a suitable reflection surface or where the orientation or location of the flaw which is not favourable for detection using single probe. Also, highly attenuating materials are often tested with through-transmission technique. Figure 7.4 shows the probe arrangement for through-transmission technique. The technique is often used in large castings and highly attenuating materials.

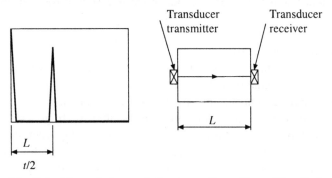

Fig. 7.4   Through-transmission inspection of bar of length *L*

7.3.3 Angle Beam Pulse-Echo Testing

Angle beam transducers provide access to areas that are inaccessible to normal beam probes. Figure 7.5 shows the angle beam test arrangement. Angle beam inspection is accomplished with shear wave probes. Angle beam test applications are explained in detail in section 7.5.

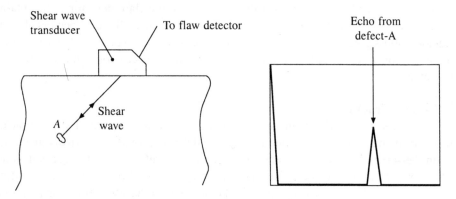

Fig. 7.5   Angle beam test arrangement

7.3.4 Criteria for Probe Selection

Some of the factors that affect the probe selection are flaw sensitivity, beam divergence, penetration, resolution etc.

7.3.5 Flaw Sensitivity

The frequency of the probe is one of the most important factors to be considered when the minimum detectable flaw size is of concern. While there are a number of other parameters that affect the flaw sensitivity, the detectability of a flaw is a direct function of the wavelength, which varies inversely with the frequency. Most favourable detection conditions exist when the flaw is somewhat larger than the wavelength. As the wavelength becomes larger than the flaw, the likelihood of detection decreases considerably. In general, it has been found that using a particular frequency probe, defect size of the order of half of its wavelength can be detected.

7.3.6   Beam Divergence
Divergence is a function of diameter and frequency of the probe, and sound wave velocity in the material. Hence selection of the proper probe is essential for assuring a satisfactory inspection.

7.3.7   Penetration and Resolution
Attenuation plays an important role in ultrasonic testing in a variety of ways. Not only does it account for the loss of signal height for equal reflectors at increasing distances from the probe, it is also a useful diagnostic tool for several types of inspection. Two of the most affecting sources of attenuation are beam spread and scattering. In general, the use of lower frequency probes will minimise the attenuation and maximise the penetration due to the fact that the longer wavelength pulse is less affected by scattering at grain boundaries etc. Lower frequency probes, then, are said to have greater ability for penetration.

What is an advantage on the one hand is often a disadvantage on the other. Lower frequency probes have lower resolution, i.e. decreased ability to resolve closely spaced reflectors. Therefore higher frequency probes are chosen for better resolution.

7.4   TECHNIQUES FOR NORMAL BEAM INSPECTION

It must be emphasized that the basic role of an ultrasonic flaw detector is to obtain and display information. Interpretation of the data must come from qualified inspectors. Automatic interpretation offers great potential provided correct data have been furnished to the instrument. In order to demonstrate the basics of ultrasonic inspection, discussion is made with the help of a few examples.

7.4.1   Fatigue Cracks
Figure 7.6 shows the normal beam testing of bars for fatigue cracks. Fatigue cracks are assumed to be planar in shape, with boundaries well defined, providing sharp distinct reflected echoes on the screen. With length L and time t for a pulse reflecting at the bar end, echos of the defect present at a distance a_1 would appear at time $(a_1/L)t$ on the screen. Multiple echoes of the flaw echo would also appear. If the probe is moved away from the location, the defect echo would disappear, while the back echo remains. For a circular shaft with a planar flaw, moving the probe in a circular fashion around the outer extremity of the end of the bar should generate a pattern of rising and falling flaw echo that will indicate the approximate size and shape of the flaw. Where access to a suitable inspection location is available, it is useful to confirm the presence and shape of a flaw by approaching it from a different direction.

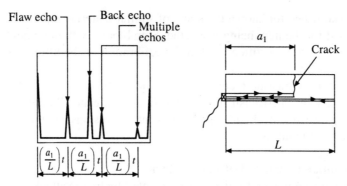

Fig. 7.6   Typical pulse-echo response from a planar reflector (fatigue crack)

7.4.2   Inclusions, Slag, Porosity, and Large Grain Structure

Many manufactured products contain internal defects that give reponse quite differently than that seen for a fatigue crack. Such defects are inclusions, slag and porosity to name a few. Figure. 7.7 shows the screen appearance and the general reflection behaviour of such defects. In these situations, where there is no flat planar reflector, the scatter at the defect may be sufficient to destroy the back echo signal. In this event, the loss of the back echo may be more informative.

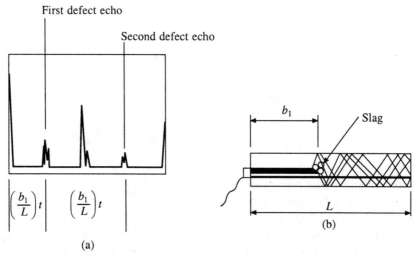

Fig. 7.7   (a) Screen appearance from slag, inclusions or porosity (b) reflection pattern for the above type of defects

7.4.3   Thickness Measurement: Corrosion Detection

Ultrasonic transit time measurements are conveniently used for determination of thickness in piping, tubing, and pressure vessels. Thickness measurement, of course, is crucial in the prevention of failures caused by corrosion. Since the longitudinal wave speed is essentially constant for a given engineering materials, changes in material thickness may be determined quite accurately using the position of the back echo obtained from conventional normal beam inspection.

Thickness measurement is based on the transit time comparison, i.e., reference transit times are first established for known thickness of similar material and the comparable travel times are obtained for the item being inspected. Step blocks with incremental thickness for the range of interest are most often used in the calibration of the ultrasonic instrument for thickness measurement.

Ultrasonic thickness measurement is also accomplished with digital instruments that automatically determine the transit time of the first back echo. Proper calibration is also required for these instruments. In all cases, the manufactures' instruction manuals should be followed in order to obtain reliable results.

7.4.4   Intergranular Cracks: Hydrogen Attack

The ultrasonic testing employed for the measurement of hydrogen attack/intergranular attack involves the measurement of velocity, attenuation and back-scatter.

It has been seen that hydrogen attack decreases ultrasonic wave velocity and increases attenuation and back-scattering. The reduction in wave velocity is caused by an overall decrease in bulk modulus of elasticity due to microcracking. Such a decrease in bulk modulus is produced when a large number of microcracks are present or the material has extensive hydrogen attack.

Attenuation measurements are often used to detect defects that have irregular growth patterns. The usual effect on the ultrasonic pulse of this type of defect is the scattering of the energy (Fig. 7.8) with a resulting loss of amplitude and little, if any, reflected energy. These irregular cracks are usually detected with a loss of amplitude using a normal beam pulse probe. Calibration for the test starts with a multiple echo display obtained using a defect free sample of the item to be inspected. Time base and amplitude adjustments are fixed so that the fourth back echo is of full screen height (FSH) in the calibration piece. Unacceptable defects are likely to be present in the item being inspected when the fourth back echo falls to less than 20% FSH and is taken as criterion for the presence of unacceptable defects.

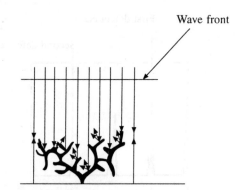

Wave front

Fig. 7.8   Scattering at intergranular type defects

Sometimes it may be difficult to apply attenuation measurements on jobs where inner surface is pitted and scatters ultrasound. In such situations, back-scattered ultrasonic waves are analysed. Back-scattering occurs from the grains because of impedance mismatch at the material grain boundaries. Back-scattering increases with ultrasonic test frequency. These measurements are usually conducted at higher frequencies such as 10 MHz. While the back-scattering method is sensitive to cavities and microcracks, the technique has to be used carefully to avoid erroneous results due to anisotropy between grains or at the boundary of two different metallic phases. To account for such effects, back-scattering measurements are compared with those made at a reference location which is having no hydrogen attack.

7.5   TECHNIQUES FOR ANGLE BEAM INSPECTION

Angle beam inspection is accomplished using shear waves inclined at some specified angle (inspection angle). The angle is specified on the probes. Ultrasonic angle beam inspection is widely used for locating cracks at certain oblique angles in the components. Weld inspection is quite frequently accomplished using angle beam probes. Typical defects possible to detect include cracks, slag, inclusions, porosity etc. The type of defects expected dictates the choice of the angle of the probe to be used.

A typical weld testing arrangement is shown in Fig. 7.9(a). Defects are assumed to be within the weld metal as well as within the heat affected zone. Since there is no back-echo for this inspection, the correct proximity of the probe to the inspection area must be established. A method for doing this is to first obtain a corner reflection as shown in Figs. 7.9(b) and (c). In this case, the probe is manipulated along a line parallel to the edge at a distance estimated to be equal to the skip distance S. The skip distance may be estimated using the specified probe inspection angle. Once the skip distance is established, a line is drawn on the piece to be inspected parallel to the weld and at a distance equal to the skip distance. Inspection is accomplished by using the skip distance line as a reference and moving the probe near and away from the weld while rotating it slightly in the plane of the plate. Typical defect indication is shown in Fig. 7.9(d).

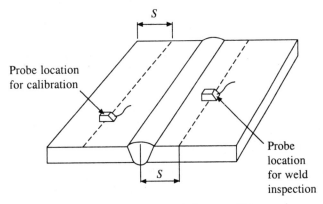

(a) Typical arrangement for angle beam weld inspection

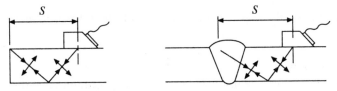

(b) Skip distance for calibration (c) Beam path for inspection of angle beam probe

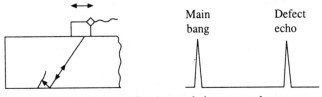

(d) Locating a crack using angle beam transducer

Fig. 7.9

The relationship between skip distance, material thickness and beam path distance are given below (Refer Fig. 7.10)

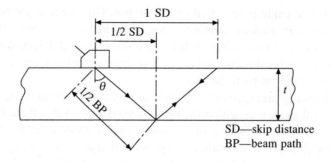

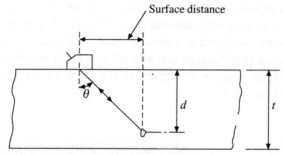

Fig. 7.10   Relationship between skip distance, beam path distance, flaw surface distance and depth

Half skip distance $= t \tan \theta$ (7.15)

Full skip distance $= 2t \tan \theta$ (7.16)

Half skip beampath (1/2 BP) $= t \sec \theta$ (7.17)

Full skip (1 BP) $= 2t \sec \theta$ (7.18)

Defect at depth d $= \text{BP} \infty \cos \theta$ (7.19)

Surface distance of the defect $= \text{BP} \infty \sin \theta$ (7.20)

where t is the thickness of the part being tested and θ the refraction angle of sound beam in the material.

7.5.1   Pipe Inspection

Pipes of virtually all sizes can be inspected ultrasonically for internal and surface defects. In pipes both manufacturing and service flaws can be detected. A typical arrangement for pulse-echo inspection of a pipe is shown in Fig. 7.11. This scheme would detect longitudinal flaws. As the probe is moved towards and past the defect, the echo will rise and fall.

7.6   FLAW CHARACTERISATION TECHNIQUES

Correct information on the flaw location, size, shape, orientation etc. are important for making confident decisions on the appropriate corrective action for equipment's 'fitness for purpose'. Echo amplitude alone is not sufficient for sizing the flaws correctly. Most widely used flaw sizing method for larger flaws (when the flaw size is comparable or larger than beam width) is 6 dB drop method and for smaller flaw, it is 20 dB drop method. Figure 7.12

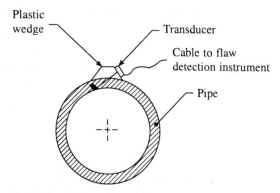

Fig. 7.11 Pulse-echo angle beam inspection of pipe

shows the principles of both the methods. The probe is so situated that maximum echo response is obtained. Further the echo is adjusted to full screen height by adjusting the gain. Next, the probe is moved laterally until the echo amplitude falls by one-half in the case of 6 dB drop method and one-tenth in the case of 20 dB drop method. For planar flaw with orientation perfectly normal to the plane of transducer, the method will correctly locate the edge of the flaw and planar shape of the flaw could be traced. The methods have the inherent problem of being unreliable for flaws of irregular shape and varying roughness.

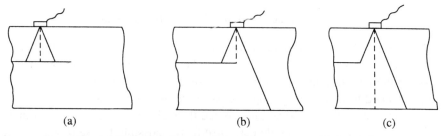

(a)   (b)   (c)

Fig. 7.12 (a) Probe location for full screen response, (b) for 6 dB drop response and (c) for 20 dB drop response

7.7 ULTRASONIC FLAW DETECTION EQUIPMENT

Many types of pulse-echo ultrasonic flaw detectors are available in the market. In a flaw detector, there are three essential working units in addition to a power supply unit that provides direct current at appropriate voltages to the three working units. Figure 7.13 shows the block diagram of a pulse-echo flaw detector.

The three essential working units are as follows: pulse transmitter, receiver amplifier and cathode-ray oscilloscope (a cathode ray tube plus a time base or a sawtooth generator). Here the free-running time base generator is more complicated than in an ordinary oscilloscope, because after the end of a sawtooth wave it waits long enough for the reverberations in the test object to die down, about four or five times the sweep time, before a new sequence of events is started. Another function of the time base generator, as in any ordinary oscilloscope, is to provide square wave signals for the cathode ray tube, ensuring that the spot appears only during the sweep period, but not during flyback or waiting time. Just after the beginning of the sawtooth wave, the pulse transmitter is triggered and it delivers a fast rising, short,

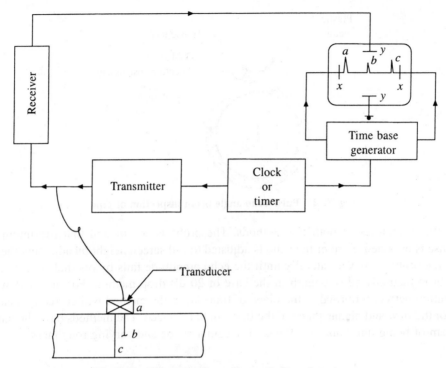

Fig. 7.13   Diagram of an ultrasonic flaw detector

high voltage spike to the probe. An alternate system is sometimes favoured. In this alternate system, the time base is of a single-sweep type (when triggered it completes one cycle and then waits for the next trigger signal). In that case, a single additional unit, a clock pulse generator, is needed to do the triggering and to set the repetition rate.

From the transmitter, the electrical pulse is fed through a cable to the probe, an external device which is not part of the flaw detector itself. It is possible to use probes of different makes with a number of flaw detectors. In the probe, the piezoelectric transducer is shock-excited by the short, high voltage pulse and made to vibrate at its own resonant frequency for a few oscillations, thus radiating an ultrasonic pulse into the test object. It is heavily damped to keep the ultrasonic pulse short, normally just a few cycles. The ultrasonic echo pulse is picked up by the same probe, which reconverts it into an electrical signal, but having a voltage many orders of magnitude smaller than the transmitted pulse, so that it must be amplified before it can serve any useful purpose.

In the receiver-amplifier, the echo signals are amplified and filtered to some extent. In most flaw detectors, there are two independent facilities to control the receiver gain: one is calibrated in decibels and the other is uncalibrated. After amplification at the ultrasonic carrier frequency, the signals are rectified and further amplified before being fed to the deflection plates of the cathode ray tube.

Some flaw detectors have various ancillary circuits, e.g. time-varying gain control to compensate for signal loss with distance in the material, a built-in monitor for semi-automatic defect indication etc.

7.8 MODES OF DISPLAY

Communicating the flaw size and shape to others is a very crucial part of the NDT process. Decisions on removal of the part, repair or continued service need full information on the flaw characteristics. Various types of presentation possible are given below.

7.8.1 A-Scan

Echoes can be displayed just as seen on an ordinary oscilloscope: X-represents time of flight of the pulses converted into distance travelled by the pulses (depth of penetration); deflection parallel to the Y-axis represents the amplitude of the echoes. This type of presentation is called an 'A-scan'. It shows the situation with the probe stationary in one position. A-scan presentation is still the most used mode of display in the ultrasonic testing.

Since the information that is available in A-scan, is basically one dimensional, interpretation with accompanying sketches and calculations is required to characterize the flaw. Imaging systems using automated probe movement control and computerized data analysis and storage greatly enhance the quality of defect characterisation and the ease of communication. There are basically two imaging techniques widely used in the ultrasonic testing of components. These are B-scan and C-scan.

7.8.2 B-Scan

In the B-scan display, the Y-axis is used in a different way. When moving the probe along a straight line on the surface of the test object, the displacement of the probe can be converted into an electrical signal (voltage) by a potentiometer and used to shift the spot on the oscilloscope screen. This dimension is normally displayed along the X-axis and the travel of the ultrasonic pulse in the object is represented by the time base moving the spot in the Y-direction (usually from the top downwards). Now a new way is needed to display the amplitude of the echoes and this is achieved by brightness modulation, or z-modulation of the cathode ray beam. The beam is always cut off, only the echo signals cause it to brighten up, producing a spot on the screen whose brightness is proportional to the echo amplitude. In this way only one line scan, i.e. a serious of dots, appears on the screen at any one time. The whole picture has to be built up on a long persistence screen, or on the screen of a storage tube, or on the film of a camera with the shutter kept open during the whole scan. This type of display is called B-scan.

The B-scan presentation gives a cross sectional view of the part being tested and shows the length and depth of a flaw in the test material. The limitations of the B-scan test system is that the areas behind a reflecting surface are in shadow, and no indications behind the surface can be obtained.

7.8.3 C-scan

In some testing problems, the depths of defects are irrelevant but their distribution parallel to the test surface is the important feature. For this purpose the presentation is rotated by 90° such that the X- and Y-directions are now both in the plane of the surface of the test object, i.e. the plane of scan. The probe radiates perpendicular to this plane, and the time base generator is switched off. Any signal which appears between the transmitted pulse and the backwall echo is gated out by a circuit and produces a bright spot on the screen. This type of display is called a 'C-scan' and it produces a plane projection of all echoes within the gate width.

A C-scan display is a very effective way to report data on flaw depth since the presence of the flaw as well as its severity can be indicated directly on a drawing of the part being inspected. This has been particularly useful in corrosion detection in pipes and pressure vessels and in the detection of delaminations in composite materials.

7.9   IMMERSION TESTING

Immersion testing techniques are mainly for laboratory and for large installations carrying out automatic ultrasonic testing of large number of components. Either B - or C - scan presentation can be obtained using automated scanning techniques. Immersion testing has the following advantages: (i) uniform couplant conditions are obtained and (ii) longitudinal and transverse waves can be generated with the same probe simply by changing the inclination of the probe. In the immersion technique, both the probe and the test specimen are immersed in water. The ultrasonic beam is directed through the water into the test specimen either as a normal beam or as an angle beam.

When the normal beam technique is used, the water path distance must always be longer than the distance S in the equation given below:

$$S = \frac{\text{Thickness of specimen} \times \text{Sound velocity in water}}{\text{Sound velocity in specimen}} \tag{7.21}$$

when the specimen is steel, the water path distance must be longer than 1/4th the steel thickness. Otherwise, the first backwall echo overlaps the second front surface echo (entry echo) and defects near to the backwall may not be seen.

7.10   APPLICATIONS OF ULTRASONIC TESTING

The pulse-echo technique is the most versatile ultrasonic method for nondestructive testing and is the most widely used. Weld testing is the largest application of ultrasonic testing. Additionally, many of the semi-finished products in the steel and non-ferrous metal industries, i.e. bars, rods, sheets, pipes, rails etc. are ultrasonically tested. Apart from these very simple shaped items, objects which are large like forgings, are tested using automatic or semi-automatic test stations. Smaller objects and those which are more complicated are tested manually. Another very important application of ultrasonic testing is the finding of dangerous incipient defects in components in service, e.g. fatigue cracks and effects of corrosion. In power plants, boiler components must be tested regularly for fatigue cracks in welds and for corrosion in certain areas.

7.11   ADVANTAGES

(a) Testing can be carried out from only one accessible surface unlike in the radiographic method where accessibility from two opposite sides is required.
(b) At a time, very large section thickness can be tested.
(c) Results are immediate. Hence on the spot decision can be made.
(d) Cost involved is cheaper as compared with other volumetric test methods.

7.12   LIMITATIONS

(a) Maximum penetration in fine grained steel and aluminum is in the range of several meters. But in coarser structures, which scatter the ultrasound waves very strongly, like castings, especially cast iron and stainless steel, it is drastically less. Some times it can be as small as 50 or 100 mm.

(b) The test method is highly operator dependent. Hence, highly skilled operator is required for data interpretation.

7.13 STANDARDS

1. IS 9664:1981	Code of practice for ultrasonic pulse echo testing by contact and immersion methods
2. IS 4225:1979	Recommend practice for straight beam ultrasonic testing of steel plates
3. IS 4260:1986	Recommended practice for ultrasonic testing of butt welds in ferritic steel
4. IS 4904: 1982	Calibration block for evaluation of ultrasonic flaw detection equipment
5. IS 6394: 1986	Code of practice for ultrasonic testing of seamless metallic tubular products by contact and immersion methods
6. IS 7949: 1986	Code of practice for ultrasonic testing of ferrous welded pipes and tubular products
7. IS 7666:1975	Recommended procedure for ultrasonic examination of ferritic castings of carbon and low alloy steel
8. IS 8791: 1978	Code of practice for the ultrasonic flaw detection of ferritic steel forgings
9. Is 11690: 1986	Method for ultrasonic testing of steel plates for pressure vessels and special applications
10. ASTM E1065-87a	Guide lines for evaluating characteristics of ultrasonic search units
11. ASTM E317–85	Practice for evaluating performance characteristics of ultrasonic pulse-echo testing system without the use of electronic measuring instruments
12. ASTM E428–71 (1985)	Fabrication and control of steel reference blocks used in ultrasonic inspection
13. ASTM E1001–84	Practice for detection and evaluation of the discontinuities by the immersed pulse-echo ultrasonic method using longitudinal waves
14. ASTM E214–68 (1985)	Practice for immersed ultrasonic examination by the reflection method using pulse longitudinal waves
15. ASTM E578–82 (1988)	Practice for ultrasonic angle beam examination by the contact method
16. ASTM E797–87	Practice for measuring thickness by manual ultrasonic pulse echo contact method
17. ASTM E500–86b	Terminology relating to ultrasonic examination

7.14 MECHANICAL IMPEDANCE ANALYSIS TECHNIQUE

7.14.1 Introduction and basic principle

The Mechanical Impedance Analysis method, which is conceived and developed in Russia, is an important and widely used technique for detecting debonds and delaminations in composites, non-metallic, multilayer and honeycomb structures. This method works on the principle of detecting the change in the mechanical impedance Z, of the test objects in the defective zones. The mechanical impedance is defined as the complex ratio of the harmonic exciting force '*F*' to the oscillatory velocity '*V*' of the structure

$$Z = F/V = R + jX = |Z| \exp(j\varphi)$$

where *R* and *X* are the real and imaginary parts of *Z* and φ is the phase factor given by

$$\tan \varphi = X/R.$$

Unlike the characteristic impedance, which is the feature of the medium, mechanical impedance is the parameter of the structure. The impedance of the structure depends on the structural features such as thickness, elastic properties and density of the layers of the component. In the area where all the layers are bonded together, the structure vibrates as a whole system and the impedance *Z* has its maximum value. The presence of any flaw reduces the connection between layers and results in the excitation of low frequency bending vibrations due to a reduced local stiffness which decreases *Z*. This can be modelled as a grounded spring system at the point of the localized defect. The spring model requires that the frequency of the harmonic force applied to the structure remains below the resonant frequency of the structure. The measure of *Z* provides the feasibility for detection of defects in composites, nonmetallic multi layer and honeycomb structures.

7.14.2   Measurement of variations in mechanical impedance

Measurement of variations in mechanical impedance at the point of contact due to presence of a defect can be accomplished using various kinds of probes, viz. (a) single contact piezoelectric, (b) twin contact piezoelectric, (c) tapping for excitation and microphone as receiver and (d) tapping for excitation and piezoelectric crystal receiver. Probes (a) and (b) operate at a fixed frequency while the probes (c) and (d) operate over a wide frequency range. Choice of the particular probe depends on the nature of the material and the type of the flaws to be detected. For example, single and twin contact piezoelectric probes are useful to detect debonds in materials such as hard metals, metal honeycomb and multi layer composites, whereas tapping probes are useful to detect debonds and voids in soft materials such as rubber, polymer and plastic based structures. Figure 7.14 gives the schematic diagrams of the four types of probes.

Single contact probe has one transmitting-receiving vibrator and has single contact area with test object. The arrangement consists of a bar like vibrator that contains a transmitting and a receiving piezoelectric transducer separated by a resonant rod. The transmitting transducer is fixed between the resonant rod and a rear mass. The receiving transducer is connected in between the resonant rod and a spherical contact tip. The input signal from a signal generator is given between the rear mass and the transmitting transducer and the output signal is taken between the spherical contact tip and the receiving transducer. The rear mass acts like a back reflector that increases the intensity of the acoustic waves in the direction of the tested object.

Twin contact probes have two identical transmitting and receiving vibrators and have two contact areas with the test object. Each vibrator consists of a piezoelectric transducer with rectangular cross section and electrodes on its lateral sides, two passive metal members and spherical contact tip. In the case of twin contact probe, the input signal from the transmitting

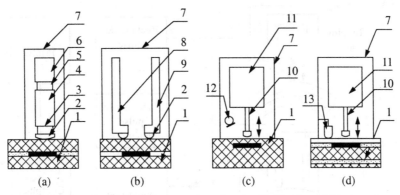

(a) Single contact piezoelectric, (b) Twin contact piezoelectric, (c) Tapping with microphone receiver and (d) Tapping with piezoelectric receiver.

1. Test object, 2. Contact tip, 3. Receiving transducer, 4. Resonant rod, 5. Transmitting transducer, 6. Rear mass, 7. Probe case, 8. Transmitting vibrator, 9. Receiving vibrator, 10. Moving system, 11. Electromagnet, 12. Microphone and 13. Piezoelectric receiver

Fig. 7.14 Probes used in low frequency acoustic flaw detectors. (a) Single contact piezoelectric, (b) Twin contact piezoelectric, (c) Tapping with microphone receiver and (d) Tapping with piezoelectric receiver. 1. Test object, 2. Contact tip, 3. Receiving transducer, 4. Resonant rod, 5. Transmitting transducer, 6. Rear mass, 7. Probe case, 8. Transmitting vibrator, 9. Receiving vibrator, 10. Moving system, 11. Electromagnet, 12. Microphone and 13. Piezoelectric receiver.

vibrator is given to the receiving vibrator through the test object. As the transmitting and receiving vibrators are identical, their natural vibration frequencies remain equal when the impedance is changed.

In piezoelectric probes, the transmitting vibrator excites the oscillations in the test object. The free vibrations are excited by quick discharge of transmitting transducer's capacitor through a thyristor. The discharge produces longitudinal oscillations in the vibrator and bending oscillations in the test object.

In the tapping type probes, short low energy rectangular pulses that are generated using electromagnetic vibrators excite the test object. The vibrator system returns to the initial position after every pulse. Tapping probes have either microphone or piezoelectric receiver for detecting the output signal.

The output signal from both contact type and tapping type probes are processed through a signal processor which compares the phase and the amplitude of the transmitting and receiving signals. From this information, transmission factor is determined and the structural impedance is obtained. The transmission factor and the impedance change are recorded as the probe is moved across the defective area.

The block diagram of a typical acoustic flaw detector with contact and tapping type probes is shown in Fig. 7.15. The presence of an unknown defect can be detected by comparing the signal from this region with that from a known defect created in an identical reference object. The spectra of the known defect can be taken as the reference standard. The measurements carried out for two different structures with twin contact piezoelectric probe are shown in Figs. 7.16 and 7.17. Figure 7.16 shows the presence of defects at various depths *t* in a reinforced plastic sheet. Figure 7.16(a) gives the reference spectrum and the Figs. 7.16(b) and 7.16(c) give the difference spectra between the reference standard and delaminations

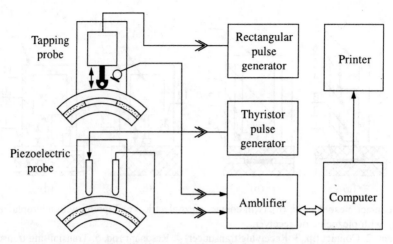

Fig. 7.15   Circuit diagram of a typical acoustic flaw detector

at h = 1.7 mm and 3.5 mm. The presence of the defects can be clearly seen in both the cases. Similarly, detection of a defect in a honeycomb structure is demonstrated in Fig. 7.17. The reference spectrum is shown in Fig. 7.17(a). The difference spectrum of the reference

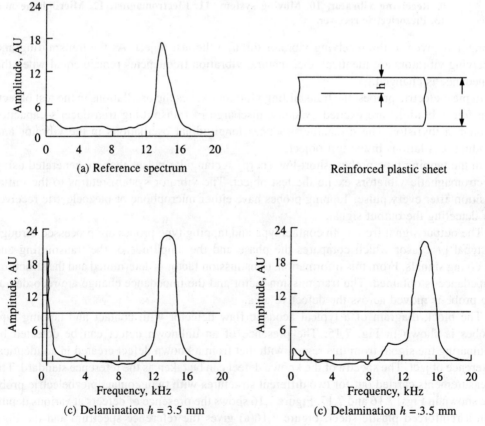

Fig. 7.16   Detection of defects at different depths in a reinforced plastic sheet.

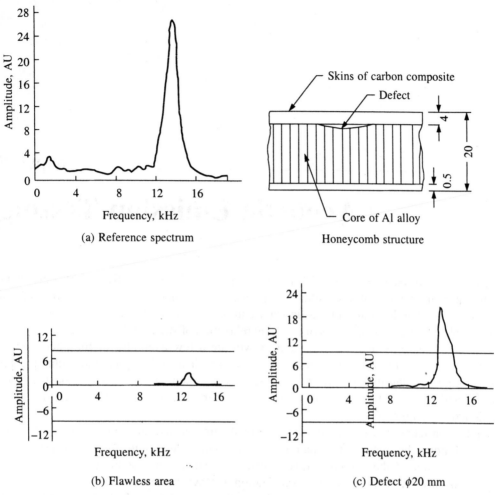

(a) Reference spectrum

Honeycomb structure

(b) Flawless area

(c) Defect ϕ20 mm

Fig. 7.17   Detection of defects in a honeycomb structure.

standard and a flawless region of the test object is shown in Fig. 7.17(b). In Fig. 7.17(c), the difference spectrum for a flaw of 20 mm diameter in a honeycomb structure is shown.

7.14.3   Applications and limitations

The mechanical impedance method is an effective technique for detecting the defects of multilayer structures and delaminations in composites and adhesively bonded structures. This technique is of particular value in testing the near edges of the structure where the moisture ingress is important. There are some limitations in this technique. Since every type of structural component to be inspected requires a calibration standard, detectability of the defect cannot be uniquely quantified. Also, the detectability diminishes with increase in the depth of the defect below the testing surface. The minimum detectable defect size is therefore dependent not only on the structure but also on the depth of the defect in the structure. There is no uniform and well defined criteria for acceptance and rejection of a component. Therefore, relative variations such as the local change in the impedance or the departure in the impedance value at a point from the component average is normally used as the basis for assessment of the components.

Chapter 8

Acoustic Emission Testing

Acoustic emission technique (AET) is emerging as a powerful tool for NDE of plant components such as pressure vessels, pipes, welds etc. Acoustic Emission (AE) is defined as the class of phenomenon whereby transient elastic waves are generated by the rapid release of energy from localized sources like places of transient relaxation of stress and strain fields. Fracture, plastic deformation, crack initiation and growth are a few examples of the phenomenon resulting in AE. This dynamic nature of AE makes it a highly potential technique for monitoring the integrity of critical structures and components in various industries like nuclear and fossil fuel power plants, aerospace, chemical, petrochemical, transportation, manufacturing, fabrication etc.

AET, as a technique for monitoring and evaluating structural integrity, is superior to other techniques because of its capability for: (i) continuous monitoring, (ii) inspection of complete volume of the component, (iii) issue of advance warning and (iv) detection and location of any crack initiation and propagation and system leaks.

The genesis of today's technology in AE was the work of Josep Kaiser. In 1950, Kaiser published his Thesis, where he reported the first comprehensive investigation into the phenomenon of AE. Kaiser used tensile tests of convetional engineering materials to determine (a) types of noises generated from within the specimen; (b) the acoustic processes involved; (c) the frequency ranges and amplitude levels found; and (d) the relation between the stress, strain and the frequencies recorded at various stress levels to which the specimens were subjected to. In this chapter, a brief description of the basic principle of AET and its applications are given.

8.1 PRINCIPLE OF AET

Acoustic emission inspection detects and analyses minute AE signals generated by growing discontinuities in material under a stimulus such as stress and temperature. Proper analysis of these signals can provide information concerning the detection and location of these discontinuities and the structural integrity.

Another important feature of AE is its irreversibility. If a material is loaded to a given stress level and then unloaded, usually no emission will be observed upon immediate reloading until the previous stress has been exceeded. This is known as Kaiser effect and is due to the fact that AE is closely related to plastic deformation and fracture. This irreversibility of AE has important practical implications because it can be used in the detection of subcritical growth of flaws, such as fatigue crack growth, stress corrosion cracking, hydrogen embrittlement etc.

Depending on the nature of energy release, the two types of AE observed are: (i) continuous and (ii) burst.

Continuous emission is characterised by low amplitude emissions. The amplitude varies with AE activity. In metals and alloys, this type of emission occurs during plastic deformation by dislocation movement, diffusion controlled phase transformations and fluid leakage. Burst emissions are characterized by short duration (10 μ s to a few milliseconds) and high amplitude pulses due to discrete release of strain energy. This type of emission occurs during diffusionless phase transformations, crack initiation and propagation, stress corrosion cracking etc.

8.2 TECHNIQUE

It is difficult to use a single all-encompassing parameter to describe an experimental result uniquely. Hence a number of AE parameters are used for interpreting the experimental results. Some of the parameters are used to identify the change in source of AE during the progress of a test, while others are used to eliminate background noise.

Figure 8.1 shows a typical AE signal and the various parameters used for interpretation. Ringdown counts is the number of times the signal crosses a threshold level set for eliminating background noise. This could be used independently or as the cumulative counts with respect to time, load or any other paramter. Count rate is another parameter commonly used.

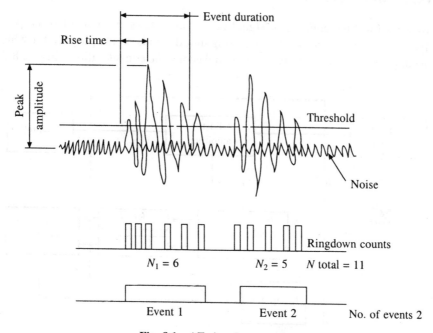

Fig. 8.1   AE signal parameters

The most common ways in which AE signals can be processed are:

(i) Counting: Ringdown counts, Ringdown count rates, events.
(ii) Energy analysis: used for both continuous and burst type emissions.
(iii) Amplitude analysis: used to characterise emissions from different processes.
(iv) Frequency analysis: used to identify different types of failures.
(v) Advanced signal analysis concepts such as pattern recognition, spectral analysis, maximum entropy etc.

In many instances, especially on large pressure vessels, it becomes necessary not only to detect AE signals but also to locate their sources. This can be accomplished by suitably spacing several sensors over the surface of a pressure vessel and monitoring the time of arrival of the signals to various sensor locations. Because of the high velocity of sound and the relative closeness of sensors on a steel vessel, time resolutions in microsecond range must be made in order to locate the source to within less than about 25 mm. The major impetus for the development of such system was the desire for safe operation of pressure vessels, particularly in nuclear-power systems.

AET is capable of detecting growing flaws at least an order of magnitude smaller than those detectable by any other known NDT method. AET is also capable of locating one or more discontinuities while they are growing. When the discontinuity approaches critical size, the AE count rate increases markedly, thus giving a warning for impending instability and failure of the component.

AE evaluation of structures depends on the ability to detect weak signals in noisy electrical and mechanical environment. Proper instrumentation and effective methods are needed to discriminate between wanted and unwanted signals.

8.3 INSTRUMENTATION

The instrument for AET consists of signal detection, data (signal) acquisition, processing and analysis units. The choice of the analyzing unit depends on the purpose for which AET is employed, the level of sensitivity required and economic considerations. Figure 8.2 shows

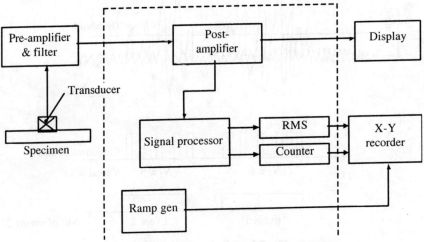

Fig. 8.2   Simple experimental test setup for AET

the typical AET experimental setup. Figure 8.3 shows the options available in organising AET system with different analysing capabilities.

Transducer for AET

The most widely employed transducers for detection and recording of AE are piezoelectric transducers with frequency of the order of 30kHz-2MHz. Resonant types are used with narrow band instrumentation and non-resonant types with wide band instrumentation. As the response of the piezoelectric crystals is different for different wave modes, a careful calibration is necessary.

Pre-amplification and filtering

The pre-amplifier follows the transducer. The preamplifier should have low noise, moderately high power gain and the input impedance matching the transducer. Filters are designed for different band widths and can be plugged in to meet specific requirements.

Post-amplification and threshold

The pre-amplifier output is of low level and hence has to be amplified further before handling with the processing circuitry. Further amplification with selectable gain is incorporated in this unit. In order to eliminate the background noise from analysis, only signals exceeding certain threshold voltage are detected and analysed.

Data acquisition

Two types of systems are in common use for acquisition of raw AE data for off-line analysis, namely video recorders and analog magnetic recorders. When real-time decision making is important with capability for on-line processing and analysis, transient recorders with computer interface are used.

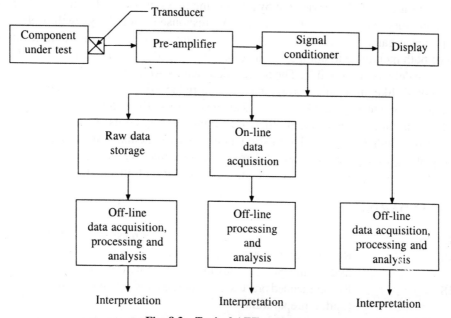

Fig. 8.3 Typical AET systems

Processing and analysis
The processing instrumentation required for AET depends on the form and quantity of raw data. Its function is to convert analog data into digital form.

Display devices
A variety of display devices are used for displaying and recording analysed data. The simplest and most commonly used recording device is the X-Y recorder.

8.4   SENSITIVITY

AE inspection is extremely sensitive compared with the other more familiar NDT methods. The minimum detectable crack size for UT, RT and ECT methods is about 0.50 mm, if ideal conditions are met for each method. Whereas AET can detect crack growth of the order of 25 microns. This corresponds to microcrack growth of the order of less than 10 μm.

8.5   APPLICATIONS

A broad classification of the applications include:

(a) Inspection during proof testing and on-line monitoring of pressure vessels, pipelines and engineering structures.
(b) Leakage detection and location.
(c) Quality control during fabrication.
(d) Investigating processes such as fatigue, stress corrosion and corrosion.
(e) Monitoring underground pipe lines.
(f) On-line weld monitoring.

In order to validate the application of AET for a given system, a number of simulation experiments are generally carried out by introducing flaws into a similar structure/component or on laboratory specimens and monitoring AE response during the growth of these flaws.

Experience gained in the field of AET of pressure vessels and other plant components made of both metallic and composite materials suggests that precise detection and location of dynamic defects are possible. The defects detected by AET have been confirmed by other NDT methods like ultrasonic testing, magnetic particle testing etc. It is also possible to find out the phase of a test cycle when severe damage occurs to the component structure. Energy and phase amplitude analysis and other AE parameters can be used to discriminate defect signals from high background industrial noisy environments. For the pressure vessels working at high temperatures, defect detection is possible even after keeping the sensors at the end of wave guides that are as long as 5 to 8 m and attached to the vessel.

8.6   STANDARDS

1. IS	Glossary of terms used in acoustic emission (in print).
2. IS	Recommended practice for acoustic emission inspection during hydrostatic pressure testing of systems (under preparation).
3. IS	Recommended practice for acoustic emission monitoring during welding (under preparation).
4. ASTM-E 569	Acoustic emission monitoring of structures during controlled stimulation

5. ASTM-E 1139   Acoustic emission from metal pressure boundaries.
6. ASTM-E 610   Definition of terms relating to acoustic emission.
7. ASTM-E 650   Guide for mounting piezoelectric acoustic emission sensors.
8. ASTM-E 750   Characterizing acoustic emission instrumentation.
9. ASTM-E 976   Guide for determining the reproducibility of acoustic emission sensor response.
10. ASTM-E 1106   Primary calibration of acoustic emission sensors.

8.7 STRUCTURAL INTEGRITY ASSESSMENT

Hydro and pneumatic testing are employed for qualification and in-service assessment of industrial components operating under pressure. While this testing can indicate that there are no through and through leaks, it would not indicate presence of harmful defects which would have grown during the testing. On-line acoustic emission monitoring during hydro and pneumatic testing would enable detection of such growing defects. By employing multi sensor approach, it would also be possible to locate the growing defects, if any. Sometimes, AE monitoring is done covering only specific regions of concern like circumferential welds between the shell and dished end or a nozzle weld etc. To illustrate the usefulness of AET for structural integrity assessment, a case study on AE monitoring during pressure testing of a Horton Sphere of a petrochemical organization is discussed below.

8.7.1 Hydro testing of a Horton sphere

During the inservice inspection of a 17 m Horton sphere, a flaw was detected during magnetic particle testing. In order to assess the impact of this flaw on the structural integrity of the Horton sphere, it has been decided to apply acoustic emission technique to monitor any growth of the flaw during hydro testing. For AE monitoring during hydro testing of the 17 m Horton sphere, a total of twelve sensors were used in 1-5-5-1 configuration. Figure 8.4 shows typical locations of the AE sensors mounted on the Horton Sphere during hydro testing, alongwith a typical AE source location map. The 12 sensors of 150 kHz resonant frequency type used in 1-5-5-1 configuration are arranged in such a way to cover the whole sphere in a triangular location mode One sensor each is located the top and bottom of the sphere. Five sensors each are located equidistant along two circumferential configuration, as shown in Fig. 8.4. Based on the response of the sensors to simulated pencil break source, the inter-sensor distance of 9.5 m in the 1-5-5-1 configuration was optimized. By this, the entire vessel could be covered to detect and locate any AE source associated with local plastic deformation and/or growing discontinuities from any part of the sphere, in addition to the flaw region identified by magnetic particle testing.

The hydro test of the vessel was carried out to a maximum pressure of 22 kg/cm^2, with periodic holds at different pressures. A reloading cycle from 20 kg/cm^2 to 22 kg/cm^2 was immediately carried out following the first cycle of hydro test. During the hydro test, it was observed that AE signals were generated only during the pressure rise. With increase in pressure, AE signals were generated in the newer areas and the areas where AE occurred in the previous pressure steps do not generate AE in the subsequent pressure steps. These signals were attributed to local micro-plastic deformation of the material. A few signals have also been generated from specific regions, particularly through out the circumference at an elevation corresponding to the concrete supports. Subsequent inspection of the vessel and simulated pencil break study after the hydro test indicated that the AE signals were generated from the cracks in the concrete columns which were supporting the vessel. Some of the signals could also be confirmed to be due to fracture of oxide scale or paint layer. The results obtained from the broadband sensor were analysed in terms of the spectral energy in different frequency bands. The overall spectral energy was found to increase with pressure rise and this increase was predominantly concentrated in the low frequency band upto 200 kHz. This was attributed to the micro-yielding taking place in the sphere. This was also confirmed from the fact that, during the repressurisation stage (20-22 kg/cm^2), the energy of the signals was at the background level, and is attributed to Kaiser effect.

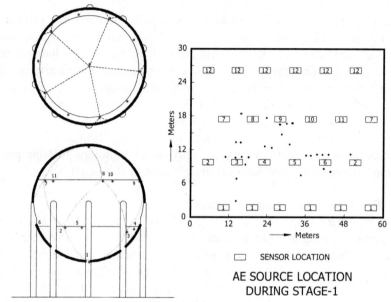

SENSOR LOCATION

AE SOURCE LOCATION
DURING STAGE-1

PRESSURISATION (STAGE-1)
RANDOM AE ACTIVITY DUE TO
1. MECHANICAL RUBBING BETWEEN SUPPORT
   STRUCTURE AND VESSEL
2. PAINT LAYER PEEL-OFF

REPRESSURISATION (STAGE-2)
NO SIGNIFICANT AE ACTIVITY

Fig. 8.4   AE Monitoring during hydrotesting of Horton sphere

8.8   ACOUSTIC EMISSION TECHNIQUE FOR LEAK DETECTION

One of the problems faced in industrial components operating under pressure is the leakage and hence its early detection and location would help in taking suitable remedial measures before any catastrophe takes place. This is particularly significant if the leaking fluid is hazardous with respect to its poisonous nature and inflammability. The feasibility of leak detection by AET depends on three factors: (i) the nature of AE radiated from the leak, (ii) the attenuation between leak and sensor and (iii) the background noise. The physical origin of leak signal is the fluctuating pressure field associated with turbulence in the fluid. The actual detection of the leak depends on the flow rate as this factor decides the energy content of the leak signal. Extensive studies have been undertaken to develop AET based methodologies for detection and location of leaks, even remotely with high sensitivity and reliability. To illustrate the usefulness of AET for detection and location of remote leaks in pressurised systems, a case study on application of AET for detection and location of leaks in an end shield system of a heavy water reactor (PHWR) is discussed below.

8.8.1 Leak detection in an end shield of a PHWR

AET has been successfully applied for detection and location of leak paths present on an inaccessible side of an end shield of unit 1 of Rajasthan Atomic Power Station (RAPS). This methodology was based on the fact that AE signals due to air and water leaks have different characteristic features. Baseline data was generated from a sound end shield of a PHWR for characterising the background noise. A mock up end shield system with saw cut leak paths was used to verify the validity of the methodology. Time domain analysis of AE signals obtained by air pressurisation of the end shield to 0.124 MPa was used for detection and location of leak paths. However, this analysis could not be applied for detection of subsequent leaks, found after repair and operation of the system, due to limit on maximum air pressurisation of the end shield to 0.035 MPa. Hence, frequency spectral analysis was

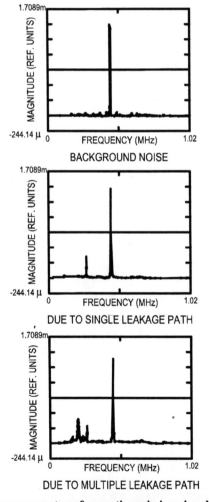

Fig. 8.5   Autopower spectra of acoustic emission signals for the end shield

used. Auto-power spectra showed presence of characteristic frequency associated with the air leaks (Fig. 8.5). The difference in the characteristic frequency of the signal for the two leak paths was attributed to the difference in size, shape and morphology of the leak paths. This can be understood if one observes the playing of a flute, i.e., the flutist generates sounds of varied frequencies by adjusting the fingers for closing and opening of the holes in the flute along with the controlled air blow.

Thermography

All objects around us emit electromagnetic radiations. At ambient temperatures and above, these are predominantly infrared radiations (IR). IR are invisible to eye. But with the aid of a suitable detector, IR can be converted into a visible image. Variation in the temperature of the surface of the object can be visualized from the thermal image of an object. This means that deviations from normal temperature can be detected from a distance. It is this advantage that the technique exploits for ever increasing applications in a number of industries.

9.1 BASIC PRINCIPLES

Thermography makes use of the infrared spectral band of the electromagnetic radiation. The infrared band is further subdivided into four smaller bands, the boundaries of which are arbitrarily chosen. They include the near infrared (0.75–3 μm), the middle infrared (3–6 μm), the far infrared (6–15 μm) and the extreme infrared (15–100 μm). The most commonly used band for commercial infrared imaging is between 0.75–15 μm.

The properties of infrared radiations are similar to those of other electromagnetic radiations such as visible light except that their transmission and absorption behavior is different from that of visible light. Infrared radiations travel in straight lines outward from the source. They can propagate in vacuum and in certain liquids, solids and gases. They can be optically focused and directed by lenses or mirrors or dispersed by prisms. IR can also be transmitted through certain materials which are opaque to light. The intensity of the emitted spectrum is dependent upon the absolute temperature of the body. The basic factors affecting the thermal measurement include (a) emissivity, (b) surroundings, and (c) atmosphere.

(a) Emissivity
This is defined as the ratio of the radiance of a body at a given temperature to the corresponding radiance of a black body at the same temperature. For the black body, the emissivity factor is 1.0. Actual objects are seldom "black". Normally, various materials and treated surfaces exhibit emissivities ranging from 0.1 to 0.95. Emissivity is a critical parameter for quantitative measurement of the temperature.

(b) Surroundings

It is important to have the object surroundings free from thermal radiation sources, otherwise the radiation from these sources would also be reflected by the object under examination leading to erroneous values.

(c) Atmosphere

The effects of atmosphere are of importance when the object is far away. The atmosphere not only attenuates the radiation from the target but also alters the spectral characteristics. However, these effects are negligible in cases where the object under investigation is located quite close and the atmosphere is uncontaminated with vapours, smoke, fog, hot gases etc. Occasionally, one may need to make some critical measurements on an object in presence of hot air/gases as in the case of furnaces. In such cases, suitable filters such as high temperature gas filter are used along with the appropriate correction factors to take into account the ambient temperature and attenuation by these filters. In case where the objects are situated at a large distance as in the case of airborne thermography, atmospheric absorption plays a very important role. The atmospheric absorption is quite a complex process and in these cases, mathematical modelling is resorted to for estimating the temperatures.

9.2   DETECTORS AND EQUIPMENT

The detection system for infrared imaging can be a contact (surface) system such as cholesterol liquid crystal or a non-contact tele-system such as a thermographic camera. Surface systems tend to be less costly and simple and can have high resolution. Camera systems are more expensive. However, thermal imaging with tele-camera systems has wider engineering applications.

The block diagram of a non-contact thermography system is shown in Fig. 9.1. It basically consists of an infrared scanner, monitor, control unit and a calculator for field applications. The output can also be stored in a modified video thermal recorder which can be analyzed later using a personal computer with image processing facilities. The infrared scanner essentially consists of an optical system, scanning mechanism, infrared detector and associated electronics. The optical system collimates the incoming infrared radiation into the detector. The commonly used materials for mirrors and prisms in the optical system are germanium, silicon, sapphire, barium fluoride and arsenic trisulphide. The scanning mechanism scans the surface within the field of view. It consists of two octagonal prisms rotating perpendicular to each other at a high speed.

The heart of the thermography system is the infrared detector. There are different modes for acquiring a thermal image.

1. Image Converters: Here the thermal image is converted into electron image through the use of converters which is then converted into an optical image.
2. Pyricon Based Devices: These are normal vidicon tubes with infrared sensitive face plates (sulphate triglycine).
3. Mechanical Scanning Devices: Here the image is scanned with a moving mirror across a fixed and cooled detector (mercury cadmium telluride or indium antimonide). This is the type of system which is used extensively in the field of NDT.

The advent of personal computers has revolutionized the field of thermography.

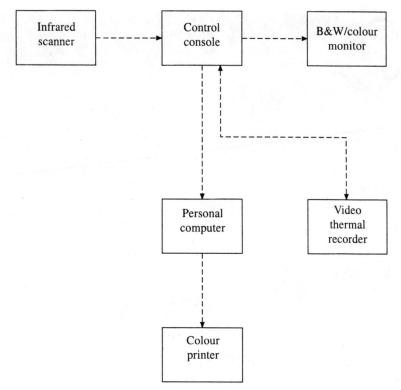

Fig. 9.1   Black diagram of a thermography system

Thermograms can be subjected to image processing and enhancement to obtain the minute details not otherwise visible. Software options for image processing include contrast stretching, spatial filtering, thermal chopping, relief presentation etc.

9.3   TECHNIQUES

Thermography can be classified basically into two categories: (a) passive and (b) active. In passive technique, the natural heat distribution is measured over the surface of a hot structure. This is generally used in temperature monitoring. In an active technique, heating or cooling is induced or applied to the part or the complete surface and the movement and redistribution of temperature profile across the test surface is measured. This is generally used in non-destructive evaluation.

9.4   APPLICATIONS

In the petroleum industry, this technique finds applications in the monitoring of stack temperature, maintenance of plant equipment such as reaction towers, refining furnaces, ducts and piping, detection of corrosion in oil tank shell and measurement of oil levels etc. Figure 9.2 shows a typical thermogram showing temperature distribution in a hot oil heater in a Petrochemical plant.

Thermal imaging has been extensively applied for condition monitoring of furnace tubes gas and fluid transfer lines, evaluation of heat resistant linings in refractory furnaces etc.

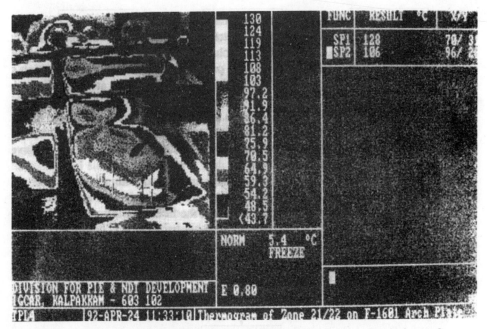

Fig. 9.2   Thermogram of archplate of a hot oil heater in a petrochemical complex

This technique is ideally suited for the wear determination of refractories in blast furnaces, hot blast stoves and steel stoves and the inspection of rotary kiln lining and estimation of temperature within the kiln.

Thermographic inspection of the entire electrical power systems can be performed. Stator lamination insulation, core insulation, slip ring temperature measurement etc. of turbo-generators are also made using thermography.

Fig. 9.3   Thermogram showing hot spot (white region) on the low voltage side of a 230 kV transformer

Application of thermography for the inspection of transmission lines, substations and distribution systems has become a regular feature in many of the countries abroad. Figure 9.3 shows a thermogram taken on 230 kV transmission line and Fig. 9.4 shows a thermogram taken on an insulator in a 33 kV switchyard. Hot spots indicating relatively higher temperature regions can be seen in the photographs. Apart from these important applications, this technique can also be applied for:

(1) Location of loose contacts on busbar joints of switchyard, switchgear etc.
(2) Location of improper jointing of lugs in cable joints
(3) Finding irregularities in distribution boards
(4) Detection of hot spots in isolators due to presence of dirt or moisture which could lead to corona.
(5) Checking the adequacy of insulation.

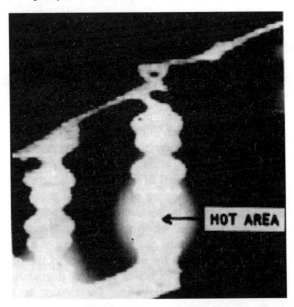

Fig. 9.4 Thermogram showing a hot spot (white region) in an insulator array in a 33 kV switchyard

9.4.1 Thermal Imaging for Condition Monitoring of Industrial Components

Figure 9.5 shows a conical reducer in a heavy water plant along with its thermal image on the right side. Cracked synthesis gas (N_2&H_2) at high temperature coming from catalyst tubes of a ammonia cracker unit is collected commonly by hairpin tubes and then flows through this conical reducer to a waste heat boiler. The conical inlet made of carbon steel is insulated inside to protect from hot synthesis gas and the maximum permissible outer skin temperature of the conical inlet is 393K. Thermal image given in Fig. 9.5 revealed that the maximum temperature in the hot region was 409K exceeding the prescribed limits. The white arrow indicates the region of hotspot. The patch indicated by the yellow arrow is due to variations in emissivity (as can be seen in the photograph as variation due to surface condition). The thermal imaging as part of the condition monitoring programme enables corrective action to keep the conical outer surface temperature within limits.

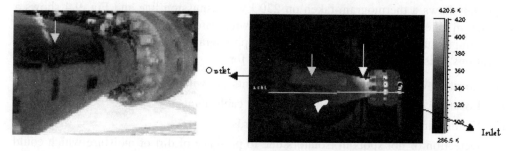

Fig. 9.5   Conical inlet of a heavy water plant along with its thermal image

Figure 9.6 shows a thermal image of a storage tank in a heavy water plant. The liquid level in the tank (arrow) can be clearly seen. This is due to the fact that thermal capacitance of the liquid is different from that of the tank. Figure 9.7 shows a typical thermal image of a set of cracker tubes of 89 mm diameter in a furnace. Ammonia flows inside these tubes and is cracked with the help of a catalyst. The designed operating skin temperature of these should be between 800K-993K for optimum yield of ammonia. The following observations are made from the Fig. 9.7:

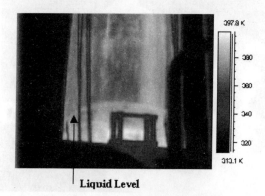

Liquid Level

Fig. 9.6   Thermal image of a storage tank in a heavy water plant

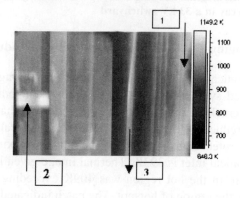

Fig. 9.7   Thermal image of cracker tubes inside a furnace

1. Flames impinging directly on the tubes (indicated by arrow 1) can be visualised. Skin temperatures of the tubes in such cases exceed the prescribed limit of 993 K.
2. IR reflections from the metal used for fastening the thermocouple makes it appear to be hotter compared to the tube (arrow 2).
3. Flames in the background between the two tubes can also be seen (arrow 3).

Figure 9.8 shows a thermal image of a hermetically sealed motor used in inert gas recirculation system of a radioactive hot cell. The image reveals hot spot in the top region, requiring attention. Wall thinning in tubes used in boilers and stream pipelines is very common. Infrared thermal imaging is an useful technique for detection of such wall thinning. Figure 9.9 shows a thermal image indicating a wall thinning of the order of 20% in a Zircaloy-2 tube of OD 100 mm and wall thickness of 8.5mm.

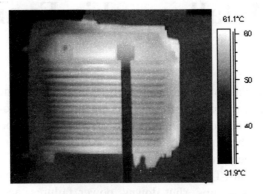

Fig. 9.8 Thermal image of a hermetically sealed motor

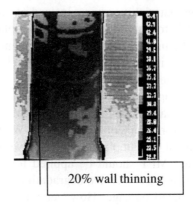

20% wall thinning

Fig. 9.9 Thermal image of a Zircaloy-2 tube

9.5 CODES AND STANDARDS

1. ASTM E 1311   Minimum detectable temperature difference for thermal imaging systems
2. ASTM E 1213   Minimum resolvable temperature difference for thermal imaging systems
3. ASTM E 1543   Noise equivalent temperature difference of thermal imaging systems.

Chapter 10

In situ Metallographic Examination

In spite of choosing best available materials for fabrication of components for service in the plants, it has been noticed that materials undergo gradual degradation by way of changes occurring in microstructure and consequently the mechanical properties during service. After considerable service, the required mechanical properties of the material of the components may fall below the safe operating limit, even when due care is taken to maintain operating parameters within design limits. This can be generally attributed to the environment, fluctuations in operating parameters, start ups, shut downs, power failures, accidents etc. For safer operation of a plant and as a preventive measure of failure, it is beneficial to have a periodic assessment of the status of the material in service. Instead of periodic testing of mechanical properties, it may be worthwhile to assess the changes taken place, if any, in microstructure such as precipitation at grain boundaries, temper embrittement, decarburization etc. which will be indicative of degradation in the mechanical properties of materials. This study can further suggest the mechanical testing of a representative specimen, if required and the further steps to be taken for safer operation of the plant. The microstructural features obtained can also reveal initial stages of material degradation before the condition becomes an acute problem, thereby allowing time for repairs or replacements. When no significant degradation is detected, confidence is gained that unplanned outages would not occur. Conventional NDE methods such as UT and MPT should be applied for the condition assessment of components to detect damage such as inservice degradation or to detect pre-existing flaws that could result in service-related damage. However, these methods cannot be used as substitutes for metallography because they are not capable of detecting and quantifying the lower levels of damage associated with the early stages of material deterioration.

In situ metallography (field metallography) is used for microstructural evaluation of plant structural components during service. Regular metallography consists of preparing a section of a material in laboratory by usual grinding, polishing and etching sequence for revealing microstructure and then examining the same under an optical microscope in the laboratory.

In the in situ metallography, instead of sectioning a component for metallographic examination, the surface of it is metallographically prepared 'in situ' by using portable grinding, polishing and electro-polishing units and it is a nondestructive method. Microstructure can be examined on the prepared spot using a portable microscope or can be registered on a replicating tape which will reveal the microstructure on processing in the laboratory.

Some of the NDT techniques such as ultrasonics is very much influenced by such characteristics of material. Nondestructive testing in conjunction with metallography is extensively used in quality evaluation of components not only during stages of manufacturing and installation, but also during inservice and maintenance. The great advantage of metallographic examination is that it can provide valuable information regarding the origin and nature of flaws and thus plays a key role in failure investigation. It also helps in determining whether indications obtained from NDT methods such as ultrasonics and magnetic particle testing are due to metallurgical structure or due to flaws present in the component being tested. Indications of magnetic particle examinations are re-checked by in situ metallographic examination to find out ghost indications due to variations in chemistry and heat treated conditions of welds. Sometimes, it becomes impractical to adopt satisfactory quality control techniques and therefore process is controlled by using combination of metallographic examination and statistical techniques.

This chapter discusses an approach to the selection of system and sites for field metallography, the procedure for obtaining a replica, and the significance of microstructural characteristics of typical power plant material for damage assessment.

10.1 APPROACH TO THE SELECTION OF SITE FOR METALLOGRAPHIC EXAMINATION

The criteria for selection of systems and sites for field metallography are based on the expected damge mechanism(s), which in turn is (are) governed by the type of materials used in fabrication of the components and service conditions. Replica locations are also selected on the basis of problematic sites identified from known experience.

For example, in components fabricated from plain carbon steels operating at temperature above 673 K, or Cr-Mo steels above 753 K, the primary mechanism expected is graphitization. This type of damage usually occurs in the portion of HAZ, nearest to the unaffected base metal. Therefore, when graphitization is of concern, sites for replication should be located primarily at the interface of weldment/base metal.

In the case of Cr-Mo steels and austenitic steels, the expected damge mechanism is creep, the time dependent deformation of materials. Creep is governed by operating stresses in addition to the temperature and time factors. Thus, when creep is the damage mechanism of concern, sites for replication should be selected from the more highly stressed locations in components and systems operating at the highest temperature.

In weldments, creep damge usually occurs first in the HAZ, or weld metal very close to the weld fusion line, where the microstructures are most susceptible to creep damage. Experience suggests that longitudinal welds in high temperature system deserve special attenuation. In the case of circumferential welds, it is important to determine the most likely location around the weld where high tensile stresses occur.

10.2 REPLICATION PROCESS

Replication process results in the production of a "hard copy" or "finger print", i.e., replica of the microstructural features for subsequent metallurgical evaluation. Replication involves the following steps:

(1) Grinding and polishing the surface to be examined. Polishing is performed by either mechanical methods or electropolishing to produce a 0.20 μm finish. Electropolishing can be accomplished much faster than mechanical polishing, but its successful application is more sensitive to metal surface temperature.

(2) Etching the polished surface with an appropriate etchant (e.g., 2–5% nital, i.e. nitric acid in alcohol in the case of carbon and low alloy steels) to develop the microstructural features.

(3) Firmly applying a thin (= 50 μm) cellulose acetate film that has been wetted and softened with a mild solvent (acetone) immediately prior to application. An alternate method is to spray the polished and etched surface with a strong solvent, e.g., acetone, and immediately apply the film. Keeping the film free of extraneous foreign particles is more difficult with this technique. In either case, it is the softening by the solvent that allows the film to capture the metallurgical features in a reverse topography, with depressions becoming protrusions. The film is allowed to dry and is then removed.

(4) Removing the film and attaching the dried film to a flat surface (usually a microscopic glass slide) for microscopic observations. It is important to keep the film flat to enable viewing at high magnification, up to 1000 using an optical microscope for metallurgical evaluation.

The metallurgical features recorded on the replica are much more distinguishable when the replica is either blackened at the back side prior to attaching the replica to the glass slide or applying a thin film of gold on the front side by vapour deposition. After etching the polished surface (step 2), the microstructural features can be directly observed using a portable optical microscope and recorded with the camera attached to the microscope. Photography is possible only when sufficient access is available for vibration free mounting of the microscope assembly. Replica provides valid images of microstructures when produced by skilled personnel.

Figure 10.1 shows the typical components used for in-situ metallography. These include grinding and polishing unit, etching set-up and portable compact optical microscope. The use of microscope for observing the microstructure at a selected spot on a stainless steel component can be seen in Fig. 10.1.

10.3   SIGNIFICANCE OF MICROSTRUCTURAL OBSERVATION

The significance of creep and fatigue damage and cracks is commonly assessed at a magnification of 200. Microcracks usually form by the coalescence of aligned cavities indicating advanced creep damage. Macrocracks develop by the growth of microcracks. From a practical stand point, the changes in base metal are not as important as in the HAZ and weld metal because the last two undergo significant creep damage well before any creep related problems develop in the base metal. For the evaluation of microstructures of various materials, ASM-Metals handbook, Vol. 8 on 'Metallography, structures and phase diagrams' may be referred to.

Microstructural features are very useful in assessing microstructural degradation, damage assessment and life prediction. Periodic measurements made during inservice inspection help in knowing any unanticipated degradation in components, thus avoiding premature failures. Many a time, after an accident, like accidental increase in temperature and pressure, fire accident etc., it is necessary to confirm that the metallurgical conditions of the components are not altered and the components are acceptable. This can be successfully verified using in situ metallography.

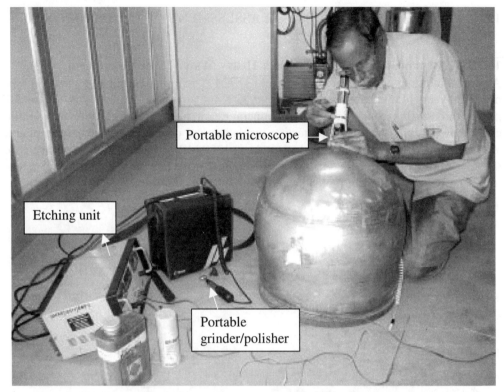

Fig. 10.1   In-situ metallographic set-up showing portable flexible grinding and polishing machine, etching control unit and a portable metallurgical microscope

10.4   DECISION MAKING

Personnel responsible for the availability and reliability of plants and industries depend on metallurgists to provide appropriate recommendations based on the microstructural characteristics revealed by replicas. Decisions like repair, replace, or use as-is with future monitoring at a given periodicity are taken.

10.5   APPLICATIONS

Metallographic examination is used for the following applications:

(1) Evaluation of material condition
(2) Condition monitoring of components
(3) Failure analysis
(4) Assessment of creep damage, temper embrittlement etc.

10.6   CODES AND STANDARDS

1. ASTM E 340   Macro-etching of metals and alloys.

2. ASTM E 3-80   Preparation of metallographic specimens.
3. ASTM E 1351   Production and evaluation of field metallographic replicas.
4. ASTM E 1180   Preparing sulphur prints for macrostructural examination.

10.7   TYPICAL CASE-STUDIES FOR ASSESSMENT OF COMPONENTS BY IN-SITU METALLOGRAPHY

10.7.1   Assessment of Degradation of a Heavy Water Plant Component

A conical inlet piping made of carbon steel (ASTM A 182 GRF1) failed prematurely after nearly 20 years of operation in a power plant. Cracked ammonia synthesis gas (N_2 and H_2) passes through the conical inlet at a temperature of 623K. During normal operating conditions, the pipe line has a protective insulation and outer temperature of the pipe ia around 393 K, and the pressure inside the tube is 1250 MPa. Due to breakage of insulation the temperature of the pipeline increased to about 623K, which went unnoticed for a long time, and hence resulted in premature failure.

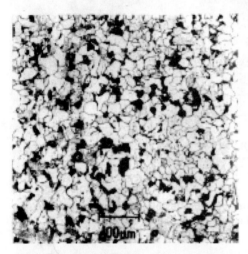

Fig. 10.2   **Ferrite/Pearlite microstructure of the pipeline operating at normal limits**

Fig. 10.3   **Degraded microstructure showing growth of ferrite area and presence of carbide network at grain boundaries**

In-situ metallographic investigation revealed normal ferrite-pearlite microstructure (Fig. 10.2) on the outer surface of the pipeline where the insulation was intact. In the failed zone, the microstructure was found to be degraded. The pearlite colonies got transformed to ferrite and spheroidal carbides (Fig. 10.3) which lowered the tensile strength of the pipe. The photo mosaic in Fig. 10.4 shows the propagation of the crack near the failure location

Creep failure in super alloy turbine blade

A nicked based super alloy aeroengine turbine blade failed in service has been investigated using in-situ metallography. The nickel based superalloys are normally resistant to creep damage due to the presence of fine and coherent ã' precipitates in austenite matrix. However, when the temperatures of the blades accidentally exceeds normal operational conditions, these fine precipitates grow in size and lead to reduction in strength, thus causing premature failure by creep damage. The grain boundary cavities observed in the microstructure (Fig. 10.5) obtained by in-situ metallography clearly indicates that the failure of the turbine blade has taken place by creep damage.

Fig. 10.4 Photomosaic of the crack near the failure location

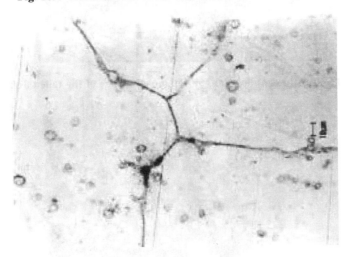

Fig. 10.5 Grain boundary creep cavities in an aeroengine turbine blade

Failures of stainless steel dished ends during storage

Stainless steel dished ends made by cold spinning process are used to fabricate cylindrical vessels. The straight portion of the dished ends is to be subsequently welded to the cylindrical shells to fabricate vessels used as storage tank to store process liquids. Several dished ends made out of type AISI 304L stainless steel developed extensive cracking during storage. The dished ends were stored in a coastal environment with an average temperature of 32Ú C, humidity ranging from 70-80% and an atmospheric NaCl content ranging from 8 to 45 mg/m^2/day. Visual inspection before welding revealed extensive cracks in the inside surface on many dished ends. Liquid penetrant testing was used to determine the extent and nature of the crack on the surface. In-situ Metallographic inspection (Fig. 10.6) on the inside surface indicated that the cracks were transgranular in nature and were also heavily branched with macro and micro branches. The morphology of the crack is indicative of transgranular stress corrosion cracking (TGSCC) as revealed by in-situ metallography (Fig. 10.7). TGSCC occurred due to significant tensile stresses on the inside of the dished ends, presence of surface contamination seen as rust and improper storage in a hot and humid coastal environment. In the hot and humid coastal atmosphere, long exposures of stainless steel components containing iron surface contaminants could result in the rusting of iron debris. Such rust particles absorb moisture and chlorides from the environment, which leads to SCC of the components.

Fig. 10.6   In-situ metallography at the inner surface of the failed dished end

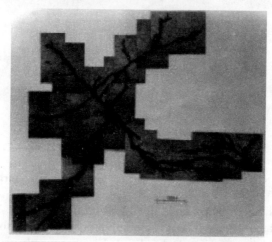

Fig. 10.7   TGSCC in the inner surface of the dished

Chapter 11

Leak Testing

Leak testing is employed to detect leaks and determine the rate at which a liquid or gas will penetrate from inside a "tight" component or assembly to the outside, or vice versa, as a result of pressure differential between the two regions, or of permeation of somewhat extended barrier. It has become conventional to use the term "leak" to refer to an actual discontinuity or passage through which a fluid flows or permeates. "Leakage" refers to the fluid that has flowed through a leak. "Leak rate" refers to the rate of fluid flow per unit of time under a given set of conditions, and is properly expressed in units of mass per unit of time. Standard leak rate refers to the rate of flow of atmospheric air under conditions in which inlet pressure is 0.1 MPa ± 5%; outlet pressure is less than 1 kPa; temperature is 298 K ± 5 and dew point is less than −298 K.

The term "minimum detectable leak" refers to the smallest hole or discrete passage that can be detected, and "minimum detectable leak rate" refers to the smallest detectable fluid flow rate. The amount of leakage required for a leak-testing instrument to give a minimum detectable signal can be determined. This amount is generally used to denote the sensitivity of the instrument. Instrument sensitivity is independent of test conditions, but when an instrument is applied to a test, the sensitivity of the test depends on the existing conditions of pressure, temperature and fluid.

11.1 MEASUREMENT OF LEAKAGE

Leakage is measured by how much fluid passes through a leak under a given set of conditions. Because leakage will vary with conditions, it is necessary to state both the leak rate and the prevailing conditions in order to define a leak properly. Therefore, leak rate is often expressed as the product of some measure of pressure and volume per unit of time. More widely used units for specifying leak rate are:

(a) torr-liters per second
(b) liter-microns per second
(c) atmospheric cubic centimeters per second

It is desirable to know the conversion factors as different personnel refer leaks and their rates using different units. Basic conversion factors are:

$$1 \text{ atm} = 760 \text{ torr}$$
$$1 \text{ Pa} = 0.98692 \infty 10^{-5} \text{ atm}$$
$$1 \text{ bar} = 10^{6} \text{ dynes/cm}$$
$$1 \text{ atm.cc} = 760 \ \mu\text{m liters}$$
$$= 0.76 \text{ torr.liters}$$
$$1 \text{ lusec} = 1.316 \infty 10^{-3} \text{ atm-cc/s}$$
$$= 0.133 \text{ mPa m}^3/\text{s}$$
$$= 0.001 \text{ torr liter/s}$$
$$1 \text{ Pa m}^3/\text{s} = 9.8692 \text{ atm cm}^3/\text{s}$$

(Appendix A given at the end of the chapter gives various conversion factors for SI units used in the leak testing)

There are two basic types of leaks: (a) real leaks and (b) virtual leaks. A real leak is an essentially localized leak: i.e. a discrete passage through which fluid may flow (hole, crack etc.). Virtual leaks are leaks that involve the gradual desorption of gases from surfaces or components within a vacuum systems.

11.2   LEAK TESTING METHODS

There are many methods of detecting leaks. Depending on the sensitivity required, Table 11.1 gives various methods of leak testing and their sensitivity.

Table 11.1   Leak Testing Methods

Method	Detector	Sensitivity (leak rate in lusecs)
Air/soap solution	Visual, bubbles, sound of escaping fluid, ultrasonic detectors	10^{-2}
Methanol/hydrogen	Visual-bubbles	10^{-4}
Hydrogen	Pirani gauge	10^{-4}
Halogen gas	Heated anode Electron capture gauge	10^{-9}
Hydrogen/helium	Mass spectrometer	10^{-10}
Radioactive gas Krypton-85	Counter	10^{-10}

Comparison of leak rate in three different ways may help to visualise the size of leak and the same is given at the end of the chapter under Appendix B.

11.3   LEAK DETECTION

Leak detection may be carried out by visual inspection using soap bubbles or mass spectrometers etc. Among the various methods of detection available, bubble testing is widely used for less sensitive applications and mass spectrometer is used for high sensitive detection. Hence discussion is limited to the bubble testing and mass spectrometer methods only. To understand about the other methods of detection, the references given at the end of the chapter may be consulted.

11.3.1   Bubble Testing

Immersion of pressurised component in water is used as a crude test in some cases to check for leak tightness. In this method, the sensitivity can be made very high if very high pressures are used. The main reason for the insensitivity of testing in water is that comparatively large bubbles are formed. Such bubbles take so long to appear that they can easily be missed. In liquids of low surface tension as compared with water, the bubbles formed are seven or eight times smaller in diameter. Hence they are emitted several hundred times more frequently, and appear as a vertical stream which is clearly visible, under proper viewing conditions.

The best combination of pressurizing medium was found to be *hydrogen* and *ether*. Ether has a low surface tension and hydrogen has a fast flow through small leaks. *Methanol* and *helium* are better than hydrogen, and can be used for detection of smaller leaks. Before use of all such materials, the inspector should become familiar with the hazards involved in handling these materials and the necessary safety precautions to be taken.

If the leak is small, the bubble may be difficult to be seen until the eye is adapted. A magnification glass (2 × to 5 ×) will be of great assistance. Good lighting and dark background will be helpful. Small stream of bubbles can be more easily detectable from above than from the side. Bubble forming solution is applied to the surface of a pressurized vessel if it is too large or not possible to submerge. The ideal liquid for bubble testing should have low surface tension and low viscosity. The bubble size depends on the viscosity of the liquid, pressure and diameter of leak. Sometimes, vibration or hammering of the pressurised component under test is applied for enhanced detection sensitivity.

Advantages: The advantages of bubble testing are that it is inexpensive, can be carried out by relatively less experienced personnel, is rapid, gives accurate location of leak, and the whole specimen is inspected simultaneously.

Limitations: The technique cannot locate very small leaks. In some cases, leaks have been known to pass gas in one direction only, and if this is inward, the bubble technique will not locate such leaks.

Applications: The technique can most advantageously be applied for checking the integrity of pressure vessels, valves, instruments, piping circuits, containments, condensers, heat exchanges, pumps, cylinders etc.

11.3.2   Helium Leak Detector

For very sensitive leak testing, mass spectrometer based helium leak detector is used. The commercial helium leak detector can detect the presence of less than one part of helium in 10 million parts of air. The helium leak detector is a portable mass-spectrometer especially designed to be highly sensitive to helium gas. A mass spectrometer is an instrument for separating or sorting atoms of different mass. Gas molecules entering the mass spectrometer are bombarded by electrons emitted from a heated filament. The ion beam produced by the electron bombardment is accelerated in the form of a narrow beam by means of an electric field. The ions then pass between the pole pieces of a permanent magnet. The magnetic field deflects the ions in circular path. The radius of the curvature of the path depends upon the mass of the ion. Ions having equal mass will all emerge from the magnetic field at a certain position. The helium leak detector is adjusted so that only helium ions are collected. The flow of helium ions to the collector induces a minute electrical current which can be detected, amplified, and used to activate an electrical meter to control the pitch of an audio signal generator. Figure 11.1 shows a schematic diagram of a helium leak detector and the associated vacuum system.

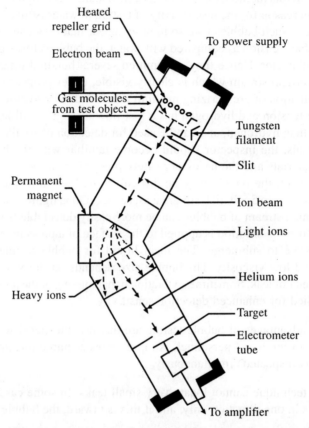

Fig. 11.1   Schematic diagram of helium leak detector

Helium is generally used for leak detection because it is an inert gas and does not react with other gases and materials in the system. Helium is not present in any significant quantity in the atmosphere, thus causing little interference in sensitive leak detection work. Helium, having a light mass, passes through small leaks more readily as compared to heavier gases.

There are five different techniques in using helium leak detector. They are:

(a) probe technique
(b) envelope vacuum technique
(c) sniffer technique
(d) envelope pressure technique
(e) pressurization technique.

In all these techniques, it is necessary to have clean test specimens/components since dirt, moisture, scale and oil may easily seal comparatively large leaks. A brief description of each of the above techniques is discussed below:

(a) Probe technique
In this technique, a fine jet of helium such as that obtained from a hypodermic needle, is passed over the exterior surface of the specimen. Helium gas will be drawn into any opening through the walls of the specimen and register on the leak detector as a visible or audible indication.

(b) Envelope vacuum technique
Sometimes it is desired to determine only the presence of leaks or the total magnitude of all the leaks. In such a case, the specimen containing helium air mixture is put into an evacuated chamber. The chamber is evacuated using an auxiliary pump and the pump outlet is connected to the leak detector for measuring the leak.

(c) Sniffer technique
In this technique, the specimen to be tested is filled with helium or a mixture of helium and air to a pressure greater than atmosphere. The surface of the test object is then scanned with a "sniffer" connected to the leak detector. Helium flowing out through any opening will be sucked into the leak detector system by the sniffer and the leak rate is indicated.

(d) Envelope pressure technique
In this technique, the test system is surrounded by a hood containing helium. The test system is then evacuated. Helium will flow through any leaks into the evacuated test system and then to the leak detector. This technique gives the overall leak rate of the component.

(e) Pressurization technique
In applying this technique, the component is first placed in a helium pressurization vessel and exposed to a helium atmosphere. The component is removed from the pressurization vessel and transferred to a second chamber which is connected to a vacuum pump and helium leak detector.

11.4 STANDARDS

1. IS 8973:1987   Glossary of terms relating to leak detection technique.
2. IS 9902:1982   Recommended practice for leak testing.
3. ASTM E 493   Test methods for leaks using mass spectrometer leak detector in the inside-outside testing mode.
4. ASTM E 1003   Methods of testing for hydrostatic leak testing.
5. ASTM E 515   Methods of testing for leaks using bubble emission technique.
6. ASTM E 499   Methods of testing for Leaks using the mass spectrometer leak detector in the detector probe method.
7. ASTM E 498   Methods of testing for leaks using the mass spectrometer or residual gas analyser in the tracer probe mode.
8. ASTM E 1002   Methods of testing for leaks using ultrasonics.
9. ASTM E 908   Practices for calibrating leaks, gaseous reference.
10. ASTM E 432   Practices for guide for selection of leak testing methods.
11. ASTM E 479   Practices for guide for preparation of a leak testing specification.
12. ASTM E 425   Definitions of tems relating to leak testing.

Appendix A: Conversion factors for leak testing (Ref: ASTM E 425–85)

To convert from	To	Multiply first column by
Leak rate		
atm cm^3/s	Pa m^3/s	1.01×10^{-1}
micron litres/s	Pa m^3/s	1.33×10^{-4}
Pascal litres/s	Pa m^3/s	1.00×10^{-3}
STD cm^3/s	Pa m^3/s	1.01×10^{-1}
Torr litres/s	Pa m^3/s	1.33×10^{-1}
Pressure		
Atmosphere	Pa	1.01×10^5
Bar	Pa	1.00×10^5
Micrometer of Hg	Pa	1.33×10^{-1}
Micron	Pa	1.33×10^{-1}
Millimeter of Hg	Pa	1.33×10^2
Torr	Pa	1.33×10^2
Viscosity		
Centipoise	Pa s	1.00×10^{-3}
Poise	Pa s	1.00×10^{-1}
Volume		
cm^3	m^3	1.00×10^{-6}
litre	m^3	1.00×10^{-3}
ft^3	m^3	2.83×10^{-2}

Appendix B: Comparison of leak rates

Std.cm^3/s Leak	Approximate equivalent	Approximate bubble (Nos) equivalent (a)
10^{-1}	1 cm^3/10 s	steady stream
10^{-2}	1 cm^3/100 s	10/s
10^{-3}	3 cm^3/h	1/s
10^{-4}	1 cm^3/3 h	0.1/s
10^{-5}	1 cm^3/24 h	b
10^{-6}	1 cm^3/2 wk	b
10^{-7}	3 cm^3/yr	b
10^{-8}	1 cm^3/3 yr	b
10^{-9}	1 cm^3/30 yr	b
10^{-11}	1 cm^3/3000 yr	c

(a)   assuming bubble of 1 mm^3 volume
(b)   bubbles too infrequent to observe
(c)   smallest detectable leak by helium mass spectrometer leak detector.

Chapter 12

Comparison and Selection of NDT Methods

Non-Destructive testing (NDT) exploits the physical principles for detection, location and evaluation of defects and assessment of microstructures and/or mechanical properties without impairing the usefulness of the part being inspected. NDT finds wide use in many areas such as process improvement, inservice inspection, life extension studies and measurement of mechanical properties. Nearly every form of energy is utilised in NDT. Each NDT method is specially suited for a particular task and hence does not compete with, but complement each other.

The purpose of this chapter is to summarize the characteristics of various types of discontinuities and to select the possible NDT methods which may be employed to detect each type of discontinuity. Before going into the selection of a suitable NDT method for detecting discontinuities, the user must know what types of defects are to be expected in any inspection. In the following section, various types of defects that can occur right from the raw material stage till the product is in service are discussed.

12.1 DEFECTS IN MATERIALS

The purpose of NDT is to detect, locate, and characterise various flaws in materials and products. Flaws or imperfections that are detected and located by inspection may be from the original material, caused by the process used, created by some human error or defects introduced during the operating life of the component or a result of combination of some of them. It is important for the NDT inspector to be able to detect and evaluate defect/flaw when it exists. In order to have a better knowledge of the types of defects that exist in a particular material/component, a clear understanding of the material, the processes, and the possible interaction between them is a must. Before discussing various types of discontinuities which can be expected in a material, let us know the definitions of discontinuity and defect. 'Discontinuity' is any local variation in material continuity such as change in geometry, structure, composition or properties or presence of holes, cavities or cracks.

When any discontinuity, single or multiple is of such size, shape, type and location that there is substantial chance for material failure to occur inservice, then the discontinuity is commonly called a simple discontinuity that is not harmful in a different application. Various types of defects/discontinuities introduced during various metallurgical processes and in service are discussed below.

12.1.1   Metallurgical Processes and Defects

12.1.1.1   Casting defects

Casting of metal involves pouring or injection of molten metal into a cavity of a particular shape where it is allowed to solidify. The cavity or mold may be of an intricate shape so that when the metal is solidified, a part is produced which, with or without further preparation, may be used for its designed purpose. Even those materials considered to be wrought, originate from cast ingots through deformation work in the solid state. The solidification from liquid at pouring temperature to the solid at room temperature occurs in three stages: (i) contraction of liquid metal, (ii) liquid to solid contraction, (iii) contraction of the solid to room temperature. The flaws which may be formed during the solidification process are discussed as follows:

(*a*) *Non-metallic inclusions*: 'Non-metallic inclusions' is a general term applied to sand, slag, oxide etc. trapped in the casting. Most of the non-metallics, generally lighter than the molten metal manage to move to the top of the ingot but some are trapped within because they did not have sufficient time to reach the surface before the molten metal above them solidifies. Usually these inclusions are irregular in shape (Fig. 12.1).

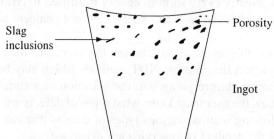

Fig. 12.1   Non-metallic inclusions and porosities in an ingot

(*b*) *Porosity*: Porosity is caused by the entrapped gas in the molten metal which gets trapped in the solid casting. The size and amount depend on the gas content of the metal and the rate of solidification of the casting. Porosity may either occur throughout or in some localised areas of the casting. It's shape is spherical or nearly spherical (Fig. 12.1).

(*c*) *Blow holes:* Blow holes or gas holes are caused by trapping of air, mold, or core gases and water vapor in the casting during solidification. They occur in single or in clusters and are of smooth, round, elongated, or oval shape of varying sizes. Sometimes an extremely large gas hole appears like a shrinkage cavity, although it differs from a shrinkage cavity in that the ends of the gas hole are rounded and smooth.

(*d*) *Shrinkage flaws:* These are cavities formed during liquid-to-solid contraction. Various forms of cavities (Fig. 12.2) can occur in a casting. They are:

(i) *Macro-shrinkage (piping defect)*: Molten material, after it is poured into the mold, starts to cool and solidity. The solidification process starts from the surface and progresses towards the center of the ingot. Since the center of the ingot is the last to cool and solidify, most of the cavity due to shrinkage forms at the center. The cavity is called the "pipe". Piping may extend along the axis from the top towards the interior of the ingot.

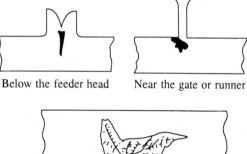

Below the feeder head   Near the gate or runner

(ii) *Center line shrinkage (Filamentary shrinkage)*: Wherever solidification cannot be correctly controlled and is not directional, a coarse form of shrinkage may occur. This type of shrinkage flaws may be extensive, branched, dendritic and interconnected. This form of shrinkage is, in general, more dispersed than macro-shrinkage.

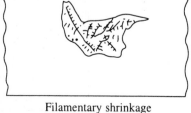

Filamentary shrinkage

(iii) *Microshrinkage*: Shrinkage cavities may also be produced on a micro-scale. During

Fig. 12.2   Formation of shrinkage flaws

the later stages of solidification, the channels between the growing dendrite arms become progressively narrower. In some places, the dendrite arms may bridge over and restrict the supply of liquid to the new isolated channels with pools of liquid. Contraction of these pools of liquid during solidification leads to formation of fine cavities. These cavities are very fine and are called "microshrinkage".

(e) *Cold shut*: Cold shut is caused by the failure of the stream of molten metal to unite with a confluent stream or with solid metal such as a poring splash, internal chill or a chaplet. Formation of cold shut is shown in Fig. 12.3. They usually look like a crack with a smooth and curved contour. It is usually exposed to surface.

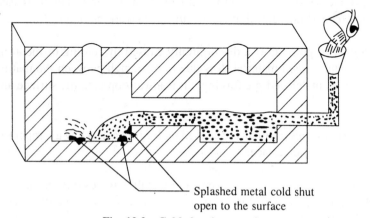

Splashed metal cold shut
open to the surface

Fig. 12.3   Cold shut in a casting

(f) *Crack*: This is a discontinuity which is due to fracture of metal during or after solidification. 'Hot tears' are cracks (Fig. 12.4) caused by stresses which develop near the solidification temperatures when the material has lowest strength. The stresses arise when the contraction of the cooling metal is restrained by a mold or core or by an already solidified thinner section. 'Stress cracks' also called as 'cold cracks' are formed when the metal is completely solid. They are the result of large contraction that builds up in large complicated shapes of castings.

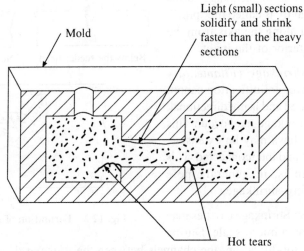

Fig. 12.4   Hot tears in a casting

12.1.1.2   Forging and rolling defects

Forging is the working of a material into an useful shape by hammering or pressing. Many times forging operations are carried out at higher temperatures. Certain materials are also cold forged.

The process of plastically deforming a material by passing it between rolls is known as rolling. The initial breakdown of ingots into blooms and billets is generally done by hot rolling before further processing into plate, sheet, rod, bar, pipe, rails or structural shapes. Cold rolling produces sheet, strip and foil with good surface finish and increased mechanical strength. The defects (Fig. 12.5) that can occur during forging and rolling are given below:

(a) *Forging lap*: A forging lap is a discontinuity caused by folding of metal in a thin plate on the surface of the forged material. It is due to mismatch between the mating surfaces of the two forging dies in "closed-die forging". It is always open to the surface and is irregular in contour.

(b) *Forging bursts or cracks*: Bursts are caused by forging at too low a temperature. They can occur internally or on the surface.

(c) *Laminations*: Large porosity, pipe and nonmetallic inclusions in slabs or billets are flattened and spread out during rolling and forging processes. These flattened discontinuities are known as laminations.

(d) *Stringer*: Nonmetallic inclusions in slabs or billets which get thinned and elongated in the direction of rolling by the rolling process are called stringers.

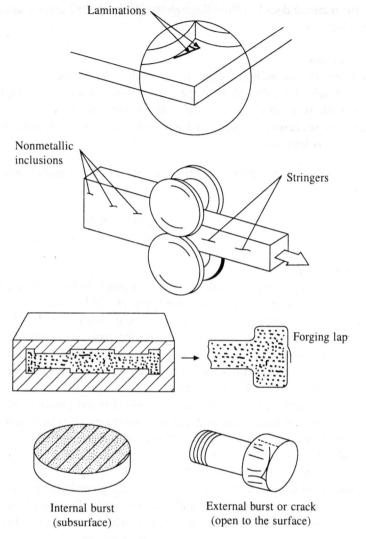

Fig. 12.5 Forging and rolling defects

(e) *Seams*: Surface irregularities such as cracks on the slab or billet which get stretched out and elongated during rolling are called seams. Seams may also be caused by folding of the metal due to improper rolling. Seams are surface discontinuities. On finished bars, seams appear as straight or slightly spiral lines either continuous or broken.

12.1.1.3 Extrusion defects
Extrusion is the process by which a block of material is reduced in cross section by forcing it to flow through a die under high pressure. Extrusion is carried out either under hot or cold condition. Following defects are generally formed during extrusion process.

(a) *Internal pipe or extrusion defect*: Trapping of oxidized outer skin of the billet into the central region of the extruded product is known as 'internal pipe'.

(b) *Cracks*: If the material does not flow through the die properly,' cracks' are generated in the finished product.

12.1.1.4   Drawing defects

Drawing operations involve pulling a material through a die by means of a tensile force applied on the exit side of the die. Most of the plastic flow is caused by compressive force which arises from the reaction of the material with the die. The reduction in diameter of a solid bar or tube by successive drawing is known as 'bar or wire or tube drawing'. The drawing defects are as follows:

(a) *Seams*: Seams can occur in rod or wire if the starting rod (raw material) has defects such as seams or pipe.

(b) *Center-burst*: The most common type of drawing defect is the 'Center-burst' or chevron cracking. Center burst is caused due to drawing at too low a temperature.

12.1.1.5   Welding defects

Welding is the process of joining materials in which the pieces to be joined are bonded with alloying taking place at the interface. Two basic types of welding are fusion welding and pressure welding. Fusion welding is essentially a casting process in which a material is melted and cast in the joint and is made to fuse with the parts to be joined. This metal is supplied by filler rods, which are generally of a composition similar to the metal being welded. Some of the well known fusion welding processes are: Tungsten inert gas, Metal inert gas, Shielded metal arc and Electron beam.

In pressure welding, both pressure and heat are applied to the pieces to be welded. The pressure produces plastic deformation and the heat produces recrystallisation across the boundary in the plastically deformed material. This results in the formation of new crystals which are integral part of both the pieces. Thus bonding takes place. The heat necessary for the welding may be generated by passing electric current through the pieces to be joined.

The general sources of weld defects include improper design and joint preparation, defects in parent material, improper welding technique and faulty solidification of molten metal. A variety of defects occur in welds. Some of these defects which are shown in Fig. 12.6a-c are discussed below:

(*a*) *Gas inclusion*: Gas may be formed in molten weld metal for various reasons and may get trapped if there is not sufficient time for it to escape before solidification. The trapped gas is usually in the form of round holes, termed porosity or blow holes, or of an elongated shape called piping or wormholes. Gas formation may be caused by chemical reaction during welding, high sulphur content in plate and/or electrode, excessive moisture in the electrode or in base plate edges, too short an arc, incorrect welding current, wrong polarity etc.

The type of porosity (Fig. 12.6a) within a weld is usually designated by the amount and distribution of the pores. Some of the types are classified as follows:

(i) *Uniformly scattered porosity*: This is characterised by pores scattered uniformly throughout the weld.

(ii) *Cluster porosity*: This is characterised by cluster of pores that are separated by porosity-free areas.

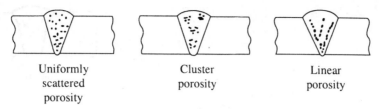

| Uniformly scattered porosity | Cluster porosity | Linear porosity |

Fig. 12.6a Various types of porosity in the weld

(iii) *Linear porosity*: This is characterised by pores that are linearly distributed. This generally occurs in the root pass and is associated with lack of penetration.

(*b*) *Slag inclusions*: Slag inclusions are oxides and other nonmetallic solid materials that are entrapped in the weld metal or between the weld metal and base metal. In most cases, the sources of slag inclusions are the materials covering the electrodes or fluxes employed in arc welding operations. In multilayered welding operations, failure to remove the slag at the end of each pass will result in entrapment of slag inclusions in these zones. Slag inclusions are frequently associated with lack of penetration, poor fusion, oversize root faces, too narrow a groove and faulty electrode manipulation.

(*c*) *Lack of fusion*: Lack of fusion or incomplete fusion is caused by the failure of complete fusion of weld metal and base metal or inter-weld passes. Lack of fusion can occur at side wall or in the interpass region.

(*d*) *Lack of penetration*: Frequently, the root of a weld will not be adequately filled with weld metal and a void is left. This inadequate penetration may be caused by too small a root opening, too large an electrode, insufficient weld current, excessive welding speed, improper groove preparation etc. In joints requiring complete penetration, this type of defect is generally not acceptable and requires its complete removal and re-welding.

(*e*) *Cracks*: Cracks are linear ruptures of metal under stress. Although sometimes wide, they are often very narrow separations in the weld or adjacent base metal. Usually little deformation is apparent in the cracked region of the weld. Cracks can occur in a wide variety of shapes and types and can be located in numerous positions in and around a welded joint (Fig. 12.6b). Cracks associated with welding may be categorized according to whether they originate in the weld itself or in the base metal. Generally four types of cracks occur in the weld metal: transverse, longitudinal, crater and hot cracks. Base-metal cracks can be divided into seven categories: transverse cracks, underbead cracks, toe cracks, root cracks, lamellar tearing, delaminations and fusion-line cracks.

(i) *Transverse cracks*: Transverse cracks lie in a plane normal to the axis of the weld. These cracks are usually open to the surface. They usually extend across the entire face of the weld and sometimes propagate into the base metal. They are the result of high residual stresses induced by thermal cycling during welding. High hardness of the parent metal, excessive restraint, and the presence of hydrogen promote their formation.

(ii) *Underbead cracks*: They are similar to transverse cracks. They form in the heat affected zone because of high hardness, excessive restraint, and the presence of hydrogen. Their orientation follows the contour of the heat affected zone.

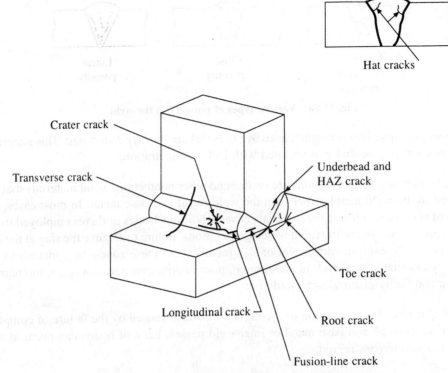

Fig. 12.6b   Various types of welding defects (cracks)

(iii) *Longitudinal cracks*: Three types of longitudinal cracks are possible. They are: (i) check cracks-open to the surface and extend from the root to some point within the weld, (ii) root cracks—extend from the root to some point within the weld and (iii) full centerline cracks—extend from root to the face of the weld. The longitudinal cracks are usually oriented perpendicular to the weld face and run along the plane that bisects the welded joint. Check cracks are caused either by build up of high contraction stresses in the weld joint, particularly in the final passes or by a hot cracking mechanism. Root cracks are the most common form of longitudinal weld metal cracks because of the relatively small size of the root pass. If such cracks are not removed, they can propagate through the weld during subsequent passes. This is the usual mechanism by which full centreline cracks are formed.

(iv) *Crater cracks*: Crater cracks are caused by failure to fill the crater before breaking the arc. When this happens, the outer edges of the crater cool rapidly, producing stresses sufficient to crack the interior of the crater. Crater cracks may be oriented transversely or longitudinally, or may occur as a number of intersecting cracks forming the shape of a star.

(v) *Hat cracks*: Hat cracks derive their name from the shape of the weld cross section with which they are usually associated. This type of weld flares out near the weld face, resembling an inverted hat. Hat crackes are the result of using excessive voltage or too low a welding speed. The cracks are located about halfway up through the weld and extend into the weld metal from the fusion line of the joint.

(vi) *Root or toe cracks*: This type of cracks can occur at the notches present in the weld when high residual stresses are present. Both toe and root cracks propagate through the heat affected zone before they are arrested in region of the base metal. Characteristically they are oriented almost perpendicular to the base metal surface and run parallel to the weld axis.

(vii) *Lamellar tearing*: This is a phenomenon that occurs in T-joints where the web plate is welded on both sides by employing full penetration welds. The stresses developed by this configuration result in separation that takes place in the base metal between the roots of the two welds extending in a plane parallel to the surface of the base metal. Such a discontinuity is often associated with laminations or other planes of weakness in the metal. Such a discontinuity is often associated with laminations or other planes of weakness in the metal. It is characterised by step like tear and is caused by the shrinkage of the weld bead thus stressing the base metal through its thickness (12.6c). This results initially in decohesion of nonmetallic inclusions and then ductile tearing at about 45° between adjacent nonmetallic inclusions to produce the step like-tears. Lamellar tearing can occur outside the heat affected zone, 5-10 mm below the fusion face.

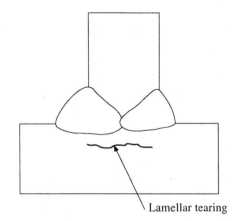

Fig. 12.6c Lamellar tearing

(*f*) *Tungsten inclusions*: In the gas tungsten arc welding (GTAW) process, the occasional touching of the electrode to the work or to the molten weld metal, particularly in manual operation, or use of excessive currents may transfer particles of the tungsten electrode into the weld metal. These are called 'tungsten inclusions'.

(*g*) *Undercut*: This discontinuity occurs when the welder has melted and flushed out some of the parent metal in the line of fusion. An undercut, therefore, is a small groove running parallel to the weld at its edge. It may be continuous or intermittent. Undercutting may be caused by excessive welding current, incorrect arc length, high speed, incorrect electrode manipulation etc.

(*h*) *Burn through*: A burn through area is that portion of the weld bead where excessive penetration has caused the weld pool to be blown into the pipe or vessel. It is caused by factors such as high current, slow rod speed and incorrect rod manipulation. These factors lead to excessive heat in a particular area.

(*i*) *Root pass oxidation*: Oxidation is the result of insufficient protection of the weld and heat affected zone from the atmosphere. Severe oxidation of stainless steels can reduce corrosion resistance if the joint is not adequately purged with an inert gas.

12.1.1.6 *Grinding cracks*
Grinding cracks are caused by stresses which are built up from excessive heat generated between the grinding wheel and the material. These cracks occur on the surface of the material at right angles to the direction of rotation of the grinding wheel.

12.1.1.7   Heat treating cracks

Heat treating is basically the process of obtaining microstructure with desired properties like strength, hardness, ductility, impact strength etc. of a material by controlled heating and cooling. While heat treating, unequal cooling between light and heavy sections of a part results in build up of stress leading to cracking. These cracks are called 'heat-treating cracks'.

12.1.2   Defects Introduced During Service

The response of metallic materials during service (life) can vary widely as a function of chemical composition, thermal treatment, mechanical working, service conditions, presence of discontinuities and other material characteristics. NDT personnel need familiarity with these material characteristics in order to evaluate their suitability for service. Products that need careful testing and evaluation are those used in load carrying applications, operating at high temperatures and corrosive environments where failure may involve complete replacement or expensive repair of the component or danger to other products, structures and human life. It is important to know the types of failures that might be expected and the causes for such failures in order to know what and how to inspect, how to eliminate the fault and how to assess the risk of failures. In the following sections, a brief discussion is made on various causes of material failures and the nature of failures.

12.1.2.1   Cause of material failures

Products and structures may be subjected to a number of varying service conditions. Imposed loads may be static (stationary or fixed) or dynamic (varying). The environment may contribute to corrosion vibration, temperature and pressures higher or lower than normal etc. The product may also be subjected to abuse. Mechanical failure is always a result of presence of stresses above some critical value, leading to deformation or fracture. Such excessive stresses are set up by some combination of (i) material defect, (ii) excess load, (iii) improper load application or (iv) design error. Some of the important causes of material failures are discussed below:

(*a*) *Static loads*: The principal reasons for failure under static loads include large discontinuities, poor dimensional control during manufacturing, overloading during use etc.

(*b*) *Dynamic loads*: Dynamic loads are varying loads that can be unidirectional or multi-directional. Multidirectional loading is a more severe condition to cause a failure. When the cycles of loading become high, failure can occur at stress levels far below those determined by static load tests.

(*c*) *Service at high temperature*: Service at high temperature reduces the allowable value of most of the desirable material properties including the ability to support load due to phenomena like creep, thermal fatigue etc. The effect of creep also increases with increased temperature. The temperature at which property values become critical depends upon the particular material and the previous treatment it has received.

(*d*) *Stresses above elastic limit*: Stresses above the material's elastic limit may cause material flow, distortion and cross-sectional weakening. These effects get further intensified at elevated temperatures.

(*e*) *Corrosive environment*: Corrosive environment or corrosion due to a combination of selective materials in contact (galvanic couple) can produce failure in two ways. Corrosion may actually reduce the amount of material available to carry the load, but even more important, in many cases, the corrosion may create small discontinuities which serve as stress risers. These stress risers become the nuclei for initiation of fatigue failure. Combined influence of stress and corrosion environment may lead to stress corrosion cracking, hydrogen embrittlement etc.

(*f*) *Vibration*: Many structures and systems are subjected to vibration during their service, such as transportation equipment, machines and devices that have moving parts. In addition, some structures may vibrate because they are excited by some outside influence. Stresses from vibration may be superimposed on the stresses from other loading sources. The principal problem created by vibration is the introduction of cyclic loading leading to high cyclic fatigue failure.

(*g*) *Abuses*: Excessive loading from abuse may be accidental. Many a time, it may be due to human error. Abuse is controlled by use of factor of safety in design, usually based on yield strength or fracture mechanics concepts. Factor of safety ranges from slightly more than one to five or more depending on the criticality of the component.

12.1.2.2 Types of material failures
There are generally two type of material failures in service. One is the easily recognized fracture or separation into two or more parts. The second is the less easily recognized excessive plastic deformation or change in shape.

(*a*) *Excessive plastic deformation*: Yielding followed by excessive plastic deformation occurs when the elastic limit of the material has been exceeded. Yielding produces permanent change of shape, which may prevent the part from functioning properly. In a ductile material under conditions of static loading at room temperature, yielding rarely results in fracture. This is because of the fact that the material strain-hardens as it deforms, and an increased stress is required to produce further deformation. Failure by excessive plastic deformation is controlled by the yield strength of the material selected for a uni-axial condition of loading. For more complex loading conditions, the yield strength is still the significant parameter. At temperatures significantly greater than room temperature, materials no longer exhibit strain hardening. Instead, materials can continuously deform at constant stress in a time dependent manner, known as 'creep'. The failure criterion under creep conditions is complicated by the fact that the stress is not proportional to strain. Further, the mechanical properties of the material may change appreciably during service, due to microstructural changes.

(*b*) *Fracture*: Brittle fracture occurs at stresses far below the yield strength. Brittle fractures are usually associated with flaws and are often catastrophic in nature, i.e. occurs without warning. Brittle failures can occur in both brittle and ductile materials under certain loading conditions. High strain rates, triaxial stresses or low temperatures can make a normally ductile material to behave in a brittle manner. In an ideal brittle fracture, all the energy is absorbed to create the new surfaces and none is absorbed for plastic deformation. Brittle surfaces are often flat and shiny, with little or no evidence for deformation.

(c) *Fatigue*: Failures occurring under conditions of dynamic loading are called 'fatigue failures'. A part can be subjected to various kinds of loading conditions including fluctuating strain, fluctuating temperature or any of these in or without a corrosive environment. The failures under dynamic loads in corrosive environments are referred to by the category 'corrosion fatigue'. Most service failures occur as a result of tensile stresses. Practically all fatigue failures start at the surface or near surface. There are three stages in a fatigue failure, viz. crack initiation, crack propagation and fracture. These stages are not completely separable. A fatigue failure is insidious because it occurs without any obvious warning. Fatigue results in a brittle fracture with no gross deformation at the fracture point. The three basic factors necessary to cause fatigue failure are: tensile stress of sufficiently high value, a large enough fluctuation in the applied stress and a sufficiently large number of cycles of the applied stress. In addition, there are also a host of other variables, such as stress concentration, corrosion, temperature, overload, metallurgical structure and residual stresses which influence the fatigue failure.

Fatigue data is usually presented in the form of *S-N* curves (Fig. 12.7), where applied stress (*S*) is plotted against total cycles to failure (*N*). The total cycles to failure includes the cycles necessary to initiate the crack and the cycles for propagation of the crack. As the stress decreases, cycles to failure increase. In steels there exists a stress limit below which fatigue failure does not occur. This stress limit is called 'fatigue limit' or 'endurance limit'. In aluminum and other nonferrous alloys, there is no fatigue limit, i.e. a finite life exists at any stress level. Since infinite life (cycles) is (are) not possible, the endurance limit for such materials is taken as the maximum stress at which failure will not occur within 10^8 cycles.

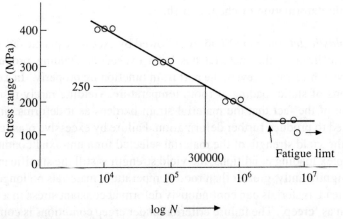

Fig. 12.7   Typical S-N fatigue curve showing fatigue limit in carbon steel

(d) *Corrosion*: In general corrosion is the deterioration of metals by the chemical action of some of the surrounding or contacting medium which may be liquid, gas or some combination of the two. To some degree, corrosion can influence all materials, but the effect varies widely depending upon the combination of the materials and the corrosive agents. Corrosion attacks materials by direct chemical action, by electrochemical action or more by the combination of the two. The effect of corrosion is always detrimental to the safe operation of critical components, assemblies and structures.

12.2 SELECTION OF THE NDT METHOD

Increasing recognition is being given to the importance of NDT in various engineering disciplines at all stages, i.e. during material production to inservice. Associated with this, there is a growing concern about the reliability of the material/technique used, cost etc. Testing and evaluation technology includes not only the measurement and presentation of data but also requires inference from such data based on comparison and interpretation. This calls for efficient and trained operators and data analysts. NDT is also used to supplement destructive tests. Observing defects in material/components helps to reduce failures and improving product quality. However, ineffective use of NDT can be disastrous in such industries as nuclear, space and defence where quality demands are very stringent. In other industries, rejection of acceptable components due to ineffective NDT can lead to financial losses. Acceptance of rejected components results in damage to the reputation of the company due to supply of products which do not meet the quality requirements. Therefore, it is needless to say that the importance of right choice of the appropriate NDT method/technique or a combination of methods/techniques depends on the type of component/structures to be inspected, the type of defect, the suitability of the technique from access point of view etc. While selecting a particular NDT method, cost factor is also to be considered. The three stages where NDT is applied are:

(a) In the pre-manufacturing stage for inspection of raw materials, (b) during manufacturing of a product, to check whether it meets the specifications and (c) during service life of the product, for fitness-for-purpose (FFS) and life prediction.

In selecting an NDT method for evaluation of a specific type of discontinuity, it should be kept in mind that the NDT methods may compliment each other and therefore several NDT methods may be capable of performing the same task. The selection of one method over another is based on the following factors:

(a) type and origin of discontinuity,
(b) material manufacturing process,
(c) accessibility of the component to perform NDT,
(d) type of equipment available,
(e) time available,
(f) cost

Capabilities of different NDT methods for detection of defects at various stages (manufacturing to inservice) are discussed below.

12.2.1 Visual Testing (VT)

The easiest and most useful method of NDT is visual examination. Important details can be collected during VT which would be useful for future analysis and also to decide on the type of NDT to be used for further analysis. Also, VT should be carried out as a complementary method to all other NDT methods VT should preceed and succeed all other examination. Inaccessible areas can be inspected by means of boroscope and fibre-optic techniques. Depending upon the severity of the surface defect and the component in use, decision will be taken for salvaging the component or not. If the product is found unacceptable during visual examination itself, further NDT need not be carried out, thus saving time and cost of inspection.

VT is selected for detecting the following discontinuities:

* surface deposits
* scaling
* erosion
* discoloration
* oxidation bulging
* missing parts

* mechanical damage
* dimensional conformance
* gross defects visible on the surface
* distortion of components during fabrication and in service
* general corrosion on the surface of a component.

12.2.2 Liquid Penetrant Testing

Liquid Penetrant Testing (LPT) is another means of enhancing the capability of visual examination. It is suitable for use on smooth surfaces of all materials, magnetic as well as nonmagnetic. It is limited to surface defects. Its inability to indicate the depth or breadth of a flaw should be kept in mind while selecting this method for a particular application.

Use of LPT for porous materials is ruled out since the absorption of penetrant into the pores would mask the presence of defects. A clean surface is a pre-requisite as penetrant cannot enter a crack that is filled with dirt, oil, or other matter.

Size, shape, weight and number of work pieces to be inspected often influence the selection of a penetrant system. The desired degree of sensitivity and the cost are the most important factors in selecting a system.

LPT can also be used for leak testing. In this case, the component casing is filled with the penetrant and developer is applied outside the surface.

LPT is selected for detecting the following types of discontinuities on the surface of a component:

* cracks of any orientation
* porosity
* pin holes
* voids
* fatigue cracks

* laminations in plates
* various types of weld defects
* corrosion cracks
* creep fissures
* forging bursts

12.2.3 Magnetic Particle Testing

While LPT is effective only for fine surface discontinuities, the need remains to detect larger surface flaws or those present just below the surface. This need is met by magnetic particle testing (MPT). This technique is applicable to only ferromagnetic materials. MPT is considered more sensitive than LPT. MPT requires a higher degree of operator expertise to ensure that the magnetic fields are aligned in the correct direction in order to detect the defect. Flaws oriented perpendicular to the induced magnetic field are only reliably detectable. Hence the challenge is to induce magnetic field lines in a given work piece so that they are most likely to be perpendicular to the flaw orientation. Therefore, prior knowledge on flaw orientation and/or introduction of magnetic fields in several directions are/is essential.

It is commonly agreed that defects breaking the surface are the most severe amongst the various discontinuities occurring in components. For dynamically loaded structures, their removal is essential. Their detection in ferritic materials is most easily accomplished by MPT. Since the depth determination of the surface breaking cracks is almost impossible, crack depth measurements may be additionally employed to assess them. Detection of subsurface defects by MPT is impossible if the components are thick, but generally it requires ideal testing conditions.

MPT is used for detecting following types of discontinuities in ferromagnetic materials.

Surface discontinuities

* cracks and tears
* porosity
* shrinkage cavities
* slag inclusions
* voids
* forging laps
* grinding cracks
* corrosion cracks
* fatigue cracks.

Discontinuities just below the surface (within around 6 mm depth from the surface) (sensitivity goes down as the defect is deeper):

* larger size cracks in various orientations
* pores
* slag inclusions
* voids
* incomplete fusion
* laminations.

12.2.4 Eddy Current Testing

LPT and MPT require some test medium (cleaner, penetrant, developer etc. in the case of LPT and ferromagnetic power and liquid vehicle such as water or kerosene etc. in the case of MPT) to be applied over the test surface. Application of such medium may not be permitted or not possible in certain components and in certain environments Eddy current testing (ECT) can be used in such conditions. In ECT, the test system need not have to be coupled directly to the material under test. The variables that contribute to the influence on ECT signals are component dimensions, electrical conductivity, and magnetic permeability. Thus, ECT gives the information that is not provided by LPT or MPT or any other method and therefore many a time it is complementary in nature.

ECT is primarily used for testing nonferromagnetic conducting materials. However, with modifications, it can also be used for testing ferromagnetic materials. One of the most important applications of ECT in engineering industry is the inspection of heat exchanger tubes and larger size tubes during manufacturing and inservice. ECT is also selected for detecting following types of discontinuities or variables:

* electrical conductivity
* heat treatment condition
* dimensional variation
  (in thickness direction only)
* hardness
* coating thickness
* cracks
* voids
* porosity
* pinholes
* corrosion
* fatigue cracks.

12.2.5 Radiographic Testing (RT)

The NDT methods discussed so far in this Chapter are used for detection of defects which are open to the surface or nearer to the surface. To detect more deeply seated discontinuities, NDT methods with test medium capable of deeper penetration and system that senses even minute changes in the characteristics and behaviour of the test medium are required. Radiographic inspection is one of the most widely used methods of NDT as this is applied to all metals and alloys, both ferrous and nonferrous, for detection of volumetric type of defects. The range of capabilities offered by the variety of sources and equipments has brought radiography to the forefront of NDT techniques.

Testing of multilayer vessels and welds is generally a difficult task due to inaccessible inner layers. RT is the only NDT method to evaluate multilayers vessels during manufacturing stages and inservice.

Development of microfocal X-ray units has made it possible to extend radiographic practice to meet the requirements of more stringent quality levels demanded for critical applications, besides a host of new application. It is known that the sensitivity in radiography depends to a large extent on the focal spot size. In microfocal radiography, the focal spot size is less than 100 μm and typically 15-50 μm as compared to a few millimeters or half a millimeter in conventional radiography. Using microfocal RT, intricate geometrical components such as tube to tube sheet welds can be tested with a sensitivity of even 1% of wall thickness of about 3 mm. Microfocal RT can be used for detection of microcracks of around 25 μm size. Another application of microfocal RT is to check the integrity of the micro welds used in electronic integrated circuits.

One of the advantages of RT is that no prior preparation of the surface of the component is necessary. The main disadvantage of the use of RT is the possible hazards due to exposure to radiation if proper care is not taken.

RT is selected to detect and size the following types of discontinuities:

* cracks (parallel to the radiation beam)
* volumetric defects such as slag inclusions and voids
* porosity
* blockages or deposits inside the pipe lines or pressure vessels,
* material thickness
* hidden foreign material inside a component.

12.2.6   Ultrasonic Testing (UT)

Ultrasonic testing involves use of high frequency sound waves coupled to the components to be inspected and studying the reflection pattern of these waves. UT is finding increased applications in various industries. Several wave modes such as longitudinal, shear and surface waves can be used depending on the orientation and location of the discontinuities. Different techniques such as pulse-echo, through transmission, and pitch-catch are employed. The advantages of ultrasonic testing are real time availability of results, higher penetrating power of these waves, higher sensitivity for planar defects, independence of sensitivity over depths, low cost for inspection, higher portability of the equipment and compatibility for automation. But the subjectivity of the results on the operators' training and skill is a stumbling block for its wider acceptance. With the advent of microprocessors and automation, operator dependability is being eliminated to a larger extent and UT is finding increased applications in industries such as power, railways, chemical and aerospace.

UT of cast metals and alloys is rendered difficult due to the influence of casting intricacy, microstructural variations and surface roughness. Defects occurring in the cast structure have irregular surfaces which scatter the acoustic waves and make UT more difficult. Hence successful use of ultrasonic testing for inspection of castings depends greatly upon the skill and expertise of the operator.

UT is used for wall thickness measurements and for detection of subsurface (volumetric) defects in almost all types of materials. Ultrasonic measurements may be applied to any material in plate or tube form to measure its wall thickness to a high degree of accuracy. Thus it is possible to make an assessment of the corrosion rate. The procedure for corrosion rate evaluation by UT is relatively simple and the level of operator training need not be high to follow the procedure.

Ultrasonic flaw detection is the only practical method having widespread use in underwater inspection applications for locating and sizing subsurface defects in components. The types of defects that are anticipated in structures such as offshore installations are surface breaking defects. Ultrasonic testing is used as a reliable means of testing and measuring the depth of these surface breaking defects that have been located using ECT and MPT.

UT is the most suitable method of NDT for inservice inspection (ISI) of components in power plants, chemical process industries etc. Many a time, RT cannot be applied for ISI due to the requirements of two side accessibility. UT is more sensitive for flaw growth monitoring as compared with RT. In view of all these advantages, the first choice for ISI is UT for volumetric defects in components except for heat exchangers, and condensers where ECT is preferred.

UT is selected to detect and size the following types of discontinuities:

* surface breaking and hidden cracks in any orientation
* Intergranular cracks
* laps
* laminations
* volumetric defects such as slag inclusions and voids
* porosity
* wall thickness measurements
* creep
* hydrogen embrittlement
* liquid level measurement
* blockages, deposits etc. in the pipe lines and pressure vessels.

12.2.7 Acoustic Emission Testing (AET)

The principal advantage of AET over other conventional NDT techniques is that it can directly detect, locate and determine the growth and severity of growing cracks. This is particularly valuable for inservice monitoring for evaluation of structural integrity. As of now, there is no other technique which can replace AET for this type of application. There are a number of advantages one can derive from the application of AET. To mention a few, ease of flaw location, ability to scan large inaccessible areas, portability of equipment etc. Its applications span a wide range covering monitoring of huge pressure vessels to the quality control of miniature electronic components.

AET has been applied for the following:

* To monitor nuclear plant components during hydrotests, preservice pressure testing of the primary system and during plant operation
* monitoring of fatigue cracks in components in aerospace and transportation systems,
* monitoring of highway bridges
* on-line surveillance in chemical and petroleum industries
* monitoring of structural integrity of off-shore structures.
* on-line and off-line monitoring of weld quality in different types of welding processes etc.

12.2.8   Thermography

According to the laws of thermodynamics, all bodies hot or cold tend to be in thermal equilibrium with their surroundings through heat transfer processes such as conduction, convection and radiation. If the body is big enough, the local discontinuities in the material give rise to local thermal conductivity changes which in turn, produce heterogeneous temperature distribution on the surface of the body. This heterogeneous temperature distributions are very common occurrences in many industries where heat generation due to any process is involved. Temperature distribution can be used to control the process and sometimes to avert dangerous and costly failures.

One of the important advantages of thermography over other NDT methods is that there is no necessity for contact between the test equipment or probing camera and the object being scanned. Hence, far away object can be tested for its temperature distributions. Thermographic NDE is applied to the following components and areas for detection of temperature distribution as an indicator to monitor the healthiness.

* converters, furnaces etc.
* linings in furnaces
* deposits or blockages in pipe lines carrying fluids
* power transmission lines and switchyards
* heat exchangers, pressure vessels etc. in the process industry
* insulation of the furnaces and other components for its effectiveness
* electronic components.

12.2.9   Summary

Table 12.1 shows the general guidelines for selecting various NDT methods Tables 12.2 (a) and (b) show the capabilities of various NDT methods in detecting different types of defects and their fitness-for-purpose application.

It many applications, more than one method of NDT is applied in a complimentary way to detect defects in a specific situation. In this connection, it may be imortant to note that X-radiography is particularly useful for detection of volumetric defects like porosities and slag inclusions. However, the reliability of detection by radiography is poor for defects like cracks. For thicker objects, radiography often loses to UT except in a few specific applications. High energy radiography units, although available, are impractial to use in most cases. Wherever applicable, both radiographic and ultrasonic techniques, when used in a complimentary manner, would provide a reliable answer to the present day safety and reliability standards.

NDT is heavily relied upon as the basis of assurance against the presence of flaws large enough to either cause immediate fracture or to grow large enough to cause premature fracture at a later time. Often, the successful implementation of a fracture mechanics based design depends solely upon the reliability of the NDT to detect flaws in the components. Thus, it is necessary that a proper and reliable NDT method and technique should be selected.

12.3   SELECTION OF INSTRUMENTATION

All NDT methods are simple in principle, but success in their use depends heavily on intelligent application and interpretation of the results. They are not easily applied as cure-alls, but can be instrumental in assuring quality products if the NDT methods are integrated into the entire spectrum of manufacturing activity from design to final inspection and in service. NDT, in reality, is a combination of art and science, which can be learnt by a person even with limited knowledge. Yet, it is a vast subject with results to be interpreted with patience. This is because of the fact that the evidence it produces is most often indirect. Also, the conditions in the practical industrial world where NDT methods are widely applied seldom measure up to the scientific concepts on which the methods are based or to the laboratory conditions in which they were developed.

In NDT, we generally apply the testing medium to the material or component under examination. The flaws or material structure modify or change the testing medium in some manner. Built into the test method, there must be a means by which we detect this change and convert the detected signal to a form that is well suited for interpretation. A variety of NDT equipments are available in the market. Though these equipments or instruments are often claimed and marketed as independent and easy to use, they are not readily applicable under plant conditions. Hence it is most important that proper NDT instrument/equipment is selected to suit the test conditions and other requirements.

Reference standards, when properly used, ensure the success of the NDT. Normally destructive tests are attempted to determine how a material or a device will perform. But, NDT is not really a test, but rather some measurements based on which, the size of a discontinuity is usually indicated rather than the performance capabilities of the component. Hence, it is imperative to have a comparative reference standard as a calibration of testing procedure. This also serves as a means to understand the NDT results in a quantitative manner. Details of various reference standards are given in codes and standards. The concerned user has to judicially select the reference standards for reliable NDT.

Therefore the selection of instruments/equipments for carrying out different NDT methods is very important and is discussed below. The motive behind the discussion is to give a clear concept in selecting the proper instruments considering various factors rather than listing the available instruments.

12.3.1 Visual Testing

One of the oldest, simplest, and cheapest NDT methods is visual testing. Here, the object is illuminated and examined directly by eye or with the help of a light sensitive device. The eye is one of the best NDT instruments that man possesses, except when the owner is tired or bored. Access and visibility are the key considerations. Unaided eye can evaluate surface finish, moderate size pits, cracks, dimensional conformance of accessible areas etc. Examination of minute cracks, deep holes, hidden deffects and inaccessible areas require the help of special devices such as magnifying lenses, microscopes and boroscopes. Selection of these aids is based on the size of the discontinuities to be detected, test object configuration and sensitivity requirements.

During under water UT and recording of data, closed circuit television (CCTV) is extensively used. By use of CCTV, all video records can be related to date, time, position, and other inspection information for future reference and comparison.

12.3.2 Liquid Penetrant Testing

For liquid penetrant testing, no special equipment is required except a source of ultraviolet (black) light for use with fluorescent penetrants. Effective inspection can be performed by using simple kit itself.

A variety of equipment is available for inspection of units in large quantity. Especially for mass production lines, package units and automatic stations are used for inspection. Also, where high reliability is required, automatic stations are used for liquid penetrant testing. Essentially, the size, shape, and production quantity of the components influence the selection of equipment.

The LPT inspection station is simply a work table on which workpieces can be handled under proper lighting. For fluorescent methods, the work table is usually surrounded by a curtain or a hood to exclude most of the white light from the area. For automatic inspection, workpieces are moved through booths equipped with split curtains, either by hand or by conveyer. In some large inspection installations, fully enclosed rooms have been built for black-light inspection.

LPT kit is most suited for inspection of plants/components, in situ applications and for limited test applications. Semi-automatic/automatic test stands are used where high reliability is required or errors due to human factor are to be avoided. Other important factors for selection of equipments are sensitivity, desired inspection coverage etc.

12.3.3   Magnetic Particle Testing

For magnetisation of the part, mobile, portable and stationary equipments are available. Selection of a particular type of equipment is based on the components to be inspected and their size and quantity and the required sensitivity. Portable equipment is available in light weight (10 to 50 kg). Generally, these portable units are designed for use at 220 or 440 V AC and supply magnetizing current outputs of 500 to 1500 amp in half-wave rectified or AC modes. Machines capable of supplying half-wave current and AC have provision for continuously variable current control and therefore can be used for MPT of wide variety of components. Primary method for magnetisation is hand-held prod. The major disadvantage of this method is the limited amount of current available. For detection of discontinuities lying deep and for coverage of a large area with prod contact, a machine with higher-amperage output is required. Also portable equipment cannot supply the full-wave DC necessary for some inspections.

Mobile units usually supply half-wave rectified or AC current outputs. Full-wave DC current is sometimes available as a single output. Inspection of parts is accomplished by use of flexible cables, yokes, prod contacts, contact clamps etc. Mobile units have an output ranging from 1500 to 8000 amp. Magnetizing current usually is controlled by a remote-control switch connected to the unit by an electric cord. Quick-coupling connectors for connecting magnetizing cables are also provided with the unit.

Stationary units may be obtained as either general-purpose or special purpose. The general purpose unit primarily uses the wet method, and has a built-in tank that contains the bath and the pump. The pump continuously agitates the bath and forces the fluid through hoses onto the part being inspected. Stationary power packs serve as sources of high-amperage magnetizing current to be used in conjunction with special fixtures, or with cable-wrap or clamp-and-contact techniques. Rated output varies from 3000 to 8000 amp and in some cases, upto about 20000 amp. The higher amp units are used for overall magnetization of large forgings or castings, which otherwise would require laborious prod inspection at much lower current levels.

12.3.4   Eddy Current Testing

In ECT, an alternating current is made to flow in a coil (probe) which when brought close to the electrically conducting surface of metallic material to be inspected, induces eddy current flow in the material. The presence of a defect or a discontinuity disturbs the eddy current flow. These eddy currents in turn generate an alternating magnetic field which may be detected either as a voltage across a second coil or by the perturbation of the impedance of the original coil. This impedance change is a function of electrical conductivity of the test material, magnetic permeability of the test material, geometry of the component and test frequency. The change in impedance is measured and correlated with the presence and extent of discontinuity.

In the through-transmission system of eddy-current testing, a signal is transmitted from a coil through a metal and is detected by a coil on the opposite side of the metal. This type of measurement completely eliminates lift-off but requires that the two coils be aligned properly. However, there is a limitation in applying this technique for higher thickness.

Various types of instruments are commercially available. Types of instruments and their capabilities are given below:

(a) Resistor and single coil (1 kHz to 5 MHz) direct reading analog meters,
(b) Inspection coil and balance coil, bridge balance (1 kHz to 5 MHz)—phase rotation of signals, storage scope, display of impedance planes, continuously variable frequency, X-Y alarm gates,
(c) Inspection coil and variable impedance bridge unbalance (1 KHz to 2 MHz) direct read-out of thickness and electrical conductivity, binary codes decimal output,
(d) Induction bridge (100 Hz to 50 MHz)—used for simultaneous measurement of four variables, analog computers, binary coded decimal output, direct digital read-out of thickness and lift-off.

An important part of eddy current testing instrumentation is the instrument used for read-out. The read-out device may be an integral part of the system, an interchangeable plug-in module, or a solitary unit connected by cable. The read-out instrument should be of adequate speed, accuracy and range to meet the inspection requirements of the system. X-Y plotters, X-Y storage oscilloscopes and strip-chart recorders are most widely used read-out instruments. Magnetic-tape recorders are fairly accurate and capable or recording at very high speed. Moreover, the data can be processed by automated techniques. When multi-channel instruments are used, microprocessors/computers are used for data storage and processing. The computers can separate parameters and calculate the variable of interest and significance, print summaries of the results and store all data on tape for reference in future.

12.3.5 Radiography Testing

NDE methods employing X-ray equipment for radiography require heavy investments. Gamma ray cameras are available at cheaper cost. The cost of maintaining a full fledged radiography facility in a pressure vessel manufacturing company comprises of consumables namely X-ray films and processing chemicals, depreciation on investments on X-ray equipment, trained staff and overheads. There has been an ever increasing trend in the cost of X-ray films. High energy X-ray and gamma ray equipment require separate rooms constructed with high density concrete for shielding purposes. Such rooms are necessary to prevent radiation hazards to operating and other non-operating personnel.

The most significant way to improve quality of radiographs is to reduce the focal spot size. This has led to the design and manufacture of microfocus X-ray equipment. The focusing and the alignment of the electron beam to the target is automatic. With a focal spot of the order of 10 μm, direct enlargement around 20X is possible. Also, high quality radiographs may be obtained with very small film-to-focal distances. Microfocal system is proven to be especially useful for examining circumferential electron beam welded parts. The improvement in X-ray real-time detection devices and the possibilities for treatment of the images by digital video image processing have made it both technically and economically feasible to inspect a broader range of products by X-ray real-time systems. The purpose of video image processing is to increase the signal-to-noise ratio and to improve the detectability of image details of interest. The video image processing is done by digitizing the analog camera video signal and digitally process the signal. The processed image can be viewed on a video monitor. The widely used video processing operations are (i) averaging to improve signal-to-noise ratio, (ii) summing to enhance the contrast, (iii) grey scale expansion/compression to provide sufficient contrat within the grey level range displayed and (iv) spatial filtering. By filtering, it is possible to enhance the contrast and to improve details and edges. Finally, substraction of video images provides a way of enhancing details.

Automatic fluoroscopic inspection system is used where critical evaluations are required and to eliminate the possibilities of errors due to human interpretation. Further, the sensitivity is superior due to dynamic conditions applied in the inspection. The system operates faster and safer than any equipment with human interpretaion. In this system, the mechanical/ electrical design is fail-safe, which means that the equipment rejects all parts until the computer has measured and found the part acceptable. The cost of film, processing etc. are eliminated.

Highly automated, self-propelled mini-crawlers which travel within pipe lines to take X-ray radiographs of pipelines from inside are available. Such a system would be suitable for both land based and off shore pipe lines for oil, gas and other fluid handling networks employing pipelines down to 250 mm bore. Such a crawler is designed for remote control from outside the pipe. It is completely self contained. The control for positioning along the length is by means of a small radioisotope source which emits a collimated beam of radiation through the pipe wall. The inensity of the beam is measured by a Geiger Muller tube and fed to an electronic logic module.

12.3.6 Ultrasonic Testing

Most ultrasonic inspection instruments detect flaws by monitoring one or more of the following variables:

(a) reflection of sound energy
(b) transit time of sound wave
(c) attenuation of sound energy

Based on the variable that is being used for knowing the healthiness of the material, a specific type of instrumentation is selected. Although the electronic equipment used by different manufacturers for ultrasonic inspection can vary greatly in detail, all general purpose equipment consist of a power supply, a pulser circuit, a search unit, a receiver-amplifier circuit, an oscilloscope and an electronic clock.

Transducers are the heart of the ultrasonic test system. Various types of transducers are available in the market. Single element normal/angle beam transducers to array type transducers are used depending upon the application, sensitivity requirement, technique of testing etc.

Generally, high frequency transducers are used for sensitive test applications. Immersion testing, generally applied to automated tube testing employs special transducers.

Conventional ultrasonic test equipment is provided with Cathode Ray Tube oscilloscope for read-out information. Data received is usually displayed on an oscilloscope in either video mode of RF mode. In video-mode display, only peak intensities are visible on the trace, whereas in the RF mode, it is possible to observe the actual waveform of the signal. RF signal mode displays are required for signal processing of received signals so as to get more information of the tested object. Signal processing is used in testing applications where signal to noise ratio is poor, for example, if the grain structure of the material is highly scattering or anisotropic etc. Signal processors are available as separate units. Modern equipment combine signal processing with limited capability along with test equipment.

Additional features are incorporated in many commercial ultrasonic instruments which include a) a circuit that electronically compensates for signal amplitude loss caused by attenuation of the ultrasonic pulse in the test piece, (useful in the case of testing thick and/ or highly attenuating materials), and (b) electronic gates which monitor returning signals for pulses of selected amplitudes that occur within the selected time-delay ranges. The set point of a gate corresponds to a flaw of a certain size that is located within a prescribed depth range. Gates often are used to trigger alarms or to operate automatic systems to sort test pieces or to identify reject objects. Various types of display modes are available. They are A-scan, B-scan, C-scan, P-Scan, Zip-scan etc. Most of the commercially available ultrasonic test equipment are provided with only A-scan display which gives defect location and roughly size of the defect (to be interpreted). B-scan facility is used where the information on the cross section of the defect is required. C-scan display gives plan view of the defect. Based on the requirements, the instruments are selected. P-Scan facility consists of a multi-headed ultrasonic detector. A computer measures the signals received from a large number of probes which are fitted to a belt wrapped around a weld. The computer processing produces a picture of the defect depending on the signals received. Zip-scan or Time of Flight Diffraction (TOFD) testing system is used for detection and sizing of defects based on diffraction of signals from crack tips. This technique is useful if the expected orientation of the crack is perpendicular to the surface.

Multichannel equipments are used for testing components by more number of probes simultaneously. Suitable manipulators are required to enable such inspection. There are various other types of advanced ultrasonic instruments such as SAFT (Synthetic Aperture Focusing Technique), ALOK and phased array. These instruments have not yet gained their popularity for application in shop floor because of advanced operator knowledge needed and the cost and sophistication of the systems.

12.3.7   Acoustic Emission Testing

Materials can speak. When stressed, they give out messages in the form of acoustic emissions. All materials exhibit this emission phenomenon. But these emissions from metals are generally inaudible. If we can detect the emissions with instrumentation and device a mechanism to decode the messages, we have an effective NDT tool to give us immediate information (on-line) regarding the internal transformations, degree of damage or state of integrity within a material or a component or a structure.

AET instrumentation consists of various units for signal detection, data acquisition, signal processing and analysis. The transducer which is used for detecting the AE signals is the heart of the system. Historically microphones were used as transducers to start with and later accelerometers were tried. The most favoured transducers for AE applications are piezoelectric transducers because of their high sensitivity and ruggedness. Resonant types are used with narrow band instrumentation and non-resonant types with wideband instrumentation. Capacitive transducers have excellent wide band frequency response but are less sensitive. Additionally, stringent requirements are imposed on the quality of the surface of the material which is used as one electrode in the case of capacitive transducers. Consequently, their usage as AE transducers is still limited to the laboratory. The pre-amplifier follows the transducer and the two together form the front end of the AET instrumentation.

The processing instrumentation required for AET depends on the form and quality of the raw data. Converting analog data into digital form and spatial filtering before analysis are some of the important aspects. Instrumentation utilized for processing and analysis is undergoing continuous evolution. Essentially two approaches are in use: one emphasizing hardware and the other emphasizing software. In completely hardware based systems, processing and analysis circuitry is completely hardwired. A system could be a single unit or a number of small units which can be plugged in as needed. A single channel system has the capability of obtaining cumulative counts, cumulative events, count rate and event rate and rms voltage. Hardware type multichannel systems are generally modular in design to provide capability for gradual expansion. In addition to the event or cumulative parameters obtained with a single channel unit, this system can locate a growing flaw. Facilities like audio monitoring and parametric distributions can be incorporated in both single and multichannel systems. If two or more sensors are allowed to be excited by a single source, the arrival sequence and the arrival time differences can be measured. These parameters are utilized for emission source location. Linear location is possible with two sensors while a minimum of three sensors are needed for planar location. With increase in number of channels needed, the hardware system looses its attraction and software system takes over. The most important advantage of software system is flexibility in operation and analysis. They have a built-in computer and the analysis is done by software. Currently, commercial systems utilizing time domain parameters are of modular design and can accommodate upto 256 channels. The most commonly used display device for visual observation of AE signals is a CRO (Cathode Ray Oscilloscope). A variety of devices are used for displaying and recording the analysed data. The simplest and most commonly used recording devices are the X-Y recorders. CRT displays are faster, more versatile and are available with multiple display and hard copy facilities. The data is also stored in magnetic disk for permanent storage and future analysis.

12.3.8   Thermography

The most common methods for detection of temperature distributions on the solid surfaces in the industries have been templistics and thermocouples. Though simple and inexpensive, these methods are obviously inadequate when large surface areas are involved or when the surfaces in question are inaccessible or difficult to reach. In such cases, a noncontact type area scanning mode thermal mapping technique, now commonly known as thermal imaging or thermography is used. The method is not only very convenient in application but in a way economical too (except for higher capital cost).

Various types of thermal imaging equipments are available. These are generally portable. Being portable in nature, the equipments are suitable for field work and in situ inspection. Thermography equipment can produce thermograms of surfaces at temperatures from 293 K to 1153 K. The accuracy at lower temperatures (around 295 K) is claimed to be 0.01 C. The absolute temperatue of a point can also be calculated using emitted radiation value. Many a time only the temperature distribution over the surface or the temperature gradient along a line of the surface is of importance. Permanent record of the thermograms called thermographs can also be made by using a 35 mm photo camera or with video recording storage facility.

12.4 SUMMARY

In most of the cases, NDT depends on human judgement for the interpretation of the results. While handling large number of simple symmetrical parts, automation can be introduced. But, by and large test results are interpreted and evaluated by persons trained in specific techniques and applications. The skill, competence, and knowledge of the person performing the test are highly important in NDT. This is the reason why certain procedures specify the certification of the personnel conducting the tests in addition to the other requirements.

Failure analysis provides invaluable inputs in identification of defects which caused the failure. Failure analysis helps in evolution of improvements and refinements in NDT techniques for detection of potentially harmful defects either during manufacturing or in service.

Table 12.1 Guide to Frequently used NDT Methods

Technique	Access requirements	Remarks
Optical	One point of access may be enough. Used to view the complex equipment.	Very versatile, little skill required.
Liquid penetrant	Requires clean surface. Flaw shall be exposed to the surface.	Applied on all except for porous materials, test is rather messay.
Magnetic particle	Requires clean and reasonably smooth surface.	Applied on only magnetic materials, surface breaking and subsurface defects are detected.
Eddy current	Surface must be reasonably smooth and clean.	Cracks, thickness measurement, comparison of materials is possible. Applicable to electrically conducting materials.
Radiography	Both sides access is needed.	Considerable skill is required for interpretation.
Ultrasonics	One or both sides.	Requires point by point search, skilled personnel are required.
Acoustic emission	Can be remote.	Detection and location of growing defects possible under stimulus. Volumetric inspection.
Thermography	Either direct or remote.	Thermal mapping for trouble shooting, or conformance to requirements. High capital cost.

Table 12.2(a) Capabilities of Commonly used NDT Methods for Detection of Different Types of Defects

Types of defects	LPT	MPT	ECT	RT	UT
Burst	+	+	x	x	*
Cold shuts	*	*	x	+	x
Cracks					
in bolts	*	*	x	*	x
grinding	*	*	x	x	x
convolution	x	x	x	*	x
HAZ	*	x	x	x	+
heat-treat	*	*	x	x	x
surface shrink	*	*	+	x	x
tubing	*	x	*	x	+
Hydrogen flacks	x	x	x	*	x
Inclusions	x	x	+	*	+
Lack of penetration in welds	+	+	+	*	+
Lamination	*	*	x	x	*
Laps and seams	*	*	x	x	x
Micro shrinkage	+	x	x	*	x
Gas porosity	*	x	x	+	*
Stress corrosion	*	x	x	+	+
Hot tears	*	*	x	*	x
Intergranular corrosion	*	x	+	x	+

Note: *-recommended methods
  + - can be used for detection
  x - not normally used

Table 12.2(b) Summary of Applicability and Capabilities of Common NDT Methods in Relation to Demonstrating Fitness for Purpose of Components

Method	Applicable component geometry		Detection capability			Length measurement	Measurement of small ligament	Through wall size measurement	Characteri-sation
	Linear	Nonlinear	Surface defects	Internal defects Vol.	Planar				
Liquid penetrant	Y**	Y**	Y**	N	N	Y**	N	N	Y**
Magnetic particle	Y**	Y**	Y**	N	N	Y**	N	N	Y**
Eddy currents	Y*	Y?	Y*	N?	N?	Y?	Y?	Y?	Y?
Radiography	Y**	N?	Y**	Y**	Y?	Y**	N	N?	Y**
Ultrasonics	Y**	Y**	Y*	Y**	Y**	Y*	Y*	Y*	Y*

Y : Yes, is applicable, has reasonable capability
N : No, not applicable, no capability
N? : Not normally practicable
Y? : Capability doubtful, but inspection may be possible with special techniques
*   : Good
** : Very good

Chapter 13

Probability of Detection Concepts in NDT

13.1 INTRODUCTION

The present day NDE engineer aims at optimization of inspection process, especially concerning evaluation of minimum detectable flaw size, reliability of instruments/sensors, reliability of operator, frequency of inspection, suitability of calibration standards etc. These aspects can be better evaluated using quantitative statistical parameters. The most important questions of engineering interest during the application of NDE include (i) What inspection methods are applicable?, (ii) How small a flaw can they detect?, (iii) What are the requirements for demonstrating an NDE procedure performance capability level?, and (iv) What type of process control is needed to maintain this level of performance? The diverse nature of different NDE processes results in different sources of variance and resultant impact on detection capabilities. For example, a manually applied liquid penetrant process is dominated by the skill of the operator in process application and interpretation. An automated eddy current process is dominated by calibration, instrument and procedure variances. Suitable guidelines are to be followed for demonstration of capabilities of specific NDE process. It is important to recognize complex and multiparameter nature of NDE process as well as the source of variance in each NDE process and to take into account the nature of the variance and process control while applying margins to the NDE processes and demonstrating the procedures. The variances in NDE process capabilities can be addressed using Probability of Detection (POD) concepts. A brief introduction to the POD concepts and their application to quality assurance, damage tolerance and fail-safe design are discussed. It should be explicitly mentioned that there are no universally fixed procedures for qualification of POD, as the procedure has to be evolved for each specific case. In view of this, the information given in the subsequent sections are to be taken as general approaches with a few examples. The examples given should not be extended to any other application without systematic assessment and expert opinion. Indeed probability of detection can vary widely depending upon the nature of crack, orientation of crack, the crack width, material within the crack, temperature and stress of the component, last but not the least, operator. However, these concepts are very valuable and are applicable to a large number of situations and thus need clear understanding to build reliability in testing.

13.2 PROBABILITY OF DETECTION (POD): THE APPROACH

The POD concept was first introduced in 1973 and was integrated into the design and quality assurance programs of NASA and US Air Force. The POD concepts and methodologies have gained widespread acceptance and continuing improvements have enhanced their acceptance as useful tools for quantifying and assessing the NDE capabilities. Probability of detection is defined as the probability that, using a given inspection procedure/system/sensor, an inspector will detect a flaw that is present in the component. The probability of detection can be determined by experimentally observing the number of times an NDE procedure can reveal flaws in a set of parts known to contain flaws. As an example, for every 100 defective parts that are inspected, if 95 are identified as containing defects and 5 parts as being free of defects, then the POD of defects is 95%. The POD can take a maximum value of 100%. Often the POD values are attached with a degree of confidence, which refers to the ability to estimate, from a limited set of samples, the probability of detection that is representative of large-scale inspection. For example, 95% POD with 90% confidence level means that there is a 10% probability that 95% is an overestimate of the true POD.

POD is measured as the probability that a specified flaw will be found in a given sample set using a specific inspection technique. Figure 13.1 shows two POD curves in which the probability of flaw detection is plotted as a function of flaw size for both a real and an ideal inspection technique. For the ideal technique, the POD of flaws smaller than a critical size is zero whereas the POD of any flaw greater than a critical size is unity. In this case, there

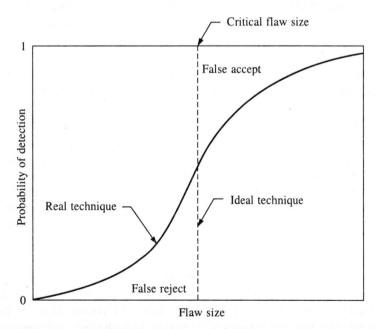

Fig. 13.1   Probability of detection (POD) curve as a function of flaw size for both ideal and real technique

are neither false rejects (FR) of good parts nor false accepts (FA) of defective ones. However, real NDE techniques are seldom, if ever, as sharp and as discriminatory as that indicated by the ideal curve, with the result that there are regions of uncertainty shown by the false reject and false accept areas.

In the context of POD, the generally asked question is: How small a flaw can be found by NDE? However, the more important question is: How large a flaw might be missed by NDE? The answer to the second question depends on (i) material, configuration, accessibility, and surface condition of the component etc. and (ii) the capabilities of NDE procedures such as, inspection environment, inspection equipment, nature of component, type of flaw, reference defects used for calibration/process control, calibration procedure followed, skill of operator and human factor (fatigue, mood etc.). It is clear from the above that the application of complex and multiparametric nature of NDE procedure always introduces an uncertainty in measurements, which can enter in many ways. Due to this, after completion of an inspection, it can only be asserted that there is a certain probability that the inspected component is free of flaws of a specific type and size. Thus, the POD concepts are being increasingly used in NDE, primarily to fix the uncertainties that arise during inspections and give a quantitative representation to the NDE process.

13.3   TYPICAL METHODOLOGY FOR ESTABLISHING POD

When an NDE process is applied to a test object, the output response to a flaw within the test object depends on the form of detection (pattern recognition), the magnitude of the feature or signal that is used in detection, and the relative magnitude of the response of the material surrounding the flaw. For example, in an ultrasonic inspection procedure, the amplitude of the response from a flaw may be used to discriminate against the response from the grain structure (noise) surrounding the flaw. If the ultrasonic procedure (measurement) is applied repetitively to the same flaw, a distribution of responses to both the flaw and the surrounding material (grain structure) will be obtained. The measured response distribution reflects the variance in the ultrasonic measurement process and similar variance can be obtained for any measurement process. The response from the surrounding material constitutes the baseline level, usually termed as "noise". This noise is different from the electronic noise of the NDE instruments. Both the discrimination capability (flaw detection) and flaw sizing (quantification) capability of the NDE procedure are dependent on their relative amplitudes as compared to noise and the rate of change of the flaw response with increasing flaw size. The variance in flaw-to-flaw and variance in signal response to flaws of equal size cause increased spread in the probability density distribution of the signal (plus noise) response. Typical probability density function for eddy current testing (ECT) of EDM notches in stainless steel plates is shown in Fig. 13.2. By applying a decision threshold (amplitude) to the responses, clear discrimination (detection) of notches is achieved. However, when the same decision threshold (acceptance criterion) is applied to a set of notches of a smaller size, clear discrimination is not noticed.

In the above example, the decision threshold could be adjusted to a lower signal magnitude to produce detection. As the signal magnitude is adjusted downward to achieve detection, a slight increase in the noise level will result in a false call. As the flaw size decreases, the noise and signal (plus noise) responses will overlap. In such cases, a downward adjustment in the decision threshold (to detect all flaws) will result in an increase in false calls. Thus,

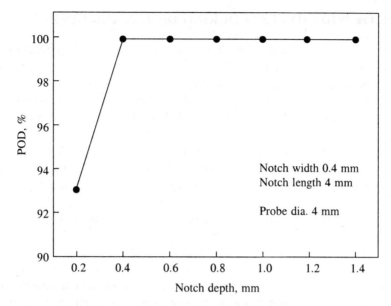

Fig. 13.2   Typical probability density function for eddy current testing of stainless steel plates using 4 mm dia. probe

it is clear that accept/reject decisions resulting from the application of an NDE procedure may result in both detection failures (MISSES) and false detection (FALSE CALLS) when the NDE procedure is operated near the limit of discrimination. Now, the probability of detection can be calculated as the ratio of total number of rejects identified to total number of actual rejects present. Similarly, probability of false alarms (POFA) can be calculated as the ratio of the total number of false calls to the total number of acceptances.

All flaws of equal size do not respond equally when an NDE procedure is applied. The physical nature of flaw initiation and growth vary considerably with the origin of the flaw, the material type involved, the load history on the test object, the environment, e.g. corrosion and the load levels immediately prior to inspection (NDE procedure application). Crack opening and crack closure effects have been studied extensively in different materials as crack closure has a dominant effect on crack detectability by X-ray, liquid penetrant, and ultrasonic inspection methods, as compared to magnetic and eddy current methods.

The POD data is usually represented as a POD curve, which is produced as follows:

Step 1: Applying a specific NDE procedure to a large number of artificial flaws of varying size that represent the type of flaws to be detected in actual components
Step 2: Recording the results of inspection with each flaw size
Step 3: Analyzing the data by fitting the results to a model that is representative of the type of data produced
Step 4: Plotting the results in the form of POD vs. flaw size.

The single valued parameter that is used to characterize the procedure is that flaw size at which the POD reaches the 90% confidence level. The single valued parameter that is often quoted in validation requirements is that flaw size at which the lower 95% confidence line reaches the 90% level (90/95 value). From sampling theory, 29 successes out of 29 trials provide a 90% confidence that the same result would be obtained if the experiment is repeated infinite number of times.

13.4   ROLE OF POD CONCEPTS DURING DESIGN AND OPERATION

During the past several years, a number of design-centered "global" approaches have been proposed that deal both with material synthesis and the manufacture of materials into finished products. Although the structure and constituent components of these approaches differ because of their different end purposes, they all depend on design, theoretical modelling, extensive computations and use of more than one NDT&E technique for confirming the measurements. Unified Life Cycle Engineering (ULCE) is an example of a global model for manufacturing, in which emphasis is placed on the development of predictive capability by the design to spell out the total set of properties important for product performance, quality, reliability, maintainability and life-cycle costs. Successful development and operation of such concepts would allow the design engineer to incorporate all trade off considerations at the time of product design, would reduce the need for retrofitting, and would undoubtedly increase the choice of the appropriate manufacturing process. Successful development of the ULCE concept could provide a new paradigm in manufacturing.

A schematic representation of the possible linkages needed for ULCE concept is shown in Fig. 13.3. With the above model of ULCE in mind, it is necessary to examine the approaches that are available to develop the linkages between the various engineering functions of manufacturing operations. Clearly, the approach needed to develop and implement the NDT&E/Design coupling is vastly different and more advanced than any encountered in current NDT&E practice. For example, this link needs to provide the designer with several pieces of quantitative information related to the design. A logical approach for the development of the NDT&E/Design link is based upon the POD concept. This concept possesses the necessary features to fulfill the above requirements. To date, all applications of the POD concept have been empirical, i.e., a statistically significant number of samples are prepared with artificial flaws, and then experiments are made by various operators utilizing specific NDT&E techniques. POD, or 'confidence results', are then drawn from these data. It is evident that such empirically derived results represent insufficient data bases for the development of NDT&E/Designer linkage of ULCE, even if coupled with expert systems or other artificial

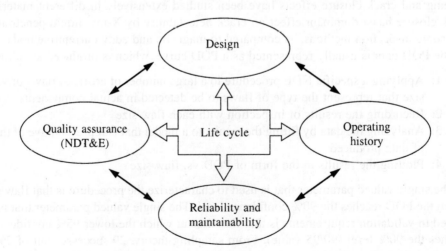

Fig. 13.3   Schematic representation of linkages needed for unified life cycle engineering

intelligence approaches. First, the empirically designed POD curves represent a convolution of operator and instrumentation capabilities. It is not possible to isolate these two sets of variables on the basis of empirical results only; hence, the degree to which any empirically determined POD curve represents the true POD determined only by the physical principles (part shapes, materials, details of measurement system etc.) is unknown. Secondly, empirically determined PODs cannot be used with confidence to predict POD values of other sets of measurement conditions.

In recent years, theoretical models that permit calculation of PODs have gained limited recognition for three major NDT&E techniques-ultrasonic, eddy current, and microfocal radiography. In contrast to empirically determined PODs, these are first principle engineering models that can be used as a basis for the NDT&E/Designer linkage in ULCE. These first principle models are analytical models of the NDT&E measurement process and depend upon the details of the measurement setup for each inspection technology. For example, the details include the geometry of the component being inspected, relative inspection configuration of probe and part, characterization of the generation, propagation and reception of the interrogating energy, critical flaw information that is obtainable from materials engineering etc. Detailed models of field-flaw interactions can be calculated for a known interrogating field, and the knowledge about the noise conditions that add to the uncertainty in the results.

Thus, we can say that POD characterization has emerged as a useful NDE engineering tool for NDE procedure design and development; for comparison of various NDE procedures; for validation of specific NDE procedures; and for personnel skill qualification. If signal amplitudes are quantified and used as the basis for acceptance/discrimination, then it is natural to use post analysis and processing at different threshold discrimination to optimize the performance of any NDE procedure. Quantification of NDE procedure capabilities provides tools for establishing an objective basis for assuring reliable NDE on a continuous basis. The obvious economic advantages of moving from more deterministic to more quantified design/analysis through POD based approaches include shorter development cycles, efficiencies in quality control, improved design efficiencies, and improvements in confidence levels for reliable performance of engineering structures.

A typical example of application of POD procedure to compare performance of different types of probes for defect detection in stainless steel plates by eddy current NDE is discussed. Notches of different length, width and depth were made in stainless steel plate and eddy current tests have been conducted using ferrite core probes of diameter 2 mm, 4 mm and 8 mm. The lift-off (noise signal) is made horizontal by suitably adjusting the signal phase. The POD data has been obtained by placing the ECT probe on defect and defect-free regions and recording the vertical output of EC signals. Typical POD curves for three probes for different notch depths are shown in Fig. 13.4. It is observed that POD increases very significantly with increase in notch depth for all the probes. When the notch depth is more than 0.8 mm, all the probes have shown a POD better than 95%. It can be inferred that there exists a minimum detectable notch-depth for each probe and it increases with increasing probe diameter. This observation highlights the need for choosing a suitable probe diameter for detecting a defect deeper than the specified depth. Similarly, POD procedure can be used to assess the inspection reliability in detecting defects of specified length and/or width for a known probe type and lift-off conditions.

Advanced methods of life assessment of materials and structures incorporate quantification of fracture and fatigue life properties based on knowledge of material/component configuration

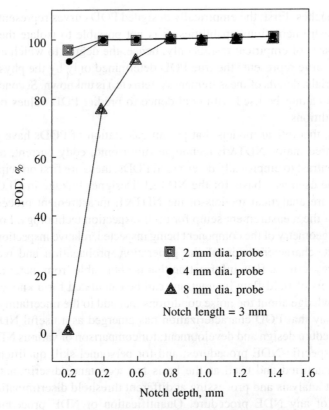

**Fig. 13.4   POD curve for eddy current testing for detection of
EDM notches using three different probes.**

and conditions. An essential element of this life analyses is the assumption of the presence
of an initial flaw of a known size at the beginning of the material/component life. Here
again, POD approaches in NDT&E provide the necessary input. Thus NDE is increasingly
applied for inservice "fitness-for-purpose" analyses, life-cycle management analyses, and
life-extension analyses.

Statistical Methods for Quality Control

The word quality refers to the totality of features and characteristics of a product or service that have bearing on its ability to satisfy a given need. Control is the process of regulating or directing an activity to verify its conformance to a standard and to take corrective action if required. Therefore quality control is a regulatory process for those activities which measure a product's performance, compare that performance with established standards, and carry out corrective action, if necessary. Quality control is a term that has been used in both a narrow sense and a broad sense. In the narrow sense, quality control means conformance to quality, often this is achieved by inspection and process control on the manufacturing floor. However, for quality control personnel, quality control has a much broader scope, which involves conformance of quality and control of the quality with respect to design and performance to the degree of customer's satisfaction. 'Total quality management' is the term now a days applied to this broad concept.

In engineering industry, activities of measuring, inspection and testing are carried out manually and also by automatic devices. The results or data, mostly in the form of numbers, are obtained in order to take corrective action in a manufacturing process for improving the quality or for taking decision on acceptance/rejection. The problem is that these data or results vary from time to time, piece to piece or sample to sample. Even if the production is carried out by fully automated machines, there is still variation in quality. Quality control uses statistical methods to separate variability due to controllable causes from that due to uncontrollable causes. Statistical quality control (SQC) is a branch of quality control. It involves the collection, analysis, and interpretation of data to solve a particular problem.

In 1924, W.A. Shewart of Bell Telephone Laboratories developed a statistical chart for the control of variation in products. This is considered to be the beginning of modern statistical quality control concept. In this chapter, the most widely used statistical methods for quality control are discussed.

14.1   PROBABILITY

One of the important problems facing production plants and engineering industry is concerned with quality improvement. It is well known that all processes, no matter how well controlled, result in variations in quality, i.e. all materials possess a wide variety of defects and each type of defect has a wide variation in the range of its characteristic parameters. A wide variety of test schemes exist, some destructive and some nondestructive to verify quality with respect to the specifications. The benefits of nondestructive inspection are many, as long as the results are reliable. It is no longer sufficient for the inspection engineer to simply specify that the component is accepted or not accepted.

There needs to be a quantitative assessment on the presence or absence of flaws and its sizes so that life prediction can be made based on this information. The probability concept when related to NDT, is the probability of the existence of a given type and severity level of defect in a particular component/item.

The probability concept can be further related to NDT as follows:

(a) in a component, what is the probability of existence of a defect when tested with a particular method of NDT?
(b) once a defect is detected, what is the probability that the size of the defect detected is within the specified range?
(c) what is the probability that a particular method of NDT could miss defect(s) of specified size?
(d) what is the probability that a defect of particular size could propagate to a bigger size and ultimately lead to failure?

14.1.1   Basic Concepts

Probability Events: Probability is the study of the likelihood of occurrence of specific events. Take for example, in the case of tossing a single coin, the probability of showing head or tail on a single toss is 50%. The probability of showing head is p(h),

$$p(h) = \frac{1 \text{ event}}{\text{no. of equally possible events}} \tag{14.1}$$

$$= 1/2 = 0.5$$

Similarly the probability of showing tail is also 0.5.

In another case, for the dice with six faces, there are six equally possible events (1, 2, 3, 4, 5 and 6) and the probability of a single event say getting a side having No. 2 is given by $p(2)$ where

$$p(2) = 1/6.$$

If a pair of dice is thrown, the probability of getting a pair of sides with both having No. 2 is

$$p(2, 2) = (1/6)(1/6) = 1/36.$$

The above discussion is to make an important point that the probability of two single independent events occurring together is the product of their individual event probabilities. The multiple event probability will be lower than any single event probability. However, it is important to note that neither event is impossible and neither event is definite. There is an element of chance, or probability in each case.

14.1.2 Probability Sample Space and Flaw Size Distribution

The categorization of a particular event under a particular situation is defined as the sample space. This sample space can be finite or infinite. A finite sample space is applicable when there is a limit on the number of possible events. Consider three coins to be tossed simultaneously in the air. This situation results in a finite number of possible 'head' and 'tail' combinations. The following probabilities may be calculated for the indicated combination of heads and tails in one toss.

(i) Probability for all the three coins showing tails:

$$p\{TTT\} = 1/2 * 1/2 * 12 = 1/8$$

(ii) Probability for obtaining any one of the combinations as HTT, THT and TTH:

$$p\{HTT\} + p\{THT\} + p\{TTH\}$$

$$= \{1/2*1/2*1/2 + 1/2*1/2*1/2 + 1/2*1/2*1/2\} = 3/8$$

(iii) Probability for obtaining any one of the combinations as HHT, THH AND HTH:

$$p\{HHT\} + p\{THH\} + p\{HTH\} = 3/8$$

(iv) Probability for all the three coins showing heads:

$$p\{HHH\} = 1/8$$

An infinite sample space is demonstrated by the concept of tossing a coin until head appears where there is no limit on the number of tosses. In the case of inspection and quality control, an infinite sample space is often practically useful in defect detection (for example fatigue cracks). The dimensions of a fatigue crack can fill infinite sample space since infinite number of groupings can be made between the possible minimum and maximum crack sizes. Usual practice, however is to categorize the data in to defined numerical categories in terms of ranges of crack size and fit the fatigue crack data within those limits. For example, inspection of a group of pressure vessels could result in the data as shown in Table 14.1 for the observed fatigue cracks. If it is required that the crack depth be recorded on a smaller interval, more crack size groupings would be required. If extremely small crack dimension range is used then an extremely large number of groupings would be required. The number of groupings in the sample space thus could in fact be very high approaching infinite depending on the size range selected for each grouping. The probability of finding a flaw

Table 14.1   Size Distribution of Observed Fatigue Cracks

Crack size range (groupings) (mm)	No. of occurrences	Probability for cracks with in a given size range
0 < d < 1.5	4	0.06
1.5 ≤ d < 3.0	5	0.08
3.0 ≤ d < 4.5	7	0.11
4.5 ≤ d < 6.0	12	0.19
6.0 ≤ d < 7.5	15	0.24
7.5 ≤ d < 9.0	11	0.17
9.0 ≤ d < 10.5	6	0.09
10.5 ≤ d < 12.0	2	0.03

p(flaw) in the specified group is equal to the number of flaws in the group divided by the total number of known flaws. This probability is given in Table 14.1 (third column) for each grouping.

14.1.3   Effect of Inspection on Flaw Size Distribution

It has been seen from the experience that any NDT inspection system detects large defects easily as compared to small ones. The probability of defect detection and flaw size distribution for an inspection system is shown in Fig. 14.1

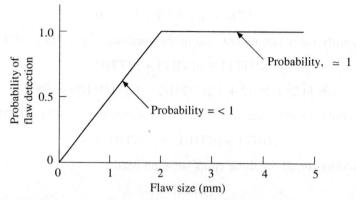

Fig. 14.1   Probability of defect detection and flaw size distribution for an inspection system

It is clear from Fig. 14.1 that for a defect of size larger than 2 mm, the detection probability is 1. It is obvious that for smaller and smaller size defects, the probability of defect detection decreases.

Probability of defect detection not only depends on an inspection system but also on various other factors such as

(a) operator knowledge
(b) proper application of the technique
(c) test environment
(d) material properties such as inhomogeneity and anisotropy
(e) defect orientation
(f) test accessibility, geometrical features etc.

The relationship between operator performance and the probability of defect detection is shown in Fig. 14.2. The 'ideal' circumstances are those in which no component with a defect size less than d will be identified as defective and all components having defects with size greater than d will be correctly identified. The other two curves represent more realistic conditions. For the 'good' curve, a small number of components will be detected with defect size less than d as defective. These defect detections are noted as 'false calls'. The curve for the 'poor' operator/system performance results in a number of 'missed defects' and a few if any false calls.

It has been seen from the above discussion that the ability to detect a flaw/defect with a particular size depends on the characteristics of the NDT system. While the probability of existence of a defect is a factor over which the NDT engineer has no control, the probability of detection is a factor that is very much in the control of NDT engineer. Therefore, while

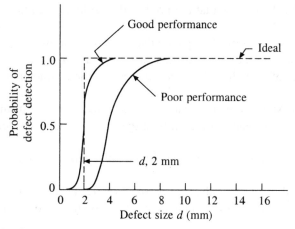

Fig. 14.2 Operator performance and the probability of defect detection

selecting an NDT inspection system, appropriate decision should be taken based on the risks involved in potential failures, false calls, missed defects and inspection cost.

14.2 STATISTICAL METHODS

During mass production of components, variations in the quality levels between each component have to be evaluated. This variation in quality from one part to another is due to a number of reasons. It is always the desire of the customer to obtain uniform products, i.e. products in narrow range of specifications. Maintaining optimum conditions closely in a process that would result in minimising the variation in the product is the key to satisfy the customer. As an ideal goal, it is commendable. But, just as there is no such a thing as a perfect circle, it is impossible to achieve exact repeatability of the quality of a product. This is due to variations in process conditions, however, small there may be. Only in the case of automated process, the reality is close to the desire.

Quality can not be controlled unless there is a means for quantitatively measuring the level of quality and for distinguishing controllable variables from uncontrollable variables. The task of evaluating these factors is accomplished largely by the application of statistical methods.

The benefits enjoyed by industry through the use of statistical quality control are immense like reduction in time and manpower requirements, waste, scrap, rework, and inspection costs. Statistical concepts can be applied in many industries involving mass production, for achieving desired quality and reliability.

14.2.1 Basic Principles

Important terms (as defined by American Society for Metals, is given in Metals Handbook Vol. 11) widely used in statistical quality control are given below:

Characteristic: A property that can serve to differentiate between units of a product. The differentiation may be qualitative (method of attributes) or quantitative (method of variables).

Distribution: Position, arrangement or frequency of occurrence of individual attributes or variables within a sample or population.

Lot: A group of individual items that are produced or sold as a unit.

Method of attributes: Measurement of quality that consists of noting the presence (or absence) of some characteristic in each of the units in the group or lot under consideration and counting the number of units that do or do not possess the characteristic.

Method of variables: Measurement of variables that consists of measuring the magnitude of a quality characteristic for each of the units in the group under consideration.

Nonconformance: Failure to meet any specified quality requirement.

Population: The totality of individual items of a single design that is available during a given period of interest, and from which samples can be taken for statistical analysis.

Sample: A finite part of a statistical population whose properties are studied to gain information about the population as a whole.

Random sampling: A process of withdrawing a sample from a lot or population in which each unit in the lot or population has an equal chance of being included in the sample.

Range: The difference between the largest value and the smallest value in a given set of observations.

Variability: Variability is evaluated as the dispersion or spread of a measured attribute about the most common value of that attribute. Both the limits of the spread and the frequency distribution of measured values within the spread must be defined to accurately evaluate the variability. Frequency distributions can be of many forms. Most industrial products exhibit a normal (Gaussian) distribution as shown in Fig. 14.3 where the most common value is centered within the range and the frequency of occurrence of any given value diminishes the

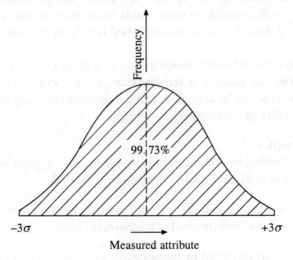

Fig. 14.3   **Gaussian distribution**

farther that value is from the most common value. Sometimes, the most common value is not centered in the normal distribution and this is known as 'skewed distribution'. Skewed distribution contains two or more peak values of frequency of occurrence. The spread can be expressed mathematically as the root-mean-square (rms) value of deviations from the process average. The rms deviation is called the standard deviation, and is usually designated by the Greek letter sigma (σ). It is inherent that, in general, in all normal distributions, 99.97% of the individual values fall within three standard deviations ($\pm 3\sigma$) of the process average.

Techniques for statistical quality control

There are two principal techniques for statistical quality control, viz. (a) control charts and (b) acceptance sampling.

14.2.2 Control Charts

The concept of control charts is developed by W.A. Shewhart and the charts are prepared by drawing samples from a population, measuring the same characteristic of every unit in each sample, and plotting the average and range of that characteristic in each sample against a sample number. The control chart relies on two fundamental principles—the central limit theorem and the relation between chart sensitivity and sample size. In simple terms, the central-limit theorem shows that, regardless of the shape of the frequency distribution of individual measurements, the distribution of averages for samples, each of which contains *n* units, will tend towards a normal distribution as *n* increases. For most industrial processes, the central limit theorem holds good for all sample sizes of five or more units, which allows statistical generalization to be applied to a wide variety of industrial processes.

The second fundamental feature of the Shewhart's control chart is that the sensitivity of the chart for small fluctuations in the production process increases as the sample size (*n*) increases.

In the control chart, upper and lower control limits define the $\pm 3\sigma$ spread for the sample average and range that is the spread within which 99.73% of all the sample averages or sample ranges is expected to fall, assuming no change in the process average or variability. If the sample average falls outside the control limits, it is a signal to immediately look for assignable cause in order to affect a change that will bring the process under control. Control charts give the average level at which the process can operate and the amount of chance variation present. On many occasions, it is not possible to reproduce the exactly given set of conditions. Whatever may be the ideal manufacturing or fabrication conditions, there is still a possibility for variation due to chance like the variation we get by tossing a coin, i.e. we are not going to get head or tail equal number of times. This type of chance variation is not possible to be eliminated in any manual or semiautomated engineering process. Inspection by this type of quality characteristics (attributes) is used as go or no go type for segregating defective products from the finished products. Many process parameters (e.g. in the case of welding; voltage, amperage etc.) can be optimized using statistical method to get products with better quality.

A typical example showing the variation in the percentage of defective rods produced with time of production is shown in Table 14.2.

Calculation of Upper and Lower Control Limits (UCL and LCL) of defective rods is as follows:

Table 14.2   Data on Ten Lots of Rods Inspected

Lot No.	No. inspected	No. rejected	Fraction of defective rods (%)
1	300	10	3.33
2	240	12	5.0
3	320	12	3.75
4	310	10	3.22
5	290	13	4.48
6	270	12	4.44
7	315	15	4.47
8	325	11	3.43
9	295	12	4.06
10	275	13	4.72
Total	2940	120	4.08 ($\bar{L}$)

$$\bar{L} \text{ Fraction defective} = \frac{\text{Total number of defective rods}}{\text{Total number of rods inspected}} \tag{14.2}$$

$$= 120/2940 = 0.0408 \text{ say } 0.04$$

$$\text{UCL} = \bar{L} + 3\sqrt{\{\bar{L}(1-\bar{L})/\bar{n}\}} \tag{14.3}$$

$$= 0.04 + 3\sqrt{\frac{0.04(1-0.04)}{294}}$$

$$= 0.04 + 0.034 = 0.074 \text{ or } 7.4\%$$

$$\text{LCL} = 0.04 - 0.034 = 0.006 \text{ or } 0.6\%$$

The data in Table 14.2 is plotted in the $\bar{L}$ chart in Fig. 14.4. UCL and LCL are also shown in this figure. In this example, it is expected that 7.4% of the rods would be defective due to chance variation in production condition and is considered as acceptable. Variations between control limits as shwon in Fig. 14.4 are known as chance variations, which are inherent in the process, i.e., from the common causes of the system. In other words, only variability beyond these fixed limits will be assumed to have come from assignable or special causes. Normally, lower control limit for components is set at 0 (zero) in the case of defect detection because it is preferable to have zero defects. In the said example, if the % defective rods is more than 7.4%, process parameters have to be optimized to produce better product or alternate method of production has to be developed. Thus, any system exhibiting variation only in common cause is a statistically controlled system.

The 'defects per unit chart' ($\bar{U}$ chart) is another type of control chart used in statistical evaluation of quality of a component or a unit which consists of many parts. In this case, the sources of defects are many or many defects are expected. Similar to the $\bar{L}$ chart, the defect per unit or $\bar{U}$ chart must consider consistent lot sizes because of the use of n in the formula for calculation of control units.

$$\text{Upper and lower control limits} = \bar{U} \pm 3\sqrt{\bar{U}/\bar{n}} \tag{14.4}$$

The following is an example (Table 14.3) of defects per unit calculations for plotting $\bar{U}$ chart.

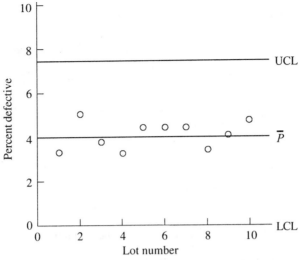

Fig. 14.4 Upper and lower control limits of defective rods

Calculations for UCL and LCL:

Average number of units, $\bar{n}$ = 49.7
Average defects per lot = 124.6
Average defects per unit $\simeq$ 2.5

Table 14.3 Number of defects found in the units for each lots

Lot No.	No. of units	Defects	Defects/unit
1	52	120	2.30
2	48	125	2.60
3	50	124	2.48
4	49	128	2.61
5	47	132	2.80
6	51	121	2.37
7	53	118	2.22
8	50	127	2.54
9	48	126	2.62
10	49	125	2.55
Total	497	1246	2.509

$$\text{UCL} = U \pm 3\sqrt{U/\bar{n}} = 2.5 + 3\sqrt{\{2.5/49.7\}} = 2.5 + 3\sqrt{0.0503}$$
$$= 2.5 + 0.67 = 3.17$$
$$\text{LCL} = 2.5 - 0.67 = 1.83$$

Defects-per-unit chart ($\bar{U}$ chart) plotted for the data in Table 14.3, with UCL and LCL are given in Fig. 14.5.

Even though control charts are used for statistical quality control methodology, the probability theory behind the generation of control charts makes them not applicable to every need. One

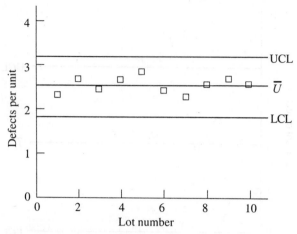

Fig. 14.5   Defects-per-unit chart showing upper and lower control limits

area for which control charts are not suited is the 'acceptance sampling', a method to determine overall quality of incoming or outgoing components. Individual items are generally classified as defective or nondefective, depending on whether the component possesses a certain set of characteristics or meets particular specifications. Instead of checking each individual component in a lot, sampling inspection with certain in-built characteristic of the sample to represent the lot is more cost effective if the requisite reliability can be ensured. Principles involved in acceptance sampling inspection are discussed below.

14.2.3   Basic Principles of Acceptance Sampling Inspection

Acceptance Sampling is another tool used widely and is of intrinsic value in the practice of acceptance of the lot based on inspection by sampling. In engineering industries, it is extremely useful to be able to make a judgment, for the purposes of accepting, rejecting or reworking a production lot, by inspecting only a few pieces from the lot.

Sampling plans depend on two major factors for their accuracy. One is randomness of the sample which determines whether a given sample is a valid group which can be used to judge the whole lot. The other is the actual number of units in the sample. An acceptance sampling plan is best described by the use of an operating characteristic curve as explained below.

Operating characteristic curve (OC curve)

An OC curve is a plot of the actual number of nonconforming (defective) units in a lot expressed as a percentage against the probability that the lot will be accepted when sampled according to the plan. The shape of the OC curve is determined primarily by sample size n and acceptance number c. Typical OC curve is shown in Fig. 14.6. It can be seen from Fig. 14.6 that the probability for acceptance is 1.0 for sample lot without any defectives. As the % defectives increases, the probability for acceptance reduces. Therefore, the curve shows the ability of the inspection procedure including sampling adopted for distinguishing the good and bad lots. The steeper the slope of the curve, the greater the efficiency of the inspection procedure. Use of a perfect OC curve would result in acceptance of all lots with acceptable quality and rejection of all other lots.

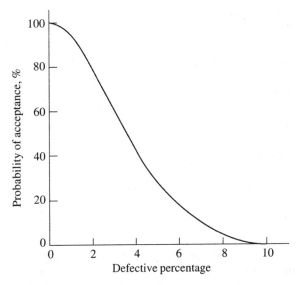

Fig. 14.6   A typical operating characteristic curve

Acceptable quality level (AQL)

On the OC curve, the quality level at which there is a 95% probability of acceptance is generally referred to as the acceptable quality level. The AQL is defined as the maximum number of defectives that, for the purpose of acceptance sampling, can be considered acceptable as a process average. While selecting the AQL, it is important to note that the value chosen shall be achieved with the existing process variables.

Producer's risk and consumer's risk

The producer's risk is associated with a high probability of acceptance, usually 95%. The manufacturer can expect that the lots with percentage of defectives correspond, to a point on the OC curve representing 95% probability of acceptance, would be acceptable. In other words, the producer's risk is the chance that a lot with fewer than the allowable percentage of defectives will be rejected on the basis of sample results. The other 5% represents the consumer's risk, that the lots whose actual percentage of defectives is equal to or less than the acceptable quality level, i.e. the chance of a 'bad' lot being accepted on the basis of the operating characteristic curve is known as consumer's risk.

Product quality auditing

Although a statistical sampling plan, in which the consumer's risk is limted is usually chosen, the actual probability that the consumer will receive lots having a greater percentage of defectives than the value specified by the OC curve (i.e. defects corresponding to 10% probability of acceptance in OC curve) for that plan depends on the quality of inspection process. The usual method of evaluating the effectiveness of the inspection and quality control is to perform an audit by randomly sampling and reinspecting the goods that have been released for shipment. On reinspection if any additional defectives were found, the control of the inspection process itself needs to be tightened. In critical instances, it may be necessary to determine the reliability of the inspection process in order to be sure that no defective lots are accepted as good ones.

Process average of material inspected
The average percent defectives of several lots of the material inspected. This is computed by dividing the total number of defectives (found by inspection) by the total number of sample pieces taken from several lots for inspection.

Average outgoing quality of material inspected
Average quality, expressed in percent defectives of material that has passed a particular sampling plan. This depends on the 'process average of the material submitted to inspection'.

14.2.4 Sampling Plans
Inspection is conducted on a 100 percent basis or by sampling, depending on such factors as desired quality level based on expectations of performance, input materials or components quality level, process control and cost of inspection. Unless performed automatically, 100 percent inspection may not be 100 percent efficient due to (i) possible variations in inspection procedure or (ii) human factors like operator fatigue the errors during manual inspection. With the use of modern statistical concepts, the quality of 'sampling inspection' can be as high as 100%. Another advantage of 'sampling inspection' is that more detailed inspection is possible on the basis of a few samples at optimum cost. Several sampling plans that available are grouped into three as follows:

(a) Single sampling plan: In this single sampling plan, acceptance or rejection of a lot depends on the acceptance or rejection of the units in the sample drawn from the lot. Single sampling plan works as follows:
   If sample size, $n = 10$ and accept No. $c = 0$, and reject no. $r = c + 1 = 1$, then inspect a sample of 10 units and accept the lot if there are no defective units in the sample. If there is one or more defectives in the sample, the lot will be rejected.

(b) Double sampling plan: This is based on selection of one sample with acceptance if the number of defectives is low, but a second sample must be inspected if the number of defectives is moderately high. If the quality of the items is good enough, most of the lots are acceptable based on the first sample itself. If too many second samples are required due to higher defect level or the part has large variations then, there is no advantages of having second sampling plan. Double sampling plan is most efficient and economical when the quality expected is either much better or much worse than the usual level. The fact that the second sample may or may not be necessary makes the inspection plan little uncertain.
   A typical example of the methodology of double sampling plan is given below.

Sample No.	Sample size (n)	Accept no. (c)	Reject no. (r = c + 1)
1	25	1	2
2	30	2	3

As per the above plan, select 25 units from the lot at random and inspect them. If none or one is defective in the sample, accept the lot. If there are three or more defectives in the sample, reject the lot. If there are exactly two defectives in the sample, then draw another random sample of 30 units. Add the number 'defective' in the first sample to the number 'defective' found in the second sample. If the total number of defectives is two or less, accept the lot. If there are three or more defectives, reject the lot.

(c) Multiple sampling plan: This sampling plan works in the same way as the double sampling plan described above except that there would be more than two stages. This type of sampling plan is usually more difficult to administer. Acceptance decision is based on three or more sets of samples inspected. This is more costlier than the other two methods. This type of sampling inspection is used when material must be inspected during continuous production process.

Criteria for selecting a sampling plan
Following points must be considered for selecting a sampling plan:

  (i)   Will the items be accumulated in lots?
  (ii) If the items are accumulated in lots, the size of the lots, conditions under which the lots will be accepted or rejected must be decided.
  (iii) The risks such as consumer's risk and producer's risk must be specified.
  (iv) The method of selecting samples must be specified when sampling inspection is performed. It must be assumed that, if defects are present, they are randomly distributed throughout the lot, i.e. the lot should be homogeneous. Therefore, any piece within a lot has an equal chance of being selected as part of the sample set.
  (v)   The sample pieces must be selected at random.
  (vi) The characteristics to be inspected must be specified, and standards for acceptance of these characteristics must be defined.

14.3   TAGUCHI CONCEPTS IN QUALITY CONTROL

Dr. Genich Taguchi from Japan has introduced some new concepts in statistical quality control, and they are named after him. Taguchi methods involve application of designed experiments for evaluation of quality during various stages, i.e. design, production and service of a product's life cycle.

14.3.1   Basic Concepts
Designed experiment: An experiment where one or more variables (called independent variables) that are believed to have an effect on the experimental outcome are identified and manipulated according to a predetermined plan. Data collected from a designed experiment can be analysed statistically to determine the effect of the independent variables. An experimental plan must also include provision for dealing with extraneous variables, that is, variables not explicitly identified as independent variables.

Quality: Quality is defined as the loss imparted to the society from the time a product is shipped. Taguchi divides quality control efforts into two categories: on-line quality control and off-line quality control.

   On-line quality control involves diagnosis and adjustment of the process, forecasting and correcting the problems, inspection and disposition of product, and follow-up action on the defectives shipped to the customer.

   Off-line quality control methods are the quality and cost control activities conducted on design and process stages of the product during the product development cycle. Three major aspects of off-line quality control are as follows:

(a) System design: The process of applying scientific and engineering knowledge to produce a basic functional prototype design. The prototype model defines the initial settings of product or process design characteristics.

(b) Parameter design: An investigation conducted to identify settings that eliminate or at least reduce the performance variation. A product or a process can perform its intended function at many settings of its design characteristics. However, variation in the performance characteristics may change with different settings. This variation increases both product manufacturing and lifetime costs. The parameter design comes from an engineering tradition of referring to product characteristics as product parameters. An exercise to identify optimal parameter settings is therefore called parameter design.

(c) Tolerance design: A method for determining tolerances that minimizes the sum of both product manufacturing and lifetime costs. The final step in specifying product and process designs is to determine tolerances around the nominal settings identified by parameter design. It is still a common practice in industry to assign tolerances by convention rather than scientifically. Tolerances that are too narrow increase manufacturing costs, and tolerances that are too wide increase performance variation and the lifetime cost of the product.

Expected loss: Expected loss refers to the monetary losses an arbitrary user of the product is likely to suffer at an arbitrary time during the product's life span because of performance variation. Taguchi advocates modelling the loss function so that the parameter design can be made more accurate. Noise is the term used to describe all the variables except the design parameters that cause performance variation during a product's life span and across different units of the product. Sources of noise are classified as either external or internal. External sources of noise are variables external to a product that affect the product's performance. For example, the performance of a perfectly designed pump can be affected by external factors such as vibration from other sources, high ambient temperature etc. Internal sources of noise are the deviations of the actual characteristics of a manufactured product from the corresponding nominal settings.

Performance statistics: It estimates the effect of noise factors on the performance characteristics. Performance statistics are chosen such that maximizing the performance measure will minimise expected loss. Many performance statistics used by Taguchi include various 'signal to noise ratios' which account jointly for the levels of the parameters and the variation of the parameters.

Some of the concepts of the Taguchi method for identifying settings of design parameters that maximize the performance statistics are discussed above. For more discussions on the subject, the reader is advised to refer to the suggested references given at the end of the book.

14.4   TOTAL QUALITY MANAGEMENT

14.4.1   Quality

The conventional definition of the term 'Quality' given by Thomas H. Berry is "A customer who buys any product or service has certain expectations. If the product or service meets or exceeds those expectations time and again, then in the mind of that customer, it is a quality product or a quality service'. From this view point, the basic definition of quality is 'meeting customers' need and reasonable expectations'.

Total Quality Management (TQM) is a management strategy aimed at embedding awareness of quality in all organizational processes. TQM has been widely used in manufacturing, education, government, and service industries, as well as science programs/organisations.

International Standard Organisation defines TQM as a management approach of an organization, centered on quality, based on the participation of all its members and aiming at long-term success through customer satisfaction, and benefits to all members of the organization and to society.

The TQM is a process for managing quality, it must be a continuous way of life; a philosophy of perpetual improvement in everything we do.

Often Japan is cited as an ideal example for quality products and quality services. In Japanese, TQM comprises four process steps, namely:

1. *Kaizen* – Focuses on continuous process improvement, to make processes visible, repeatable and measurable.
2. *Atarimae Hinshitsu* – Focuses on intangible effects on processes and ways to optimize and reduce their effects.
3. *Kansei* – Examining the way the user applies the product leads to improvement in the product itself.
4. *Miryokuteki Hinshitsu* – Broadens management concern beyond the immediate product.

TQM requires that an organisation maintains quality standard in all aspects of its activities. This requires ensuring that things are done right the first time and that defects and waste are eliminated from operations.

Although W. Edwards Deming is largely credited with igniting the quality revolution in Japan starting in 1946 and trying to bring it to the United States in the 1980s, Armand V. Feigenbaum was developing a similar set of principles at General Electric in the United States at around the same time. "Total Quality Control" was the key concept of Feigenbaum's 1951 book, *Quality Control: Principles, Practice, and Administration*, a book that was subsequently released in 1961 under the title, *Total Quality Control,* Joseph Juran, Philip B. Crosby, and Kaoru Ishikawa also contributed to the body of knowledge now known as TQM .

14.4.2 Deming's Philosophy

Dr. Edwards Deming was a physicist specialized in the field of statistics and worked in United States Bureau of Census. His greatest contribution on the evaluation of statistical methods for ensuring the quality of census assessment established him as a leader in the field of Total Quality Management. In fact he is considered as the "Guru" of Total Quality Management.

Deming also enunciated 14 principles for quality management which include innovation, the philosophy of quality to be inculcated in all individuals, appropriate and complete supervision, absence of fear and openness, ensuring quality form design through to maintenance, work standards in production, training of every worker in statistical methods, retraining people to new skills and so on.

14.4.3 Concept of Total Quality Management

TQM represents a comprehensive procedure, methodology and approach towards Quality

Assurance and Management, that transcends the barriers of materials, processes, countries, time and space, in order to satisfy the customer right from the introduction of any product or service in the market, through its evolution and use, till the complete phasing out of the product or service, only to be replaced by a better one. TQM is the highest destination in the ladder with steps of Quality Control, Quality Assurance, Quality Audit, ISO 9000, Quality Improvement and TQM. The TQM is related to the character of the company, vision of the leader, an ideal (rarely realisable) and guaranteed profits through customer delight, brand status, commitment of the employees and the employer to a common focus, policy of the company through quality circles and quality improvement etc.

In a way, TQM is the sum total of all small, yet important aspects. Strict control, documentation and updating of data in the following areas are mandatory for TQM: (a) Choice of raw materials, (b) Processes, (c) Final Product, (d) Marketing, (e) Services (with respect to both Spatial Efficiency and Temporal Efficiency), (f) Product Support: Customer Support, (g) Product Upgradation, (h) Education to the customer about the product or the service, (i) Gradual phasing-out of any product and its related services, (j) Gradual re-introduction of the new product (k) the beginning of the next equivalent cycle leading to a better product or service.

The possibility of defects in processes is always present. For strict quality control, concept like Six Sigma is very popular and was pioneered by Bill Smith at Motorola in 1986. Originally, it was defined as a metric for measuring defects and improving quality; and a methodology to reduce defect levels below 3.4 Defects Per (one) Million Opportunities (DPMO).

Six Sigma concept has now grown beyond defect control. It can be defined as a methodology to manage process variations that cause defects, defined as unacceptable deviation from the mean or target; and to systematically work towards managing variation to eliminate those defects. The objective of Six Sigma is to deliver world-class performance, reliability, and value to the end customer.

Different concepts are present for strict quality control but our ultimate aim should be the concept of zero-defect. The concept of zero-defect (100% quality assurance) should be accorded prime importance as a part of the TQM by incorporating suitable non destructive methods in the total chain of TQM. The adoption of the technology of intelligent processing of materials (IPM) with provision for feedback control to the process based on on-line measurements and of course understanding the vital correlations between measured parameters, process variables and quality specifications is another step towards achieving TQM. Multi-sensor data fusion and integration can be defined as the synergistic use of information from multiple sources to assist in the accomplishment of a task with TQM. One of the emerging possibilities of effectively utilizing the multi sensor data together with the knowledge explosion is to explore the concepts of artificial intelligence (AI) wherever applicable. Successful implementation of AI concepts in the form of verified and validated knowledge based systems and knowledge based inference mechanism are currently being developed for various specific problems.

Achieving quality is not only in the hands of the inspector but also with all. The inspector's function is the last; even though he may be good, he alone can not achieve quality as said by proverb 'a single sparrow won't make a summer'. Total quality management is like a relay race where each runner and every lap are equally crucial. Each individual, each division, each sector of an organisation has a role to play and if these roles synchronize, then only quality is achieved in any organisation. We can say that total quality management is a total war.

For example, if the design is not good whatever be the best inspection methods employed, quality can not be achieved in the final product. In the same way, the reverberation in the organisations going such as how the personnel department is treating the employees and taking care of employees, the health care system the organization has and so on. All quality means quality of output at every stage and of every division, by every employee. Quality then is synonymous with the pursuit of excellence.

14.4.4 Key Ingredients of Total Quality Management

Quality cannot be just a 'drive', a 'programme' or a 'campaign', which will only bring short lived result. Total quality management has to be a way of life, a systematic movement towards performance leadership, the very essence of the strategy and structure of the organization.

If any organization has to have a total quality management then it requires the following three key ingredients.

1. Work ethics and work culture that think and act for quality and excellence.
2. Quality of leadership should inspire the rank and file.
3. Quality of Human Resources.

All the three are equally important but the first two are essential to ensure the third in an organization. In order to excel in quality, the process of analysing the activities of the organisation in search for better understanding of where improvements can be made is to be continuously thrived upon. This process analysis is essentially a top-down process of improvement with reviews from the bottom-up. Leadership oriented approach is based on leaders who brought in the sense of quality and pride in all the people. As the leader knows all his people, it is relatively an easy task to interact and understand all of them. The leader does not need a manual or document to describe his quality policy. He shows it in action everyday to his people and his customers. If an organization has a work culture that thinks and acts quality, if its leadership is capable of providing inspiration and motivation, then it will also attract to its fold the best of human resources available.

14.5 SUMMARY

In this chapter, a discussion is made on the usefulness of probability and statistical concepts for quality control applications. Probability for defect detection can be applied for inspection methodologies to arrive at the testing sensitivity and reliable defect detectability. The information so generated is useful for fracture mechanics based design concepts. Statistical concepts are mainly used in mass production industry to identify variations in process conditions so that corrective actions can be taken and more uniform quality can be achieved. Statistical quality control methods can be used to ensure reliability of the quality of the products to the desired levels. Some of the modern quality control concepts introduced by G. Taguchi are also briefly discussed in this chapter.

Chapter 15

Codes, Standards, Specification and Procedures

The modern concept of quality control states that, in each and every activity of the organisation, there are certain elements which affect the quality of the product cycle. Therefore, it is essential to identify these elements and control them for ensuring the quality. Development of an organizational structure is needed to receive, analyse and disseminate the information on quality for its improvement. If these activities are carried out routinely and actions are taken from time to time to remove the deficiencies in the quality noticed at any stage, there would be a continuous improvement in the quality of the product that is delivered to the customer. However, such an improvement in quality is sustained only when the quality control activities are carried out in accordance with the written procedures. These procedures are issued by a standardizing organisation. Nondestructive testing is employed for assuring the quality. Basic objectives of the NDT of materials and structural components is the assessment of their healthiness through detection of defects or disorders that may lead to premature failure. The use of NDT in industry depends on Standards. Standards are used to ensure reproducible results during inspection/testing, no matter when, where or who conducts the examination. Standards also help to compare results and to take decisions on acceptance/rejection.

Nondestructive tests are specific for a given application and selection of the equipment to accomplish these specific needs is based on specifications. At times, capabilities of one test overlap with those of another. It is also true that no single method is capable of revealing all surface and subsurface discontinuities in all types of materials. For these reasons, it is sometimes necessary to use a combination of tests to obtain complementary information and thus helps in complete evaluation of the quality of the component. Specifications/Procedures indicate when and what NDT methods should be applied, what is the intent of NDT and what are the acceptance limits.

Documents containing written procedures used for quality assurance activities are classified into Codes, Standards, Specification and Procedures. The concepts of Code, Standard, Specification and Procedure are discussed below.

15.1 CODE

Code is a comprehensive document relating to all aspects like design, material, fabrication, construction, erection, maintenance, quality control as well as documentation for specific industrial components like pressure vessels, air-crafts etc. Codes are prepared by professional bodies or Government agencies for a specific subject. For some of the activities like design requirement, material qualification, NDT etc., Codes may refer to Standards which are independent and parallel documents.

Various types of Codes are available, viz. Indian Power Boiler Code, ASME Boiler and Pressure Vessel Code etc. The adoption of Codes by various industries and their effectiveness in reducing human casualties due to accidents is widely recognized. ASME Boiler and Pressure Vessel Code is an important code which was established by a committee set up in 1911 with members from Government, utilities, insurance companies and manufacturers.

ASME Boiler and Pressure Vessel Code has 11 Sections dealing with various subjects. Among these Sections, Section V deals with NDT. It is divided into Sub-sections. Sub-section 'A' contains the details on use of various methods of NDT, whereas Sub-section 'B' deals with the various Standard Practices of testing. One of the features of the ASME Code is that continuous improvement based on the experience gained is attempted by issuing revisions half yearly, i.e. the summer addenda and the winter addenda. Any questions about interpretation of the rules may be submitted to the Committee in a letter of inquiry and answers from the Committee are published as Code Cases from time to time.

15.2 STANDARDS

Codes will often refer to the Standards which are more specific documents giving the details on how a particular operation is to be carried out. These Standards take into account: (i) available technological levels and (ii) operational skills of the operators, while laying down the requirements of the Standards. To take an example with regard to manual ultrasonic testing, the test results depend greatly on person's skill. Hence, the procedures for testing and evaluation must be standardized in detail so that the test results will be least affected by difference in personal skill.

As the name implies, 'Standards' attempt to standardise material or a specific activity such as testing and inspection. The body making the Standards takes into account the various industrial requirements and prepares the Standards in such a way that a few Standards would be enough for a large variety of industrial applications. 'Codes' in turn, find it convenient to make use of these ready-made Standards.

For example, an Ultrasonic Standard is a document issued by a standardizing organisation to ensure reproducible results from an ultrasonic examination, no matter when, where or who conducts the examination. Following are some of the organizations whose NDT Standards are internationally used:

(a) ASME (American Society of Mechanical Engineers)
(b) ASTM (American Society for Testing Materials)
(c) BS (British Standards Institution)
(d) DIN (German Standards Organisation)
(e) ISO (International Standards Organisation)
(f) IS (Bureau of Indian Standards)

Various types of Standards, formulated by different agencies are as follows:

    (a) International and National Standards
    (b) Industrial Standards
    (c) Government and Military Standards
    (d) Industry Practices
    (e) Company Standards

A brief description of these Standards is given below:

15.2.1 International and national standards

This is the formal level in which fundamental parameters (characteristics) are defined either internationally (ISO) or by the national authorized agency. In the case of International System of Units, the reference standards of various units are developed and maintained by the Federal Conference on Weights and Measures, which is intended as a basis for worldwide standardisation of measurement units. International System of Units, abbreviated as SI Units, is universally adopted.

The national authorized agency for India is the Bureau of Indian standards (BIS). These Standards include such basic parameters as linear length, weight, resistance and frequency. It is necessary that all qualified calibration centres (for example, the regional test centres of BIS) must have their master instruments calibrated in a specified manner with the master instruments available at the national standards organisation (like BIS or National Physical Laboratory in India). The accuracy of these master Standards is generally several times greater than the accuracy required in industrial laboratories because it is necessary to transfer Standards through several levels before they reach an individual company.

15.2.2 Industry standards

Industry Standards are usually product-oriented. These are defined and maintained by the concerned trade association or a technical society. The main requirements for this type of Standards include product nomenclature and the need for interchangeability of manufacture's products. An example of such industry Standards is the colour code for electrical components.

15.2.3 Government and military standards

Government organizations, in particular military (defence) specify their own Standards for production and testing of most components. In many cases, the defence components must meet stringent requirements. Thus special Standards suitable for evaluation of the defence components are prepared. In numerous cases, nonmilitary companies may adopt military Standards at their company Standards to take benefit of the stringency of these Standards.

15.2.4 Industry practices

Industry practices are followed within an industry. These practices are formulated by the industry and adopted by consumers. The reason for including Practices under Standards is that they amount to actual Standards as far as their use within an industry is concerned. Examples of such functions are accounting, inspection, purchasing etc.

15.2.5 Company standards

With many years of experience, a company develops its own Standards and Practices both formally and informally. They are unique to a particular company. These Standards and Practices define the steps to be used by every one in the company who is performing a certain function such as inspection, rectification, purchase and selling. These practices also specify the limitations of authority within that particular business cycle or transaction.

15.3 SPECIFICATION

The document that prescribes in detail, the requirements with which the product or service has to comply with is termed 'Specification'.

'Specification' is of paramount importance in achieving the quality. In many cases, poor products or services are the result of inadequate, ambiguous or improper Specifications. For a product to be manufactured and operated properly, different specifications for raw material, process, inspection, acceptance, installation, operation, documentation etc. have to be finalized and adopted with reliability. The Specifications are either evolved by national bodies or by the manufacturers based on their own experiences.

15.4 PROCEDURES

These are the last level documents to be adopted in the shop-floor for any process or service. The Procedures are formulated in such a way that these documents give all the specific details pertaining to the activity. This is essential since it is a shop-floor document which has to be complied with strictly by different levels of personnel. No change in Procedure is allowed to be made without the written approval from the authorised person in the organisation. The Procedure is prepared in such a detailed manner that the shop-floor personnel can follow it without any ambiguity.

Written Procedure helps to attain reproducible test results in NDT. For example, in the case of ultrasonic testing, there are many factors which affect the ultrasonic examination. These factors include various steps from transmission of voltage pulse which generates the ultrasonic pulse till the reflected pulse is received and displayed on the CRT. Paragraph T-522 of Article 5 Section V of ASME 1991 Ed. specifies the requirements of a written Procedure to help achieve reproducible results. This is as follows:

When required by the referencing Code, any examination shall be performed in accordance with a written procedure. For example, in the case of ultrasonic testing, each procedure shall include at least the following information, as applicable.

(a) Material type and configuration of item to be examined, dimensions, product form (casting, forging weld etc.)
(b) the surface(s) from which the examination shall be performed
(c) surface condition
(d) couplant details like brand name, type etc.
(e) technique (straight beam, angled beam, contact, immersion etc.)
(f) angles and mode(s) of wave propagation in the material
(g) search unit type, frequency(ies), and transducer size(s)
(h) special search units, wedges, shoes, and their types
(i) type of ultrasonic instrument
(j) description of calibration blocks and techniques
(k) direction and extent of scanning
(l) data to be recorded and the method of recording (manual or mechanised)
(m) automatic alarm and recording equipment or both

(n) rotating, revolving, or scanning mechanisms

(o) post examination cleaning

(p) personnel qualification requirements

(q) review or demonstration of the procedure as required by the referencing Code.

15.5   INDIAN NATIONAL STANDARDS FOR NDT

Recognising the need for standardization in the field of NDT, a separate technical committee to deal with the NDT work, called 'Non-Destructive Testing Sectional Committee, MTD21', was formed in 1965, under the Metallurgical Engineering Council of the BIS. So far 36 standards have been formulated by this committee. These standards include codes of practices, test methods, definitions, safety codes and specifications. These Standards are developed based on the discussions within the Committee consisting of experts with primary interest in specific materials and products. To formulate the Standards, concerted effort is made to obtain a broad involvement and agreement between groups with varied interests. The Standards thus formulated by the committee represent true conscience documents. Participation of producers, consumers, national laboratories and other technical institutions ensure meeting this objective.

Indian Standard Codes, recommended practices and the specifications applicable for various NDT techniques have been given at the end of each chapter in this book.

15.6   INTERNATIONAL STANDARDS FOR NDT

A separate technical committee ISO/TC135 was set up by ISO in 1969 to deal with standardisation work in the field of NDT at International level. The committee functions through six subcommittees, each concerned with a particular technique. India, being a participating member of the committee, maintains close liaison with its working. International Standards and recommendations are always kept in view while formulating corresponding Indian Standards. This is done as a matter of policy because these international Standards are adopted by many other countries as the basis of product inspection, product approval and certification system and they tend to govern product acceptance throughout the world. It is essential that India participates in the development of International Standards to ensure that the view points of Indian interests are incorporated in International Standards.

The modern approach to quality control lays emphasis on manufacture of quality products at the first instance rather than correcting it later or sorting out the good and defective products. The data on quality has to be collected not only at the production stage but at all possible stages right from planning to the use of the product. This has given rise to the concept of total quality management (TQM). Under this concept, due consideration is given to the quality aspect of the product at each stage of the product cycle namely, marketing, design, purchasing, production engineering, manufacturing, inspection and testing, packaging, shipping, installation, condition monitoring etc. The role of NDT at each and every stage in a production process in achieving total quality management is well discussed in the introductory chapter of this book. It will be beneficial to the reader if the concept of total quality management, which is discussed in detail in ISO 9000 series Standards is known to him/her.

15.6.1   ISO Standards for Quality Systems

The International Organisation for Standardisation (ISO) Technical Committee, ISO/TC 176

'Quality Management and Quality Assurance', deals with standardisation in the field of generic quality management including quality systems, quality assurance, and generic supporting technologies. Standards which provide guidelines on the selection and use of these quality standards also come under the preview of this committee.

ISO/TC 176 has so far published twelve ISO standards on quality systems and supporting technologies. In addition, ISO/TC 176 has prepared a series of Committee Drafts (CD) and Draft International Standards (DIS). A CD is a document circulated for study within the ISO technical committee or subcommittee. When the committee finally reaches an agreement on the text, it is sent to the Central Secretariat for registration and publication as a DIS. The DIS is circulated to all ISO member bodies for voting. If 75 percent of the votes cast are in favour of the DIS, it is accepted for publication as an International Standard.

Quality system standards based on ISO 9000 series are gaining importance world over. More than 55 countries have already adopted these standards in to as their national Standards. Further, around 50 countries have applied for quality systems registration/certification from ISO.

ISO 9000 series are standards containing guidelines to all activities concerning manufacturing, i.e. from marketing, design, purchasing, process, inspection and testing, handling, storage, packing and delivery, quality audits etc. towards achieving total quality of a component. It also helps in identifying the weaker links in the chain of activities and in translating the requirements to reality. There are five standards in the ISO 9000 series. The ISO 9000 standard provides some basic definitions and concepts and summarizes how to select and use the other standards in the series. The effectiveness of the good management resulting from adoption of ISO 9000 standards depends largely on the careful recording of all non-conformities and the action taken for corrective action.

The ISO 9001, 9002 and 9003 standards pertain to external quality assurance under contractual situations.

ISO 9001 ensures conformance to specified requirements during design and development, production, installation and servicing. ISO 9001 requires procedures for design control and vertification. It is worth noting that about 60% of failures have been attributed to errors in design, specification and planning. This document aims at preventing such failures.

ISO 9002 is used when conformance to specified requirements during production and installation is to be ensured.

ISO 9003 is used for quality assurance and conformance in final test and inspection.

ISO 9004 contains guidance on the technical, administrative and human factors affecting the quality of product and service. This standard is only for internal use and is not to be used in contractual situations.

The standard ISO 9000 lists the essential elements in some detail that make up a quality system starting with the responsibilities of management. Various sections are devoted to each aspect of the quality system: marketing, design, procurement, production, inspection, materials control, documentation, safety and use of statistical methods etc. This standard could be used to evaluate a company's progress towards a fully implemented quality system.

Careful understanding of the ISO-9000 series of Standards shows that it is prepared based on commonsense. It contains nothing that good management would not subscribe to in any event. The main impact of the standard is due to its assumption that 'quality is everybody's business'. An organisation cannot comply with ISO 9001/2/3/4 unless this fact is clearly understood and accepted at every level. This is the reason why adoption of the ISO-9000 series standards has resulted in a complete cultural turn-round in many organisations. The main thrust for implementation of the standard is to allow this turn-round to be as smooth and painless as possible.

It would be worth mentioning here that Bureau of Indian Standards has its standard series IS 14000 which is same as ISO 9000 series standards. The IS 14000, 14001, 14002 and 14003 standards are identical to ISO 9000, 9001, 9002 and 9003 respectively. The IS 14004 is even more comprehensive than ISO 9004.

15.7   CONCLUSION

The process of standardisation is dynamic and the Standards formulated by the committee are reviewed periodically to make them up-to-date and bring them in line with the latest technical developments. While reviewing them, comments are invited from the users of the Standards so as to ascertain any difficulty that might have been faced in implementing the Standards and to make the Standards widely acceptable and unambiguous.

General References

1. Warren J. McGonnagle, Nondestructive testing, Gorden and Breach, 1971.
2. Robert C. McMaster, Nondestructive testing, Vol. 2, 2nd ed., ASTM and ASM, 1982.
3. Robert C. McMaster, Nondestructive testing hand books, Ronald Press Company, 1991.
4. D.M. Lewis, Magnetic and electrical methods of nondestructive testing, George Allen & Unwin Ltd, 1950.
5. Don E. Bray et al, Nondestructive evaluation, a tool in design, manufacturing and service, McGraw-Hill Book Company, 1989.
6. Metals Hand Book, Vol. 11, Nondestructive testing and quality control, 8th ed., ASM, 1976.
7. Jack Blitz et al, Electromagnetic and visual methods of testing of materials, Butterworths, 1969.
8. H. L. Libby, Introduction to electromagnetic nondestructive test methods, Wiley Interscience, 1971.
9. Eddy current manual, Vol. 1, AECL-7523, Rev. 2, Atomic energy of Canada, 1983.
10. R. Halmshaw, Industrial radiology techniques, Wykenham Publishers, 1971.
11. Justin G. Schneeman, Industrial X-ray interpretation, Index Publishing Company, 1968.
12. Lawrence E. Bryant, Paul Mclintire, Radiology and radiation testing-nondestructive testing, 2nd ed, Vol. 3, 1985.
13. J. Szilard, Ultrasonic testing, Wiley Interscience, 1982.
14. M.G. Silk, Ultrasonic transducers for NDT, Adam Hilger Ltd., 1984.
15. Krautkrammer and Krautkramer, Ultrasonic testing, Narosa Publishing House, New Delhi, 1993.
16. Drouillard, T.F. et al, Monitoring structural integrity by acoustic emission, ASTM STP-571, ASTM, 1975.
17. Halmshaw, R., Nondestructive testing, 2nd ed., Edward Arnold, Division of Hodder and Sloughton, London, 1991.
18. Baldev Raj et al., An overview of nondestructive test applications of thermography, Jr. of Nondestructive evaluation, Vol. 10, No. 3, 1990.
19. P.J. Mudge, Practical aspects of NDT reliability in nondestructive testing, Vol. 2, Pergamon Press, England, 1988.
20. O. Forli and B. Pettersen, The unreliability of nondestructive testing, ibid.
21. B.J. Dikstra and A.T. McIntyre, Reliability aspects of automated ultrasonic inspection, ibid.
22. W.D. Dover and D.A. Topp, Assessment of the effectiveness of underwater NDE for fatigue cracks in offshore structures', ibid.
23. O. Forli, B. Pettersen, The performance of conventional ultrasonic and radiographic examination, Brit. Jr. of NDT, Vol. 27, No. 6, 1985.
24. G. Barrie Wetherill, Sampling inspection and quality control, 2nd ed., John Willey & Sons Inc., New York, 1977.
25. Irving W. Burr, Elementary statistical quality control, Vol. 25, Marcel-Dekker Inc., 1979.
26. A.V. Feigenbaum, Total quality control, 3rd ed., McGraw-Hill Book Company, 1983.
27. Harrison M. Wadsworth, Kenneth S, Stephens, A. Balnton Godfrey, Modern methods for quality control and improvement, John Willey & Sons, New York, 1986.

28. Santhi Swarup, and V.K. Jain, NDT standards an aid for inspection and quality assurance, Jr. of Nondestructive Evaluation, Vol. 10, No. 2, 1990.

29. B. Ram Prakash, ISO 9000 and NDE Vol. 2, Interline Publishing, Bangalore, 1993.

30. M.G. Silk, Ultrasonic transducers for nondestructive testing, Adam Hilger Ltd, Bristol, 1984.

31. Wiliam Lord, Electromagnetic methods of nondestructive testing, Gorden and Beach Science Publishers, London, 1985.

32. W.E. Gardner, Improving the effectiveness and reliability of nondestructive testing, 1st ed, Pergamon Press Ltd, Oxford, U.K., 1992.

33. Fong, J.T. et al, NDE Reliability through round robibn testing, The American Society of Mechanical Engineers, New York, 1986.

34. G.L. Fitzpatrick, Imaging Near Surface Flaws in Ferromagnetic Materials using Magneto-Optic Detectors, Review of Progress in Quantitative NDE, Eds. D.O. Thompson and D.E. Chimenti, Plenum Press, New York, 1985, Vol. 4B, pp. 807–818.

35. B. Wincheski, D.R. Prabhu, M. Namkung and E.A. Birt, Review of Progress in Quantitative NDE, Eds. D.O. Thompson and D.E. Chimenti, Plenum Press, New York, 1992, Vol. 11A, pp. 871–878.

36. S. Simms, MOI: Magneto-Optic/Eddy Current Imaging, Materials Evaluation, Vol. 51, No. 5, 1993, pp. 529–534.

37. J.C. Moulder, M.W. Kubovich, E. Uzal and J.H. Rose, Pulsed Eddy Current Measurements of Corrosion-Induced Metal Loss: Theory and Experiment, Review of Progress in Quantitative Nondestructive Evaluation, Vol. 14, eds. D.O. Thompson and D.E. Chimenti, Plenum Press, New York, 1995, pp. 2065–2072.

38. J.H.J. Stalenhoef, and J.A. de Raad J.A., MFL and PEC Tools for Plant Inspection, Insight, 42, Feb. 2000, pp. 74–77.

39. R. Hockey, D. Riechers, R. Ferris and R. Kelley, Passive Pulsed Eddy Current Inspection of Sheet Metal, Review of Progress in Quantitative Nondestructive Evaluation, Vol. 15, eds. D.O. Thompson and D.E. Chimenti, Plenum Press, New York, 1996, pp. 1099–1104.

40. D.M. Stevens and H.L. Whaley, Inspection for Corrosion Under Insulation, PD-Vol. 54, Non Destructive Evaluation, ed. D.E. Bray, ASME, 1993, pp. 43–47.

41. Gary W. Carriveau and R. Austin, Nondestructive Evaluation of Corrosion Through Insulation, Review of Progress in Quantitative NDE, Eds. D.O. Thompson and D.E. Chimenti, Plenum Press, New York, 1996, Vol. 15B, pp. 1741–1746.

42. A. Sophian, G.Y. Tian, D. Taylor and J. Rudlin, Electromagnetic and Eddy Current NDT: A Review, INSIGHT, Vol. 43, No. 5, May 2001, pp. 302–306.

43. Neutron Radiography Handbook Ed. P. Vander Hert and H. Rottger, D. Riedel Publishing Co., Holland, 1981.

44. Neutron Radiography — Principles and Applications, Ed. B. Venkatraman, Baldev Raj, K. Viswanathan, Neutron Radiography Working Group of India, 1999.

45. Practical Applications of Neutron Radiography and Gaging, ASTM STP 586, 1975.

46. W.D. Rummel and G.A. Matzkanin, Non Destructive Evaluation (NDE) Capabilities Data Book, NTLAC: DB - 97–02, Nondestructive Testing Information Analysis Center, Texas Research Institute Austin, Inc., November, 1997.

47. D.O. Thompson and T.A. Gray, The role of NDE in global strategies for materials synthesis and manufacturing, Material Research Society Symposium Proc., Vol. 142, 1989.

48. R.W. Nicholas and S. Crutzen, Impact of PISC results on Codes, Standards and regulatory activities, PISC Report No. 28, 1993, EUR 15104 EN.

49. Baldev Raj, C.V. Subramanian and T. Jayakumar, Non-destructive Testing of Welds, Narosa Publishing Hours, New Delhi, 2000.

50. N.R. Mandal, Aluminum Welding, Narosa Publishing House, New Delhi, 2002.

51. H.S. Khatak and Baldev Raj (Eds), Corrosion of Austenitic Steels—Mechanisms, Mitigation and Monitoring, Narosa Publishing House, New Delhi, 2002.

52. N. Parida, B. Ravikumar, Parvesh Kumar, D.K. Bhattacharya, T. Jayakumar, C.K. Mukhopadhyay, V. Moorthy, S. Devangan, Baldev Raj, D.C. Patel, S.P. Hariharan and A. Joseph, Acoustic

Emission Testing of LPG Horton Sphere, in Fourth National Workshop on Acoustic Emission (NAWACE-97), Aug. 22-23, 1997, BARC, Bombay, India.

53. P. Kalyanasundaram, T. Jayakumar, Baldev Raj, C.R.L. Murthy and A. Krishnan, Acoustic Emission Technique for Leak Detection in an End Shield of a PHWR, Nuclear Engg. & Design 116 (1989) 181 and J. Pressure Vessel and Piping 36 (1989) 65.

54. Non-Destructive Testing of Welds, Baldev Raj, C.V. Subramanian, T. Jayakumar, Narosa Publishing House, New Delhi.

55. Placid Thoughts, Total Quality Management, IGC Newsletter, Vol. 38, October 1998.

56. Thomas H. Berry, Managing the Total Quality Transformation, McGraw Hill, New York.

57. http://en.wikipedia.org/wiki/Total_Quality_Management

Index

The Rampant Lions Press

Catalogue of an exhibition at
The Fitzwilliam Museum · Cambridge
11 May - 27 June 1982

With a foreword by the Director
of the Fitzwilliam Museum
and an introduction by Brooke Crutchley

The Rampant Lions Press

A printing workshop through five decades

THE RAMPANT LIONS PRESS · CAMBRIDGE

Published by The Rampant Lions Press, 12 Chesterton Road, Cambridge CB4 3AB

© The Rampant Lions Press 1982

ISBN 0 905291 11 8 cased   ISBN 0 902591 12 6 paperback

Photographs: carvings by Edward Leigh; jackets and bindings by John Leigh
Designed and printed by Sebastian Carter at The Rampant Lions Press
on Vintage cartridge from M. W. Raggett
Set by The Stellar Press in Monotype Ehrhardt   Offset plates printed by The Stellar Press

Printed and made in Great Britain

Foreword

In establishing a policy for exhibitions in our Adeane Gallery we seek opportunities for those which can display the variety of local talent which has reached international distinction. It is fitting that, following the outstanding success of *Cockerell Bindings 1894-1980* last year, we should be able to show this year the achievements of the Rampant Lions Press, another example of father and son sharing the work, developing and extending it. Will and Sebastian Carter, in accepting our invitation, realised that we did not have an inadequate budget for exhibitions – we have no budget. So they have provided not only the material, almost all available from their stock, but also any special mounting required for the exhibits – as well as this catalogue which they, of course, have printed. Our visitors, with us, should be grateful to them for their efforts in aid of this celebration. It comes by chance in Will's seventieth year and just thirty-three years after he decided to make his part-time printing press a full-time business in the den of those Rampant Lions whose banner hangs over the exhibition. On their behalf as well as the Fitzwilliam's I thank the former Printer to the University, Mr Brooke Crutchley, for contributing the introduction proper to this catalogue. Mr Paul Woudhuysen has been responsible for coordinating within the Museum detailed arrangements for the exhibition itself.

Crutchley generosity includes also the loan to us of the family breadboard, carved by Will Carter. Lord Rothschild has lent his family tree. Olwyn Hughes has lent Rainbow Press books. The Royal Air Force Museum has lent a copy of *They fell in the battle*. Mr Colin Franklin has lent an Arabic inscription, another of Will Carter's carvings. We are gratefully indebted to each of these lenders.

The exhibition is assisted by a contribution from the Eastern Arts Association.

It is particularly gratifying that the carver has volunteered to demonstrate his skill, on two afternoons during the exhibition, across the landing from the Adeane Gallery in the Hamilton Kerr Room: 20 May and 17 June, 2.30-4.50 pm. There are further admirable examples of his most recent handicraft in the lettering of the boards at the doorways of the Gallery. These boards commemorate the splendid benefaction to the Museum of the former Patron of the Friends of the Fitzwilliam, the late Sir Robert Adeane. They were commissioned by Lady Adeane; and they make a most welcome and worthy memorial to the vital lead which Sir Robert gave to the fund for building the 1975 Extension, of which the Gallery named for him is the principal feature.

MICHAEL JAFFÉ

5

Introduction

'Fine printing' has two purposes: to satisfy the craftsman's aspirations and to please connoisseurs and collectors. But it has an incidental usefulness: to provide a standard by which those responsible for ordinary commercial printing can measure their own performance. The great private presses – Kelmscott, Doves, Ashendene, Eragny – were doing just that at the turn of the century, when some sort of guide-light was desperately needed.

Today printing is in a similar state of uncertainty, mainly but not wholly because of changes in technology which have not yet been worked out in typographical terms. In this predicament the mantle of Morris and his associates has fallen upon an equally small number of dedicated printers, prominent among them the Rampant Lions Press of Will and Sebastian Carter. Visitors to this exhibition of their work will be able to see how it has progressed from modest beginnings to an assured place on the typographical scene, its reputation now well established at home and overseas.

However, although the roles of Kelmscott and Rampant Lions might be similar, there could hardly be a greater difference than exists in the appearance of their books. Morris made do with only three types, two of these being different sizes of the same semi-gothic design; despite the floriated initials for paragraphs and occasional engraved borders and headings in red, there is a solid sameness about his books, magnificent but impenetrable. By contrast, Rampant Lions books are often imposing but never to the detriment of lucidity. Types are chosen to suit each particular text and arranged to assist the message to the full. Thus honour is done to the author and respect paid to the reader. The printer, having done his job, retreats into the background.

Will Carter's interest in printing was aroused when he visited the Oxford University Press at the age of twelve and was given a packet of type to play with. On leaving school he spent two years with Unwin Brothers, the book-printers of Woking, followed by a period with the Shenval Press of Hertford and London, then managed by one of the most imaginative printers of the time, James Shand. In 1934 he arrived in Cambridge to take up a post in Heffers' printing works and in Cambridge he has remained, apart from wartime service in the Royal Navy and various sojourns abroad; these have included spells in the Frankfurt workshop of Paul Koch, son of Rudolf, in 1938 and as resident artist at Dartmouth College, New Hampshire, in 1969.

While still with Heffers he operated a small print-shop in rooms in Jordan's Yard off Bridge Street, where he produced on a flat-bed Adana press miscellaneous items such as noteheads and visiting cards for himself and customer friends. Before long, to this equipment was added a Crown Albion hand-press and later an Adana platen. Along with these

went the occasional pamphlet and hard-bound book, including those standbys of the private press – *The Song of Solomon* (5), *Ecclesiastes* (8) and Elizabeth Barrett Browning's *Sonnets from the Portuguese* (7). There are features of these early productions which were to be characteristic of all Rampant Lions work – a general acceptance of the classical tradition of typography as currently practised by Bruce Rogers, Francis Meynell and their peers but (as with them) realised in a personal way. The most obvious manifestations of their individual styles are in the treatment of title-pages and headings, and in the choice of pattern papers for covers. Many of the papers used by the Carters for this purpose and for the endpapers of books are printed from their own designs.

In 1939 Will Carter married and moved into the house in Chesterton Road which he occupies today. The semi-basement, looking across a lawn to the river Cam, suited him well as a workshop and there he continued with the practice of his craft, or rather crafts, his delight in letterforms having led him to try cutting in wood and later in stone and slate. In these fields, and in the practice of calligraphy, he was to become no less skilful and reputable than in his first love and drawn lettering is used to good effect on the title pages of many Rampant Lions books.

The Press's equipment at that time, besides type and compositor's tools, consisted of the Adana press from Jordan's Yard, an old Bremner platen purchased from Heffers and a Thompson cutter, still in use. Later a small lithographic machine (Rotaprint) was added, subsequently replaced by a larger model, and an automatic Victoria platen with a bed size of 31 × 45cm. A Vandercook proofing press and a Monopol crown platen, similar to the Victoria in operation, eventually completed the plant.

Working at Heffers, Carter missed the challenge and satisfaction of total responsibility for design and execution, such as he was able to enjoy in his own workshop. By 1949 he had decided that these things were all-important and courageously, with his wife Barbara's whole-hearted support (they had by then two children and a third was to follow shortly), he resigned from Heffers and set up on his own.

Necessarily, for the next few years most time and effort had to be applied to jobbing work, with its quick financial return. All items were designed by the printer himself, set mostly in Bembo and Walbaum types, with occasional use of ornaments and coloured inks, everything well spaced out and impeccably printed. The good taste and consistent quality of his output won the admiration of Beatrice Warde, the Monotype Corporation's publicity manager, who dedicated a whole issue of the *Monotype Recorder* to him in 1954. At the same time he was carrying out occasional commissions for the designing of work printed elsewhere, including the Festival of Britain guides.

By 1960 the business was well enough established, and the cash position sufficiently sound, to allow greater concentration on the printing of books, and an association was started with Douglas Cleverdon which led to the publication of a number of volumes under the imprint of Clover Hill Editions or Chilmark. All of them are interesting, both for content and typographic style, but outstanding is *The Story of Cupid and Psyche* in two volumes; the fascinating story of the unearthing of forty-four blocks, cut by William Morris from drawings by Burne-Jones for a book the two men planned but never brought to birth, is told in the catalogue entry (62).

In 1966 Will Carter was joined by his son Sebastian who, after reading English and Fine

Arts at Cambridge, had been employed designing for John Murray, Ruari McLean Associates and the Stellar Press, and had spent two years with the Trianon Press in Paris. He brought to the partnership new ideas, and skills comparable with his father's; in fact, father will admit that son is more expert in setting type, though he claims for himself a marginal superiority in presswork. Though sharing a room, they very rarely cooperate on any particular book; usually each works on his own, designing, composing and printing the copies. Most of their books are produced to the order of a publisher or private client; a few are their own conceptions from the start and they believe the proportion is likely to grow.

Although books have now become the major preoccupation, the Carters continue to carry out jobbing commissions, many of them for University departments or colleges. Undoubtedly, this experience influences the design of their books in a healthy way. An exhibition notice or a concert programme must be composed for instant recognition and intake. There is no room, nor time, for extravagances. Ornaments, if any, must serve to point the message; colour can be used for the same purpose, its strength precisely adjusted. Both in jobbing and bookwork the Carters tend to mix the makers' inks to get the exact hue, and the overall effect, that they want. A recurring feature is the use of grey inks, varying in tone, in title pages and headings, by way of variation from the starkness of black.

The number of copies they print of any book is seldom more than five hundred, a fact arising from the nature and potential market of the books that come their way rather than from deliberate choice. Robert Gibbings, who owned the Golden Cockerel Press between the wars, used to say that after about seven hundred copies he felt his attention flagging, but the Carters have not found this difficulty on the rare occasions when they have had larger numbers to print. A large proportion of their books are poetry, a 'natural' for a press of their kind, where each poem or page can be adjusted by eye, rather than mechanically following a standard placement which ignores variations in line length. Several books of poetry have resulted from an association set up in 1971 with the Rainbow Press of Ted Hughes and his sister Olwyn (see page 40).

Another difference between Kelmscott and Rampant Lions which stands out is in the use or non-use of italics. Neither Kelmscott nor any of the other private presses of its day possessed any italics. The lack was not important for the kind of text they printed and italics were not used by the early Italian printers whom they sought to follow. The Carters, on the other hand, make frequent use of italics in headings and sidenotes and occasionally for a complete book of poetry. Particularly graceful, and rarely seen, are the 'cancelleresca bastarda' of Jan van Krimpen used in *Sonnets from the Portuguese* (7) and Frederic Warde's version of the Vicenza italic of Arrighi used in *The elegies of a glass Adonis* (32). Another fine italic face, Palatino, is used in a number of books, including the Clover Hill *Sixe idyllia* with Anthony Gross's etchings, one of the Press's most notable productions (45).

Gross is one of several contemporary artists whose work figures in Rampant Lions books, either by way of illustration of the text or in some cases as the actual *raison d'etre* of the book with text subordinate, as in George Mackley's wood engravings (29 and 33), Michael Rothenstein's wood-prints (see page 44) and Douglas Cleverdon's 'survey' of the engravings of David Jones (87). Sometimes the printing is from original engravings in wood or copper or from other types of intaglio plate; otherwise reproductive processes are used such as line block, collotype and photolithography. Designing the text page to

9

live with, and up to, an artist's pictures is always a challenging problem, never more successfully solved than in Gross's *Very rich hours of Le Boulvé* (83).

Although many of the smaller books and pamphlets produced by the Press command our admiration, it is in the larger volumes that it seems to come to its greatest fulfilment. John Piper's *India love poems* (68), Lubbock's *Light and the mind's eye* (58) and Christopher Fry's *Root and sky* (63), with its splendid long-tailed 'y' on the title-page, as arresting as the long 'I' on the first page of the Doves Bible – all these rank with the most handsome products of the printing press in this century. *The story of Cupid and Psyche*, already mentioned (62), is another work of prime importance; although its design was in a sense prescribed, its execution is faultless and the link with Kelmscott particularly happy – the tribute of a leading small press of today to the most influential of its forerunners.

BROOKE CRUTCHLEY

The catalogue

Note

This catalogue gives details of a selection of books printed at the Rampant Lions Press by Will and Sebastian Carter, either for publication by the Press, or by some other publisher, or for private distribution by a customer. A complete checklist of books appears on p.93.

The order of the catalogue follows that of the checklist, and arranges books alphabetically under each year. Although we can give a chronological order for recent books, we cannot do so precisely for the earlier ones; and while this system leads to a few anomalies (e.g. *The deluge* precedes *The psalms*, although the second book we printed in the Golden Cockerel type), we think it better to adhere to it throughout.

Dimensions are in centimetres, height before width. Since many books are untrimmed, the sizes are rounded to the nearest half-centimetre.

Usually the two partners of the Press design and print their books independently, though each may call on the other for hand-composition and other manual labour. In the catalogue, the designer-printer is indicated after the dimensions by *W.* for Will Carter and *S.* for Sebastian Carter. In a few books, both were fully involved, and this is indicated as *W&S*.

The catalogue was compiled and annotated by Sebastian Carter, with additional notes by Will Carter.

Synopsis: **1-89**: *books* **90**: *jobbing printing* **91**: *book design* **92**: *calligraphy* **93**: *type design* **94**: *letter cutting*.

The Rampant Lions Press

In September 1924, shortly before his twelfth birthday, Will Carter was taken on a visit to the University Press at Oxford, and was allowed to print a visiting card for himself, using pica Fell type. He clearly showed such interest that a few days later John Johnson (who was appointed University Printer the following year and started the great collection of printed ephemera which bears his name) sent him a packet of type and hoped in the covering letter that it would make the basis of 'an amusing and useful hobby'.

It did. Augmented by a gift of an Adana flatbed press, and with the encouragement of Will's elder brother John (later to be, among many other things, exposer of the Wise forgeries and author of many bibliographical works including his *ABC for book collectors*) and of his cousin, the wood-engraver Reynolds Stone, the Rampant Lions Press began production. It took its name around 1930, from the Carter coat of arms; printed its first book in 1934 (1); but until 1949 remained a spare-time hobby while Will gained useful experience with various printing firms (Unwins of Woking, Shenval of Hertford, and Heffers at Cambridge, with a break for war service in the navy) as trainee, then order-clerk, then designer.

The Press was based at two family houses, at Little Faringdon near Oxford, and Chalvey Park in Windsor; then at Cambridge, first in Jordan's Yard off Bridge Street, and finally, in 1939, in its present home in Chesterton Road.

Rampant Lions Press device engraved by Reynolds Stone

1

A PREFACE

Being that written by John Baskerville for his 1758 edition of Milton's *Paradise lost*. Rampant Lions Press, 1934.

50 copies on hand-made paper.   12.5×9 cm.   *W*.
Hand-set in 12pt Centaur.
Pamphlet-sewn at the Press.

¶ This was printed on one of the very early Adana presses, an 8vo flat-bed, and the paper was damped. A copy was found in the library of the great American type-designer Frederick W. Goudy, which contained a note from the printer saying, 'This was printed on a little wooden press 8″×5″ and was the first effort of more than one page. The pathetic part about it was that I took the text from Updike and, beyond noticing a certain abruptness in the ending, didn't realise that it wasn't complete.'

The object of damping is to soften the hard fibres of rag papers and make a clean impression on them easier; at the same time it reduces wear on the type. The labour involved in damping large quantities of paper, though in our opinion amply repaid by the better results, discourages many hand-printers; but we have developed over the years a method which greatly reduces it. We divide the pile of paper into swatches of about twenty-five sheets (more or less depending on the thickness of the paper), and interleave each swatch with a damp blanket, wrung out to a degree one soon learns to recognise. We use ordinary bed blankets, and have found that man-made fibres disintegrate less quickly than wool. We wrap the pile of paper and blankets in polythene, and leave it. We do not favour weighting the pile, since paper expands considerably when damp, and it is not a good idea to hinder its movement. After a day, we remove the blankets, rearranging the swatches to help the degree of dampness to even out, and keep the pile wrapped. After another day, the paper is ready for printing. After printing we hang the sheets in racks to dry, and then flatten them out under a weight.

2

A SPANISH TRIPTYCH

Being three poems of compassion by Robert Nichols. Rampant Lions Press, 1936.

116 copies on Millbourn hand-made paper.   24×15 cm.   *W*.
Hand-set in 18pt Centaur italic.
Sewn square-back with printed paper covers. About 12 copies bound in hard-covers for the author, but the details not in the colophon.

3

A PRAYER

Rampant Lions Press, mcmxxxvij.

No record of number printed. 8 pages on various hand-made papers, rubricated by Will Carter.   15 × 12 cm.   *W*.
Hand-set in 24pt Goudy Text.
Pamphlet-sewn at the Press, with the title hand-written on the cover.

4

MEMORANDOMS BY JAMES MARTIN

Edited by Charles Blount. Rampant Lions Press [1937].

150 copies on Howard Smith grey antique wove.   16 × 12 cm.   *W*.
Machine-set in 12pt Caslon. Illustrated with 19th-century chap-book wood-engravings, printed from the wood.
Bound by Heffers in buckram, with a fold-out map, printed by offset, inside the back cover.

¶ James Martin was an English convict who was deported to Australia in 1787, escaped, and after many adventures was recaptured and returned to England. His account of his ordeal, from a manuscript in the Bentham papers at the Library of University College London, was here printed for the first time.

The chap-book blocks, which had been unearthed by Reynolds Stone while working in Taunton with the printers Barnicott and Pearce, turned out to be remarkably apt for the book, and Stone kindly agreed to lend them.

Block from *Memorandoms by James Martin* (4)

16

Lino-cut by Harry Hicken (reduced) from *The song of Solomon* (5)

5

THE SONG OF SOLOMON

According to the Authorised Version, illustrated with lino-cuts by Harry Hicken, and rubrication by Will Carter. Rampant Lions Press, mcmxxxvii.

125 copies on Arches mould-made paper.   33×25 cm.   *W.*
Hand-set in 24pt Goudy Text.
Bound by Heffers in quarter canvas, plain paper sides. Some copies bound in half leather, with buckram sides.

❡ This bears strong signs of the influence of the Koch school at Offenbach. Unfortunately the best of the 'gotisch' types from Monotype were cast on continental type-height, and the Press was not up to this sort of complication at that time.

6

CLERIHEWS

An unofficial supplement to *Biography for beginners* [edited by John Carter]. Rampant Lions Press, 1938.

An unlimited edition, on various colours of Abbey Mill antique laid papers.
12×18.5 cm.   *W.*
Hand-set in 24pt Walbaum.
Sewn square-back with printed paper covers.

❡ An enlarged edition was issued in 1946, printed on pale yellow paper.

17

7

SONNETS FROM THE PORTUGUESE
Elizabeth Barrett Browning. Rampant Lions Press [1939].

145 copies on antique wove paper; plus 50 copies on various colours of T. H. Saunders hand-made paper for Charles Scribner's Sons, New York; plus 5 copies on vellum. 14.5 × 11 cm. *W.*
Hand-set in 16pt Cancelleresca Bastarda.
Bound by Heffers in quarter cloth with Cockerell marbled paper sides. The vellum copies bound by John P. Gray in full leather.

8

ECCLESIASTES
Reprinted from the Authorised Version. Rampant Lions Press, Cambridge, MCMXLI.

150 copies on Basingwerk Parchment. 28 × 19 cm. *W.*
Hand-set in 16pt Bembo, with red initials engraved on wood by Reynolds Stone.
Pamphlet-sewn at the Press, with stiff wrappers and cut-out paper label.

¶ John Dreyfus, at that time an undergraduate at Trinity College, helped most generously with the type-setting during evening sessions, and thus begun a long friendship. He later went on to succeed Stanley Morison as typographical advisor to the Monotype Corporation and to be Assistant Printer at the Cambridge University Press, to advise the Curwen and Yale University Presses, and to write excellent books on the Nonesuch Press, Jan van Krimpen, and many other typographical subjects. It was at a party at his house in 1948 that Will Carter finally made his decision to make the Rampant Lions Press a full-time business.

9

THE LAST CHAPTER OF *URNE BURIALL*
Sir Thomas Browne [edited by John Carter. Rampant Lions Press, 1946].

175 copies on grey Basingwerk Parchment. 20.5 × 12.5 cm. *W.*
Hand-set in 14pt Walbaum.
Pamphlet-sewn at the Press in printed paper wrappers. These and the title-page designed by John Piper.

Drawing by John Piper from *Urne buriall* (9)

10

EMBLEMS OF EXPERIENCE
Siegfried Sassoon. Cambridge, The Rampant Lions Press, 1951.

75 copies on Basingwerk Parchment, of which 10 with initials hand-written by
Kenneth Breese.   25.5 × 16.5 cm.   *W*.
Hand-set in 16pt Bembo italic.
Sewn square-back with printed paper wrappers.
Printed for Siegfried Sassoon and Geoffrey Keynes, November 1951.

❡ This was the first book printed at the Press after it became a full-time business at the beginning of 1949. For the first years, almost all of its time was spent in keeping the wolf from the door by jobbing printing (see 90), but commissions such as this from early supporters like Geoffrey Keynes were very welcome.

II

LUCRETILIS
William Cory [edited with an introduction by John Sparrow]. Rampant Lions Press [1951].

175 copies on toned Basingwerk Parchment. 27.5 × 19 cm. *W.*
Hand-set in 18pt Walbaum italic. Title-page lettering by Will Carter.
Bound by Heffers in quarter cloth with Cockerell marbled paper sides and printed paper spine label.

¶ William Johnson Cory, author of 'The Eton boating song' and 'Heraclitus', was an Eton master and a great great uncle of the printer. *Lucretilis* consists of Latin verses written for teaching purposes, but they were described by H. A. J. Munro as 'the best and most Horatian Sapphics and Alcaics that have been written since Horace ceased to write'. (See also **23**.)

12

ITALIC HANDWRITING
Some examples of everyday cursive hands, selected by Wilfrid Blunt and Will Carter, introduced by Joseph Compton. Newman Neame [1954].

An unlimited edition (there were 3 impressions) on Chariot cartridge. 22 × 28 cm. *W.*
The introductory matter machine-set in 12pt Bembo. Title-page calligraphy by Will Carter.
The plates printed by offset lithography at the Press.
'Perfect'-bound at the Press, in printed covers reproducing the title-page.

¶ Our offset machine, a Rotaprint R40, was bought for long runs of stationery (it has now been replaced by a newer model, the TTR), and was not big enough to print more than one page at a time. The pages had therefore to be bound singly with an adhesive back, the so-called 'perfect' binding which unfortunately does not last.

This was one of the first books in this selection to be set by machine. All our machine-setting is done on Monotype machines to our specification by different suppliers. Monotype type designs are generally the best, thanks to the labours of Stanley Morison and his colleagues, and the system of composition, being of separate letters, allows us to correct and adjust to our hearts' content. Slug, or whole-line, composition, such as the Linotype system, would be useless for this reason.

The decision whether to hand-set a book or have it machine-set depends on many things. Some typefaces, especially the rarities like Kelmscott Troy, Golden Cockerel roman or Warde's Arrighi, but also Palatino, are not available on the Monotype, and large sizes cannot be set on a composition machine; but long texts in small sizes clearly call for the Monotype keyboard.

20

13

SEVEN POEMS IN PATTERN
John Farrow. Rampant Lions Press [1955].

250 copies printed on Millbourn hand-made paper.   25.5 × 16 cm.   *W.*
Hand-set in 16pt Lutetia italic.
Bound by Mansell in quarter cloth with Cockerell marbled paper sides.

14

THE SONG OF DEBORAH AND BARAK
Taken from the fifth chapter of The Book of Judges, with a Latin verse translation by
H. A. J. Munro. Rampant Lions Press [1956].

150 copies on Abbey Mill antique laid.   21.5 × 14 cm.   *S.*
Hand-set in 14pt Bembo. An offset frontispiece from a steel engraving after a painting by
James Northcote, tipped in.
Pamphlet-sewn at the Press, in green Bohemia wrappers, with a label.

§ This was the third book printed by Sebastian Carter, then aged fifteen, though the first
to appear in this selection. After this, he printed a series of pamphlets when not at school
or, later, university (see 17, 18, 19, 22, 26), and also helped his father with larger books
such as *The ancient mariner* (24). After spells with John Murray, the Trianon Press in
Paris, Ruari McLean and The Stellar Press, he joined the Press full-time in 1966.

15

THE FIRST TEN
Some ground covered at the Rampant Lions Press by Will Carter, 1949-58 [1959].

About 500 copies on Basingwerk Parchment and assorted Abbey Mill papers.
27.5 × 17.5 cm.   *W.*
Machine-set in 14pt Bembo.
'Perfect'-bound at the Press, in printed covers.

§ This production celebrated the first ten years of the Rampant Lions Press in business,
and it was illustrated with a flurry of examples of work done. It was initially distributed
gratis to valued customers and cognoscenti, but a sudden awareness of its interest persuaded

Frontispiece by Lynton Lamb from *A song to David* (16)

us also to offer copies for sale. It immediately took off and was soon out of print, and confirmed our conviction that there was a market for this kind of collection of ephemera (see 31, 59 and 89).

16

A SONG TO DAVID

Christopher Smart, edited by J. B. Broadbent, Fellow of King's College, Cambridge. Rampant Lions Press, distributed by The Bodley Head [1960].

600 copies on Abbey Mill antique laid.   30.5 × 19.5 cm.   *W.*
Hand-set in 18pt Walbaum. Frontispiece drawn by Lynton Lamb.
Bound by Mansell in quarter imitation vellum with Curwen patterned paper sides. Jacket.

17

KUBLA KHAN

Samuel Taylor Coleridge, Rampant Lions Press, MCMLXI.

4 (+1) copies on light blue Millbourn hand-made paper.   30 × 21.5 cm.   *S.*
Hand-set in 22pt Caslon.
Bound by Vere Stoakley in full dark blue buckram, with a paper label.

¶ The copies were divided among the printer, and two undergraduate friends; one copy was sold to defray expenses; and one ad personam copy was presented to Will Carter. The edition was dedicated 'to the person on business from Porlock, without whom this poem would have been much longer'.

18

LOBSTERS

Alexis Lykiard. [Published by] Sebastian Carter, mcmlxi.

About 100 copies on different papers.   18 × 11 cm.   *S.*
Hand-set in 16pt Fairbank italic, with display in 12pt Egyptian expanded.
Offset frontispiece of a photograph of Alexis Lykiard by Christopher Angeloglou.
'Perfect'-bound at the Press in printed wrappers designed by Rackstraw Downes.

19

THE PEN OF MY AUNT

Written by Glyn Daniel, and published by him at The Merry Boys, St John's Street, Cambridge, 1961.

180 copies on Abbey Mill antique laid.   18 × 12 cm.   *S.*
Machine-set in 12pt Bell.
Pamphlet-sewn at the Press in wrappers made at the Twelve by Eight Mill.

¶ This was the first of two pamphlets (see also 26) printed for Glyn Daniel, the archaeologist, editor of *Antiquity* and of the 'Ancient peoples and places' series, quondam questionmaster of 'Animal, vegetable, mineral' and later to be Disney Professor of Archaeology at Cambridge. It records some of the extraordinary versions of English taught in foreign phrase-books, in particular that of Pedro Carolino, the coiner of 'English as she is spoke'.

20

DOUBLE CROWN CLUB

Roll of members, list of dinners, and rules, 1962.

150 copies printed on Basingwerk Parchment.   21.5 × 12 cm.   *W.*
Machine-set in 11pt Bembo.
Sewn square-back, with blind-printed paper wrappers.

¶ The Double Crown Club is a printers' dining club which began meeting in London in 1924 and has included among its members most of the foremost living typographers and illustrators in Britain and, through its honorary membership, in Europe and the USA. To print for the Club is both an honour and an ordeal, since the clientèle is forbiddingly discriminating and our predecessors, in the case of the *Roll of members*, included virtually every printing house of distinction in the country.

21

TACT IN TYPOGRAPHICAL DESIGN

Stanley Morison. A type specimen [1962].

600 copies printed on Basingwerk Parchment; plus 100 advance copies specially printed for the 165th meeting of the Double Crown Club, held at Magdalene College, Cambridge, on the 22nd June 1962.   21.5 × 14 cm.   *W.*
Machine-set in 14pt Octavian.
Pamphlet-sewn at the Press, in printed paper covers.

¶ This was printed for the Monotype Corporation and was the first official showing of Octavian, Series 603, designed by Will Carter and David Kindersley (see 93). The type was machine-set by the Cambridge University Press who were renowned for their close word spacing. In spite of this we put the whole job through the stick and reduced the spacing throughout. It showed, as subsequent use has confirmed, that it is hard to set this type too close.

   An interesting difference of opinion occurred between Morison and the printer, who was firm that the type was designed to be leaded, whereas Morison declared that a type specimen should show the type straight from the womb: that is to say, set solid. Compromise was reached: the Note was set solid, but the text was leaded 2pts.

22

THE THRISSIL, THE ROIS AND THE FLOUR-DE-LYS
A sample-book of state poems and love-songs showing affinities between Scotland, England and France in the sixteenth and seventeenth centuries, edited with a commentary by Helena Mennie Shire. The Ninth of May, M.CM.LXII.

150 copies on Glastonbury antique laid.   24.5 × 15.5 cm.   *S.*
Machine-set in 12pt Times.
Pamphlet-sewn at the Press in dark blue Bohemia paper covers, printed, with a strip-wrapper printed in red with a description of the contents and the price.

¶ The Ninth of May (so named after the traditional feast-day of medieval Scotland, the Translation of the bones of St Andrew) was an imprint edited and published by Mrs Shire and devoted to the printing of texts, many for the first time, to throw light on early Scottish literature. The two titles before this were *Poems from Panmure House*, 1960, and *Poems and songs of Sir Robert Ayton*, 1961; and a late addition to the series was *King Orphius and Sir Colling*, 1973.

23

CORY'S *LUCRETILIS*
F. J. Lelièvre. Rampant Lions Press, Cambridge [1964].

300 copies on antique wove   24.5 × 14.5 cm.   *W.*
Machine-set in 11pt Walbaum.
Pamphlet-sewn at the Press in printed terra cotta covers.

¶ See 11.

Clover Hill Editions

Up to the early 1960s, such books as were fitted in between ephemeral jobs were modest in scale and content. But around 1963 the Press was approached by Douglas Cleverdon and asked to print a new edition of Coleridge's *Rime of the ancient mariner*, which would be illustrated by reprinting ten copper engravings made for him by David Jones in 1928. Although Cleverdon is best known as a radio producer, and especially for the first performance of *Under Milk Wood*, his first occupation was as a bookseller and publisher in Bristol. While there, he became friendly with Eric Gill (the first public appearance of the letterform known, when later cut as a typeface, as Gill Sans was on a sign which Gill painted outside his bookshop). Through Gill he met David Jones, who was working with Gill at Capel-y-ffin, and asked him to illustrate *The ancient mariner*, which appeared in 1929 with typography by Stanley Morison. Unfortunately, its publication was followed by the Depression, which badly affected the market for fine printing, and the last seventy copies of the book were remaindered at Blackwell's for 7s.6d.

The plates, however, survived the bomb which destroyed Cleverdon's bookshop in 1940, and, with the encouragement and backing of Louis Cowan, a fellow enthusiast of Jones' work whose Chilmark Press published *In parenthesis* and *The anathemata* in the United States, Cleverdon decided to reissue them, and asked us to print the letterpress. This was the first of many fruitful and stimulating collaborations between Douglas Cleverdon and ourselves.

He first used the Clover Hill imprint in 1938, for the first, and last, piece of printing he undertook himself, the unfinished *Bamboo dancer*. His name is derived from Clyfyr-dun, an Anglo-Saxon place-name in Devon which means Clover Hill, and this was the name he revived when, some years before his retirement from the BBC, he again took up his publishing activities. The Clover Hill Editions are editorially, with the exceptions noted below, his personal pieces of bookmaking, whatever the publishing arrangements accompanying their financing and distribution. (The first six books all appeared under the Chilmark Press imprint although we and Cleverdon became increasingly involved financially in the publishing; then Louis Cowan withdrew, feeling that he could not effectively distribute this kind of book in the United States, and shortly afterwards he and his wife were tragically killed in a fire at their New York apartment. After *Cupid and Psyche*, we left the partnership to be able to concentrate on our own projects, but agreed to go on printing the Clover Hill books for Cleverdon.) The exceptions are *The elegies of a glass Adonis* and *Shades*, for which the impetus came from Cowan, and *The mountains* and *Cupid and Psyche*, where we and Cleverdon were closely involved in the projects from the outset.

All the Clover Hill books are described in their due place, but for the record they are listed here, with the catalogue numbers in parentheses.

1. *The rime of the ancient mariner*, 1964 (24).
2. *The elegies of a glass Adonis*, 1967 (32).
3. *The mountains*, 1968 (34).

4. *Shades*, 1970 (40).
5. *Lessons of the war*, 1970 (38).
6. *Sixe idyllia of Theocritus*, 1971 (45).
7. *An introduction to The rime of the ancient mariner*, 1972 (46).
8. *The story of Cupid and Psyche*, 1974 (62).
9. *The Chester play of the deluge*, 1977 (70).
10. [*The innocent diversion*]
11. *The book of Jonah*, 1979 (79).
12. *The engravings of David Jones: a survey*, 1981 (87).

Number 10 is an odd-man-out, being printed by Skelton's Press, as an unlimited edition. Numbers 1-6 were published with the Chilmark Press of New York; 7-8 jointly by Douglas Cleverdon and the Rampant Lions Press; and 9-12 by Douglas Cleverdon on his own.

Clover Hill device engraved by Eric Gill for Douglas Cleverdon

24

THE RIME OF THE ANCIENT MARINER

Samuel Taylor Coleridge, with ten engravings on copper and with a foreword by David Jones. Chilmark Press, New York City, 1964.

200 copies on specially made grey Barcham Green hand-made paper; plus 115 copies signed by David Jones with an extra set of the engravings on RWS paper (including 5 discarded engravings).   31 × 25 cm.   *W&S.*
Machine-set in 16pt Bembo, with shoulder-notes in 12pt Bembo italic. The plates printed by Thomas Ross.
Bound by Mansell; the ordinary edition in full green cloth; the special edition in quarter vellum with cloth boards and the extra prints in a separate wallet; both editions in a specially marbled slipcase.

¶ The first of the Clover Hill Editions. We followed the pagination of the 1929 edition, so that the engravings would fall in the same relationship to the text. As before, the plates

were printed leaving a thin film of ink over the plate area, partly (in Jones' words) as an aid to the unification of these essentially linear designs.

David Jones agreed to contribute an introduction to this new edition, describing his approach to illustrating the poem. But as he wrote his interest increased, and his foreword outgrew the space available, reaching about 16,000 words. Luckily, the opening section, which dealt specifically with the engravings, could be used as a foreword on its own, and this was done. The full text was to be published on its own later, as a companion volume, but it was delayed by a footnote which threatened to outgrow its parent. The *Introduction* was finally published, without the footnote, in 1972 (46).

25

SARAH

By her friends and for them. Privately printed, 1965.

300 copies on T. H. Saunders mould-made paper.   25 × 19 cm.   *W.*
Machine-set in 14pt Centaur. Seven photographs (five by Cecil Beaton) printed by the Cotswold Collotype Company.
Bound in quarter leather with specially made Cockerell marbled paper sides. Some copies bound in full morocco, with marbled end-papers.

26

OXFORD CHICKEN PIE

Glyn Daniel, published by the author at The Merry Boys, St John's Street, Cambridge, 1965.

200 copies on suede Basingwerk Parchment.   18.5 × 12 cm.   *S.*
Machine-set in 11pt Modern No.7.
Pamphlet-sewn at the Press in pink Swedish Ingres wrappers.

¶ This was the second booklet printed for Glyn Daniel (see 19), and was a birthday present for his wife Ruth. Glyn Daniel is a bon viveur of some note: the editorials of *Antiquity* are full of passing references to the good things of life, and he is the author of the indispensable guide, *The hungry archaeologist in France*, Faber, 1963. This book assembled as many recipes as he could find directly associated with Oxford or Cambridge, and included a learned discussion of the origins of *crème brulée*.

27

THE FATIGUE
David Jones, Anno Xti MCMLXV.

298 copies on Basingwerk Parchment.   22×14 cm.   *W&S.*
Machine-set in 12pt Joanna.
Sewn square-backed with Fabriano Roma hand-made paper wrappers and printed label
on the front.

¶ This was a seventieth birthday tribute to the author, subscribed by friends and well-wishers, under the patronage of W. H. Auden, Kenneth Clark, Igor Stravinsky and Helen Sutherland. The editorial work was undertaken by Douglas Cleverdon. The number printed was limited to those who subscribed before a closing date, their names being printed in the opening pages, plus fifty copies for David Jones himself.

28

THE PAPER MAKERS CRAFT
Verse by Oliver Bayldon, illustrations by Rigby Graham. Twelve by Eight Press, Leicester, 1965.

Something under 400 copies on various papers from Millbourn, Wookey Hole, Hayle Mill and the Twelve by Eight Mill.   30×19.5 cm.   *W.*
Machine-set in 16pt Bembo. Seven leaves of line block illustrations by Rigby Graham.
Bound in limp imitation vellum.

29

WEEDS AND WILD FLOWERS
Some irreverent words by Armida Maria-Theresa Colt, with wood-engravings by George Mackley. The Two-Horse Press, London [1965].

250 copies on Hollingworth Original Turkey Mill mould-made paper.   30×23 cm.   *W.*
Machine-set in 16pt Centaur italic.
Bound in quarter cloth with Japanese paper sides.
There was a separate portfolio containing a set of the engravings printed on Japanese Hosho paper.

¶ This was the first time we had encountered George Mackley's work, and his highly skilled engraving made the blocks most rewarding to print. (Scratchy work on the wood, with blunt tools, can make the printing a most unsatisfying and frustrating business.)

⸿ Two of the special typefaces held at The Rampant Lions Press

---

Hunt roman

Hermann Zapf's Hunt roman was designed in 1961 for the Hunt Botanical Library in Pittsburgh. The Library generously permitted the Press to have some cast at the Stempel foundry for its own use. Hunt roman is used as a display face throughout this catalogue, its first use by the Press in a book. The sizes held are 24pt, 18pt, and 14pt, shown here.

ARRIGHI

The history of Frederic Warde's Arrighi is outlined in the note on number 32 on the facing page. Of the two versions, this is the Vicenza; the Vicentino has swash ascenders, like this. There are variants g & g and ligatures ll, sp, ct & st.

30

HENRY JAMES IN CAMBRIDGE
Geoffrey Keynes. Cambridge, W. Heffer & Sons Ltd [1967].

1,000 copies on Abbey Mill antique laid.   24.5 × 15.5 cm.   *W&S*.
Machine-set in 12pt Ehrhardt. Plate printed by the Cotswold Collotype Company.
Bound in printed paper boards, with jacket.

31

PORTFOLIO ONE
Specimen sheets of printing, type-design and letter-cutting carried out by Will Carter
at the Rampant Lions Press workshop between 1959 and 1967.

500 copies on various papers.   28 × 21.5 cm.   *W*.
Mostly hand-set in various types. Photographs printed by The Stellar Press.
Single sheets collated into a rust-red card portfolio made at the Press.

¶ This was a follow-up to *The first ten* (**15**) and we adopted a simpler format of single
sheets for ease of handling and arrangement. The foreword pointed out that the time
covered was less than ten years, but its completion coincided with the occasion of Sebastian
Carter's joining the firm full-time, and it seemed appropriate to complete this production
with one pair of hands before continuing with two.

See also **59** and **89**.

32

THE ELEGIES OF A GLASS ADONIS
C. A. Trypanis, with a typographical note by Will Carter. Chilmark Press, New York
[1967].

450 copies on Saunders mould-made paper, signed by C. A. Trypanis.   28 × 20 cm.   *W*.
Hand-set in 18pt Arrighi-Vicenza.
Bound by Mansell in Fabriano Roma paper boards, in the Tintoretto (dark sea-green)
shade.

¶ The type used for this fine poem by Constantine Trypanis, the second Clover Hill
Edition, is the Arrighi italic designed by Frederic Warde and cut by hand in 1925 by

Georges Plumet of Paris. There is only one size, in two versions: one with seriffed ascenders called Vicenza, which we used, and one called Vicentino which differed by the addition of a set of letters with swash ascenders. The type was later adapted by Monotype, with considerable modification, as the companion italic for Centaur. The most consummate use of the Warde type was made by Mardersteig at the Officina Bodoni, notably in the exquisite Ovid *Amores* of 1932. The only other fount in Europe belonged to the Fanfare Press, and was used to print Robert Bridges' *The tapestry*, 1925, and Douglas Cleverdon's 1929 *Ancient mariner*. After our edition of this book (24) we enquired into having some more Arrighi for our own use. We were able to borrow the matrices from the Metropolitan Museum of Art in New York, and had the type cast by the foundry of the Oxford University Press.

The 'Typographical note' investigates the complicated history of the type, and considers the rival claims to authorship, craftsmanship and ownership.

33

ENGRAVED IN THE WOOD

A collection of wood-engravings by George Mackley, with an appreciation by Ruari McLean, and with a glimpse of the artist by Armida Maria-Theresa Colt. The Two-Horse Press, London [1968].

300 sets on T. H. Saunders mould-made paper. A booklet signed by George Mackley, containing editorial matter, ornamented with some of the smaller engravings; plus 68 separate prints of engravings, printed from the wood in all but 13 cases.   30.5 × 24 cm.   *W*.
The booklet hand-set in 18pt Palatino italic.
The booklet square-back sewn, with printed paper covers; the engravings contained in a rust-red folder, and the whole enclosed in a buckram-covered box made by John P. Gray, with a printed title-strip on the spine.

¶ This production followed on from *Weeds and wild flowers* (29).

'Cow parsley': wood-engraving by George Mackley (reduced) from *Engraved in the wood* (33)

Rhayadr Ogwen (or Benglog Falls)

THE
MOUNTAINS

R. S. THOMAS

Illustrated with ten drawings by
JOHN PIPER
engraved on the wood by
REYNOLDS STONE
with a Descriptive Note by John Piper

CHILMARK PRESS · NEW YORK

34

THE MOUNTAINS

R. S. Thomas, illustrated with ten drawings by John Piper, engraved on the wood by
Reynolds Stone, with a descriptive note by John Piper. Chilmark Press, New York [1968].

240 copies on Wookey Hole mould-made paper; plus 110 copies signed by R. S. Thomas,
John Piper and Reynolds Stone, with an extra set of the engravings on Japanese Hosho
paper.   30.5 × 22.5 cm.   *W&S*.
Hand-set in 18pt Palatino.
Bound by Cambridge University Press: the ordinary edition in quarter cloth with Ingres
paper boards printed with an enlargement of one of the engravings; the special edition
in quarter morocco with dark blue cloth sides, and the same enlarged engraving used as
endpapers; both editions in slip-cases.

¶ The third Clover Hill Edition. Just after the second world war, John Piper and Reynolds
Stone, both enthusiasts of nineteenth-century topographical guide-books, decided to produce a modern equivalent, to illustrate the mountains of Snowdonia. They used wood-
engraving both as a reproductive process, so that the pictures could be printed together
with the text, and as creative interpretations of the drawings, which in several cases Piper
did directly on the blocks. Unfortunately John Murray, the first choice as publisher
because of their close association with Piper and Stone, and the kinship of the project with
the nineteenth-century *Murray's guides*, could not undertake it, and the blocks languished
for twenty years, their joints opening slightly as they did so. (Wood-engravings are cut on
the end of the grain of boxwood, which never grows to a large diameter. So blocks of more
than the smallest size are made of several pieces of wood jointed together with reinforcing
fillets. In time, especially if the engravings are stored in a dry atmosphere, the joints open,
and this shows up in printing as a grid of white lines. In the case of the *Mountains* blocks,
we left them in cool damp conditions for several months, and the lines closed again in
nearly all cases.)

We were eager to print these magnificent engravings, and as the Carters and the Stones
are close cousins, negotiations were simplified. Douglas Cleverdon persuaded the Welsh
poet R. S. Thomas to write some rich poetic prose to accompany them, and we set this in
our new Palatino from the Stempel foundry in Frankfurt, which we have been using ever
since. The text was printed in grey so as not to overpower the engravings, which were in
black.

The Hosho paper engravings in the special edition were tipped lightly on to extra signa-
tures of the text paper included in the binding. This was the only time we tried this method
of enclosing extra sets.

35

ASPECTS OF ART AND SCIENCE
Prints and text by J. G. Lubbock. Twelve by Eight Press, Leicester, 1969.

80 copies on Richard-de-Bas hand-made paper from Ambert in the French Auvergne,
signed by J. G. Lubbock.   32.5×25 cm.   *W.*
Hand-set in 18pt Palatino. The plates printed by the artist.
Bound by George Percival of Leicester in full niger morocco, blocked on the front board
with a design by the artist; in a slip-case.
Lent by the Fitzwilliam Museum.

¶ Joe Lubbock is an engineer who began writing and illustrating books in his retirement.
The book-dealer Colin Franklin wrote in *Fine print*, v.3. 1979: 'His are extraordinary and
visionary books. Nobody else has steered his course in taking on the universe – for that is
the theme, nothing less.' He makes and prints his own plates, with a wide variety of
methods: in his own words, 'The prints are hand-made . . . from copper-plates worked by
engraving, etching, aquatint and soft-ground etching. The colours are applied from intaglio
and relief, and additional colours are added by hand to some pages after printing.' Lubbock
planned the relationship of text and plates in each book, and was an excellent collaborator
in adapting his text to fit the space available, and permitting the printers to do likewise,
often without submitting proofs.
    One book, *Art and the spiritual life*, 1967, had been printed at The Stellar Press to Will
Carter's design. The present title was the first printed at the Rampant Lions Press, and the
partners alternately undertook the ones that followed. They are:

Reflections from the sea, 1971 (44).
Light and the mind's eye, 1974 (58).
Perceptions of the earth, 1977 (69).
Garden to galaxy, 1980 (81).

36

THE AGAMEMNON OF AESCHYLUS

Text edited by Raymond Postgate, with an introduction, a commentary and a translation into modern English prose. Rampant Lions Press, Cambridge [1969].

500 copies on Hollingworth wove, of which 250 copies were signed by Raymond Postgate. 25 × 14.5 cm. *W&S*.
Machine-set in Porson Greek and 11pt Baskerville, with commentary in 8pt Baskerville.
Bound in terra cotta cloth by Mansell, with a blocked label on the spine.

37

CATALOGUE OF BOOKS AND MANUSCRIPTS BY RUPERT BROOKE, EDWARD MARSH & CHRISTOPHER HASSALL

Collected, compiled and annotated by John Schroder, with a frontispiece by Joan Hassall. Rampant Lions Press, Cambridge [1970].

400 copies on Wookey Hole pure rag paper; plus 50 copies on T. H. Saunders mould-made paper, signed by John Schroder and Joan Hassall, with a signed proof of the frontispiece. 29 × 19 cm. *S*.
Machine-set in 12pt Baskerville, with display in Modern No.20. The plates printed by the Cotswold Collotype Company.
The ordinary edition bound in full green buckram by the Wigmore Bindery; the special edition by Sangorski and Sutcliffe in quarter green morocco with green buckram boards; both editions with a blocked label on the spine.

❡ John Schroder's catalogue of his large Brooke collection was, for us, chiefly an exercise in the difficult business of making complicated setting look reasonably tidy. We were helped in this by a generous budget. One of the benefits of the job was that we accumulated a large number of 32-em leads which were needed for all the spacing-out that had to be done; and they are being put to good re-use in the present catalogue.

38

LESSONS OF THE WAR
Henry Reed. Clover Hill Editions, Chilmark Press, New York, 1970.

530 copies on Wookey Hole mould-made paper, of which 110 copies signed by Henry Reed. 29×21 cm. *W&S.*
Machine-set in 14D Walbaum.
Bound by the Wigmore Bindery, the ordinary edition in quarter oatmeal canvas with specially designed patterned paper boards, the signed edition in full dark green cloth with patterned endpapers.

¶ The fifth Clover Hill Edition.

39

OLD RECTORY, OR THE INTERVIEW
Martyn Skinner, Rampant Lions Press.

Three volumes, printed on T. H. Saunders mould-made paper.   25.5×19 cm.   *W&S.*

  The prologue, 300 copies, 1970
  The session, 200 copies, 1973.
  The epilogue, 150 copies, 1978.

Machine-set in 14pt Ehrhardt.
Bound in Ingres paper boards, with printed label on the front.

¶ Martyn Skinner was referred to us by John Betjeman, who has been a friendly public-relations man on our behalf, quite apart from his activities as Poet Laureate. *Old Rectory* is an ambitious exercise in that difficult and unfashionable genre, the long philosophical poem.

40

SHADES
David Piper, an essay on English portrait silhouettes. Chilmark Press, New York [1970].

500 copies on St Paul's Cray rag paper.   27×20 cm.   *S.*
Machine-set in 14pt Octavian. Title-page lettering by Sebastian Carter. The plates printed by offset lithography at The Stellar Press.
Bound by Mansell in quarter black buckram, with paper boards printed with a repeat motif of a silhouette.

¶ The fourth Clover Hill Edition. David Piper was at the time director of the Fitzwilliam Museum (he afterwards became director of the Ashmolean). The illustrations were an opportunity to do some varied framing in a second colour.

The type, Octavian, is the nearest thing we have to a private type. It was designed by Will Carter and David Kindersley (see 93); because it was cut by Monotype for hot-metal composition only in 14pt, very few printers have it. One who does is The Stellar Press, who both set *Shades* and printed the plates.

Sebastian Carter won the first Francis Minns Award at the National Book League British Book Production 1971 exhibition for the design of *Shades*.

41

TRIBUTES TO ALLEN LANE

At a service of thanksgiving for his life and work, 1902–1970. Privately printed, 1970.

750 copies printed on Abbey Mill antique laid. 23 × 14 cm. *W.*
Machine-set in 11pt Ehrhardt.
Pamphlet-sewn at the Press in Cockerell marbled paper wrappers, with printed paper label.

42

WITH LOVE AND EIGHTY CANDLES FOR M.E.K.

[Poems and speeches celebrating the eightieth birthday of Lady Keynes, 1970.]

200 copies on T. H. Saunders mould-made paper. 28.5 × 21.5 cm. *S.*
Machine-set in 12pt Plantin light.
Pamphlet-sewn at the Press in blue covers, printed with title.

¶ This booklet reprinted the invitation to the birthday dinner (which we had originally printed) in facsimile, the menu (which we had not) and, from standing type, an acrostic sonnet by Jon Stallworthy. (We had already printed this poem in Arrighi-Vicenza, also for private circulation.) The lines of the sonnet begin with the letters of 'Margaret Keynes', since by good fortune the letters in each word exactly tally with the octave and sestet of the Petrarchan sonnet. There is also a translation of the poem into Latin by Nicolas Barker with the acrostic duly Latinised.

The Rainbow Press

The Rainbow Press was founded in 1970 by the poet Ted Hughes and his sister Olwyn, to publish fine first editions of the work of Hughes and his circle. They had given the manuscript of *Crystal gazer*, poems by Hughes' first wife, Sylvia Plath, to a friend to print, but he had done nothing with them. They decided to have it printed themselves, and went to the Daedalus Press in Norfolk. When the third Rainbow book, *Lyonnesse*, was being planned, Daedalus were too busy to take it on, and recommended us. (This was not the only good turn they have done us, since it was from them we bought our Monopol platen press.) Since then we have printed a number of Rainbow books, here listed:

> *Lyonnesse*, 1971 (43).
> *Pursuit*, 1973.
> *Mandrakes*, 1973 (56).
> *Spring summer autumn winter*, 1973 (57).
> *Earth-moon*, 1976 (65).
> *Moortown elegies*, 1978 (75).
> *Adam and the sacred nine*, 1978.
> *Henry Williamson*, 1979 (77).
> *Remains of Elmet*, 1979 (78).
> *Dialogue over a ouija board*, 1981 (85).

Device for the Rainbow Press drawn by Leonard Baskin

43

LYONNESSE

Poems by Sylvia Plath. London, Rainbow Press, 1971.

400 copies on Hodgkinson hand-made paper. 29×19 cm. *W.*
Machine-set in 12pt Ehrhardt. Title-page lettering by Will Carter.
300 copies bound by Davis and Hodges in quarter leather, with Japanese printed paper
sides; 90 copies by Zaehnsdorf in full calf; and 10 also by Zaehnsdorf in full vellum.

44

REFLECTIONS FROM THE SEA

Original prints and text by J. G. Lubbock. The Twelve by Eight Press, Leicester [1971].

85 copies on paper hand-made at the Richard de Bas mill at Ambert in France, signed
by J. G. Lubbock. 33×25 cm. *S.*
Hand-set in 18pt Palatino. Title-page lettering by Sebastian Carter. The plates printed
by the artist in his studio.
Bound in full dark blue morocco by George Percival at Leicester, with a design by the
artist on the front board.

¶ See note on 35.

45

SIXE IDYLLIA

Chosen out of the Sicilian poet Theocritus and translated into English verse, with eight
etchings by Anthony Gross, and with an introduction by Douglas Cleverdon. Clover Hill
Editions, Chilmark Press, New York, 1971.

270 copies printed on J. Green mould-made paper; plus 135 copies signed by Anthony
Gross, with an extra set of the prints in final state; plus 12 copies also signed with extra sets
of the prints in both first and final states and an original drawing. 33×24 cm. *W&S.*
Hand-set in 20pt Palatino italic. The plates were printed by Studio Prints.
The ordinary edition bound by the Wigmore Bindery in quarter buckram with Swedish
marbled paper boards; the special edition also bound by the Wigmore Bindery, in quarter
morocco with canvas boards blocked with a bull design by Anthony Gross, with the extra
set of prints in a separate dust-proof box; and the extra-special edition bound by
Sangorski and Sutcliffe in full morocco, also blocked with the bull design, with the extra
material in a quarter morocco solander box; all editions with slip-cases.

¶ The sixth Clover Hill Edition. We knew Anthony Gross, probably the most eminent printmaker in England, through the Double Crown Club (see **20**), and discussions between him and Douglas Cleverdon led to the plan of illustrating Theocritus in the style of the etchings Gross had been making of the part of south-west France around his summer home at Le Boulvé, where classical antiquity seems ever present. Cleverdon unearthed a charming anonymous sixteenth-century translation of six of the idylls, and Gross produced a set of densely detailed images of nature to blend with it.

We laid in a good supply of the beautiful 20pt Palatino italic (it had to be a good supply, since the sixteenth-century text had more than the usual complement of lower-case *e*s, and we had to buy proportionately more founts), which has stood us in good stead ever since.

Studio Prints, the plate printers, was a workshop which had been set up by a former Slade pupil of Gross', Dorothea Wight; the creation and printing of the prints were the subject of a BBC television film, 'In a print-maker's workshop'.

The contact established with Anthony Gross during the making of this book bore fruit ten years later with the publication of *The very rich hours of Le Boulvé* (**83**).

Binding design by Anthony Gross (reduced) for *Sixe idyllia* (**45**)

46

AN INTRODUCTION TO *THE RIME OF THE ANCIENT MARINER*
David Jones. Clover Hill Editions, London [1972].

330 copies on a special making of W. S. Hodgkinson grey mould-made paper, of which 115 were signed by David Jones. 31 × 25 cm. *W.*
Machine-set in 14pt Ehrhardt. Title-page engraving on copper by David Jones.
Bound in full green cloth; the signed copies in quarter vellum with green cloth sides, in a marbled paper slip-case.

¶ The seventh Clover Hill Edition. See note on **24**.

47

IN FAIR VERONA

English travellers in Italy and their accounts of the city from the middle ages to modern times. January the eighth MCMLXXII.

100 copies on Amalfi hand-made paper. 29.5×19.5 cm. *W.*
Machine-set in 12D Dante. Title-page emblem engraved on wood by Reynolds Stone.
Sewn square-back in limp Japanese paper wrappers with a gold-blocked label on the spine.

¶ This was a presentation volume for Giovanni Mardersteig of the Officina Bodoni, at the time the world's greatest living printer (he died in 1977; see also the note on 32). It was subscribed by his friends on his eightieth birthday. As befitted the occasion, it was a co-operative production, with texts chosen and linked by Nicolas Barker, designed by Hans Schmoller, set by the Curwen Press, printed by us, and bound by the Cambridge University Press. This was one of the very rare occasions when we have printed a book designed by someone else.

48

KERDRUC NOTEBOOK

Michael Collie. Rampant Lions Press, 1972.

200 copies on Abbey Mill suede antique laid. 19.5×19.5 cm. *S.*
Machine-set in 14pt Octavian, with display in Placard.
Bound in full brown buckram, with a jacket.

49

SEED LEAVES

Homage to R. F. Poetry by Richard Wilbur, prints by Charles Wadsworth.
David R. Godine, Publisher, Boston [1972].

160 copies on Glastonbury sage green antique laid. 26×16.5 cm. *W.*
Hand-set in 12pt Palatino. The two pages of illustration printed by the artist.
Pamphlet-sewn in Swedish marbled paper wrappers with printed paper label; a folder, quarter buckram with marbled paper sides, was then made by John P. Gray, and the pamphlet tucked in a pocket inside.

Michael Rothenstein

The series of three portfolios we have published with Michael Rothenstein began with a fan letter. We admired Rothenstein greatly as one of the most inventive and ambitious woodcut artists working in England: he cut massive sections from riven trees and printed directly from them, or composed prints from packing-case wood and pieces of timber he found. We wrote to him in October 1970, asking him if he would be interested in collaborating on a book, and to our great pleasure he agreed.

This first book led on to two others. The three titles we have published are:

1. *Suns and moons*, 1972 (50).
2. *Seven colours*, 1974 (60).
3. *The song of songs*, 1979 (80).

The format of all three is the same. It had to be large – Imperial folio – because that is the way Rothenstein works; and we were forced as a result to consider new approaches to book production. There was first the question of type. We had nothing in large enough quantity of the size we should need, 24pt at least; and to use type of that size as a text face demands qualities we had not considered before. Bembo, for example, is an excellent type, and its 24pt size is a fine display face at a normal scale; but a poem set in it on a large folio page looks spindly. So we chose Berthold Wolpe's Albertus in its light cutting, which has been produced only in 24pt. It is a fine type which is both rugged and lithe, and we think it is unjustly neglected in favour of its plumper sibling, Albertus 'regular'.

This is a sample of 24pt Albertus light.

There was next the problem of printing a large page, since our Victoria platen press was not big enough to take even the folded sheet. The solution was to damp the paper more than usual, and wrap the folded sheets round the cylinder of our Vandercook proofing press. When we came to *Seven colours* two years later, we had put in a Monopol Crown platen press, so that we could print the folded sheets flat.

The portfolios were all organised as eight letterpress folders with Michael Rothenstein's prints loosely inserted, and one title at the front, which was letterpress only in the first two portfolios, but had an extra print in *The song of songs*. The paper for the folders of the first two was the splendid 'not'-surfaced (which means not hot-pressed) J. Green mould-made, 140lb Imperial, which is no longer made. The paper for the prints, which were all printed by Shelley Rose at Rothenstein's studio, was Barcham Green Crisbrook waterleaf in all three portfolios. The boxes were all made to our specification by Grays of Cambridge.

44

50

SUNS AND MOONS

Eight colour woodcuts by Michael Rothenstein, with accompanying poems chosen by the artist. The Rampant Lions Press, Cambridge, 1972.

85 copies on J. Green mould-made paper, signed by Michael Rothenstein.   55.5 × 38 cm.
S.
Hand-set in 24pt Albertus light. Title-page lettering by Sebastian Carter. The prints on Crisbrook hand-made paper, printed by Shelley Rose at the artist's studio. Each print signed by the artist.
The folders loosely laid in a box made by John P. Gray, in black canvas with printed paper label on the front.

¶ Michael Rothenstein had for some time been working on the twin images of the sun and the moon, and the idea grew between us of producing a portfolio of eight prints, each enclosed in a folder on which was printed a poem selected carefully for its visual suggestiveness but yet not calling for too specific illustration. After some discussion, we settled for four sun poems to alternate with four moon poems, from Donne, Shelley, Yeats, Baudelaire, Sylvia Plath and Odysseus Elytis. When Michael Rothenstein sent the first proof – of the last print which accompanies the wonderful Yeats poem 'The crazed moon' – all our hopes were justified. Rothenstein, with his printer Shelley Rose, had printed from a piece of sea-bitten marine ply, and had kept so much of the texture that a bit of calico stuck to the lower part shows up perfectly. And they had developed a way of inking the wood with merged bands of different colours, to richly subtle effect.

51

THE NORTH

Samuel Beckett, with three original etchings by Avigdor Arikha. Enitharmon Press, London, 1972.

137 copies on J. Green mould-made paper, signed by Samuel Beckett, of which 12 copies ad personam, with the name of the persona printed on the colophon page.   38.5 × 29 cm.
W.
Hand-set in 18pt Palatino. The etchings printed by Studio Prints, and signed by Avigdor Arikha. Title-page lettering by Will Carter.
The sheets unsewn, contained in a heavy hand-made paper folder, blind printed with the title only, inside a natural linen folder ink-printed on the front and spine. The whole contained in a slip-case. Bound by John P. Gray.

52

THE QUEST OF GILGAMESH

D. G. Bridson, with an original lithograph by Michael Ayrton. Rampant Lions Press, MCMLXXII.

110 copies on T. H. Saunders mould-made paper; plus 15 copies on Amalfi hand-made paper signed by D. G. Bridson and Michael Ayrton. 26.5 × 19 cm. *S.*
Machine-set in 14pt Octavian. The frontispiece drawn on the plate by Michael Ayrton and printed at The Stellar Press.
The ordinary edition bound by Mansell in quarter grey-green canvas with Swedish marbled paper boards; the special edition by Sangorski and Sutcliffe in quarter morocco with cloth sides.

53

AREOPAGITICA

A speech of Mr John Milton for the liberty of unlicensed printing to the Parliament of England [Edited with an introduction by Isabel Rivers. Deighton, Bell and Company, 1973].

500 copies on J. Green mould-made paper. 33 × 24 cm. *S.*
Main setting hand-set in 18pt Palatino roman; two-column setting machine-set in 12pt Plantin light; display in Sistina and Grot R.
Bound by John P. Gray; 400 in full black canvas with a leather label; plus 100 in full black morocco.

¶ In 1971 we were approached by Deighton Bell, the well-known Cambridge booksellers, who wanted us to print a fine edition which they would publish. After discussion, we agreed on Milton's great condemnation of censorship, *Areopagitica*. We decided on a new, purely typographical treatment in which we would try to overcome the resistance commonly felt by the reader to the text of *Areopagitica*, with its long paragraphs, details of contemporary disputes, and appeals to historical precedent. We would set the main argument by hand in large type, breaking the paragraphs where the sense demanded, and the supporting arguments by machine in a smaller type in two unjustified columns. The result was a series of pages of considerable abstract beauty and variety. This scheme also had the advantage of our being able to paste the book up in advance, using the galley proofs of the Monotype setting and a cast-off, as accurate as we could make it, for the hand-set sections. The space between the sections allowed enough margin of error.

We were lucky to find an editor, Isabel Rivers, who was in sympathy with the typographical aim of the edition, and wrote an excellent introduction.

AREOPAGITICA

o

A SPEECH OF MR

JOHN MILTON

FOR THE LIBERTY OF
UNLICENSED PRINTING
TO THE PARLIAMENT
OF ENGLAND

THOM GUNN

Illustrated by Leonard Baskin

THE RAINBOW PRESS

54

BOOK-COLLECTING IN THE 1930s

A. N. L. Munby. Brighton, 1973.

110 copies on Amatruda hand-made paper, signed by A. N. L. Munby.   19×12 cm.   *S.*
Machine-set in 9pt Ehrhardt.
Pamphlet-sewn at the Press, in Swedish marble paper wrappers, with a paper label.

¶ This essay by the late Tim Munby, the librarian of King's College, Cambridge, first appeared in *The Times literary supplement*, and was here reprinted as a Christmas book for the bookseller Tony Appleton. (Others in the series are *The Cambridge Christmas books*, 1976 (**66**), and *The English language*, 1981.)

55

FIRST PRINCIPLES OF TYPOGRAPHY IN THE 1970s

Sebastian Carter. Bowaters United Kingdom Paper Company Limited, 1973.

525 copies on Nimrod cartridge.   21.5×13.5 cm.   *S.*
Machine-set in 10pt Ehrhardt.
Pamphlet-sewn at the Press, with printed wrappers.

¶ In a moment of enlightenment the Bowater Paper Company offered prizes for essays on a choice of topics in the theory of typography, a worthy attempt to promote discussion in a field relatively unencumbered with standard works. The judges were Michael Twyman, Hans Schmoller and Peter Stockham. The response was so slight that the attempt was short-lived, and in this first year no first prize was awarded. This essay came second – in other words third – but Bowaters generously sponsored this printing of it.

56

MANDRAKES

Thom Gunn, illustrated by Leonard Baskin. The Rainbow Press [1973].

150 copies on J. Green mould-made paper, signed by Thom Gunn.   29×19 cm.   *W.*
Machine-set in 14pt Ehrhardt semi-bold. Title-page lettering by Will Carter. Five line drawings by Leonard Baskin printed from line blocks.
Bound by Sangorski and Sutcliffe in quarter white goat vellum, with buckram sides, in a slip-case.

57

SPRING SUMMER AUTUMN WINTER
Ted Hughes. Rainbow Press [1973].

140 copies on Barcham Green Dover laid hand-made paper, signed by Ted Hughes.
20.5 × 21.5 cm.   *S.*
Machine-set in 14pt Centaur, with display in Palatino and Sapphir.
Bound by John P. Gray in natural calf.

58

LIGHT AND THE MIND'S EYE
Original prints and text by J. G. Lubbock. Bertram Rota, London [1974].

70 copies on Richard de Bas hand-made paper from the Auvergne, signed by
J. G. Lubbock.   33 × 25 cm.   *W.*
Hand-set in 18pt Palatino. Title-page lettering by Will Carter. The plates printed by the
artist.
Bound in full morocco by George Percival, with a design by the artist blocked in gold on
the front, and with the title blocked on the spine, also in gold. In a Cockerell marbled paper
covered slip-case.

¶ See the note on 35.

59

PORTFOLIO TWO
Projects, backward glances and jeux d'esprit put together by Will and Sebastian Carter
at the Rampant Lions Press, Cambridge, 1974.

About 500 copies on various papers.   28 × 21.5 cm.   *W&S.*
25 items, in a wide variety of settings. Photographs printed by The Stellar Press.
Portfolio of blue card made at the Press.

¶ See also 31 and 89.

60

SEVEN COLOURS

Images by Michael Rothenstein, poems by Edward Lucie-Smith. Rampant Lions Press,
MCMLXXIV.

50 copies on J. Green mould-made paper signed by Michael Rothenstein and Edward
Lucie-Smith; plus 25 copies signed as above and also by Shelley Rose and Sebastian Carter,
with 3 extra prints, of which 5 copies also contained some proof material.   55.5×38 cm.   S.
Hand-set in 24pt Albertus light. Title-page lettering by Sebastian Carter. The prints on
Crisbrook hand-made paper, printed by Shelley Rose at the artist's studio. Each print
signed by the artist.
The folders loosely laid in a box made by John P. Gray, in oatmeal linen with a printed
paper label on the front. A few of the ordinary copies bound to order.

¶ Michael Rothenstein and Edward Lucie-Smith had served together on various print-
making juries and selection committees, and had decided to collaborate on a portfolio
similar to *Suns and moons* (50). They exchanged drafts and proofs until the poems had been
written and the prints designed, and then approached us to produce the portfolio in the
same way as before.
   Whereas the *Suns and moons* prints had been wood-cut assemblages, here some silk-
screen images were superimposed on backgrounds printed from the wood.

61

SPECIMEN PRINTED ON THE ORIGINAL KELMSCOTT PRESS WATERMARKED PAPER

[Rampant Lions Press, 1974.]

52 copies.   29×20.5 cm.   W.
Hand-set in Kelmscott Press Troy.
Pamphlet-sewn at the Press in Morris patterned paper wrappers with printed paper label.

¶ This pamphlet was issued to coincide with the publication of *The story of Cupid and
Psyche*, described next.

62

THE STORY OF CUPID AND PSYCHE

William Morris, with illustrations designed by Edward Burne-Jones, mostly engraved
on the wood by William Morris, with an introduction by A. R. Dufty.
Clover Hill Editions, London and Cambridge, 1974.

Two volumes: Volume 1 containing the introduction with collotype plates of preparatory
drawings and comparative material; Volume 2 the poem and engravings.
270 copies on J. Green mould-made paper; plus 130 copies with a set of collotype
reproductions of the Burne-Jones drawings in the Ashmolean Museum and a set of the
engravings on single sheets.   34.5 × 24 cm.   *W&S.*
100 boxed sets of the engravings on single sheets also issued.
Volume 1 machine-set in 12pt Ehrhardt with display in Palatino; the collotype plates
printed by the Cotswold Collotype Company. Volume 2 hand-set in Kelmscott Press Troy.
The ordinary edition bound by John P. Gray (who also made the boxes) in quarter cloth
with Morris patterned paper sides, in a slip-case; the special edition by Sangorski and
Sutcliffe in full niger morocco in a slip-case, with the extra material in a solander box.
The patterned paper used in all the editions photographed from a Morris and Company
chintz in A. R. Dufty's collection and printed by offset lithography at The Stellar Press.

❡ This publication, the eighth Clover Hill Edition and the most ambitious undertaken,
was suggested by a chance remark during an after-dinner speech. In December 1969, the
book-dealer Colin Franklin gave a talk to the Double Crown Club (see **20**), called 'Golden
asses at the private presses'. In it he discussed the various ways the different presses had
treated Apuleius' fable, and in particular the tale-within-a-tale, the story of Cupid and
Psyche. One of the editions he mentioned was the Gregynog Press *Eros and Psyche*, which
was illustrated with rather weak wood-engravings done after drawings by Edward Burne-
Jones in the Ashmolean Museum; and he observed in passing that the Gregynog people
were apparently unaware that these drawings had already been engraved by William Morris
himself as a young man in 1865, for an abandoned folio edition of Morris' poem *The earthly
paradise*, and that the blocks had survived.

The two senior partners of Clover Hill Editions, Douglas Cleverdon and Will Carter,
were at the dinner, and gazed at each other with a wild surmise. Franklin had brought along
proofs of the forty-four blocks, which were almost all by Morris and the only ones he ever
engraved himself, since when he started the Kelmscott Press a quarter of a century later
the borders and illustrations were done by a trade engraver, W. H. Hooper. The proofs
were a revelation. When compared with contemporary mid-Victorian work, and with the
Gregynog versions, they were splendidly robust, and though some were amateurish in
execution, what they lost in proficiency they gained in vigour. They closely reflected
Morris' growing interest in early German wood-cut book illustration, and yet remained
recognisably pre-Raphaelite in flavour.

The idea of printing the blocks together with Morris' poem, and thereby completing the
abandoned project after a century had passed, was too appealing to resist. We learned that

Wood-engraving by William Morris (reduced) after a drawing by Edward Burne-Jones from
The story of Cupid and Psyche (**62**)

the history of the engravings, and the 'big book' they had been intended for, had been thoroughly researched by A. R. Dufty, secretary to the Society of Antiquaries, who were the residuary legatees of the estate of Morris' daughter May, and so owned the blocks. Dufty agreed to allow us to publish his monograph as an introduction to our edition (in the event it proved so long that we issued it as an accompanying volume), and was instrumental in persuading the Society of Antiquaries to allow us to print from the blocks, with a limit on the number of impressions.

One of the reasons why Morris and Burne-Jones could not complete their book in 1865 was that they could not find a type strong enough in colour to go with the engravings. Specimen pages were pulled at the Chiswick Press in Caslon and Basle types, and both were found to be too weak. In 1897, after Morris' death, spreads were proofed at the Kelmscott Press using the Troy type, which was far more successful; but then Burne-Jones died and the project was dropped for the second time. When we came to consider the typography of our edition, our experience was the same, and we concluded that nothing suited the engravings as well as Troy. Fortunately, the Kelmscott Press typographical material was in the Cambridge University Press collection, and through Brooke Crutchley, the University Printer, we were able to borrow some original Troy for trial pages.

The trial spreads established the number of lines we could get on each page. Douglas Cleverdon then pasted up xeroxes of the poem from the first edition of *The earthly paradise*, making them correspond to our edition page-for-page by counting the lines and placing the illustrations as close to where they fall in the story as a balanced layout would allow. Two of the blocks were of an episode which Morris later dropped from the poem; they were printed in Volume 1 for completeness' sake, and put at the end of the extra sets.

Even though we could thus plan the volume page-for-page, there was not enough original

53

Troy to set four pages at a time. As our production method was for one partner to print one spread while the other set and proofed the next, we had some more type cast at the foundry of the Oxford University Press from the original matrices in the Cambridge collection. The type used in the book is therefore new, except for the commas, of which we thought we had enough. We were wrong, so that while most of the commas are originals from the Kelmscott Press, a sharp eye will detect some wrong-fount ones – chiefly in their inverted form, as opening quotes – which are actually 18pt Monotype Klang. (Troy is cast on a Great Primer body, the equivalent of 18pt.)

Before the book itself, we printed the suite of engravings on single sheets. This was to get the measure of the blocks, trying them out under the best conditions, before starting the more exacting task of printing them with type. In the event, we found them in remarkably good condition, very little warped or split: this we put down to their having been stored in the basement of Burlington House, which was reasonably cool and damp. Most of the make-ready that was needed could be done on the back of the blocks, since there are no extreme contrasts of solid and void in the designs, and that made our job easier when it came to printing the engravings with a forme of type.

The introductory volume was editorially the most complicated and the last printed; it was also the first book we printed on our newly installed Monopol platen press. Because it included a section of collotype plates, which need ample margins for grip, it had to be trimmed, and the extra eighth-of-an-inch all round needed for the trim meant that we could not fit it on our Victoria, which was already stretched to the limit with the deckle-edged text volume.

63

ROOT AND SKY

Poetry from the plays of Christopher Fry, compiled and arranged by Charles E. and Jean G. Wadsworth, collagraph-intaglios designed and printed by Charles E. Wadsworth. Rampant Lions Press, Cambridge [1975].

220 copies on W. S. Hodgkinson grey mould-made paper, signed by Christopher Fry and Charles Wadsworth.   32.5 × 25 cm.   *W*.
Machine-set in 14pt Ehrhardt. Title-page lettering by Will Carter. The plates printed by the artist on Umbria hand-made paper from Italy.
Bound by John P. Gray in quarter sage green cloth with Swedish marbled paper sides, in a slip-case.

SEVEN COLOURS

IMAGES BY MICHAEL ROTHENSTEIN

POEMS BY EDWARD LUCIE-SMITH

RAMPANT LIONS PRESS

MCMLXXIV

Are feeble in this miserable place."
But for their words she did but mend her pace,
Although her heart beat quick as she passed by.
🖙 Then on she went, until she could espy
The wan, grey river lap the leaden bank
Wherefrom there sprouted sparsely sedges rank,
And there the road had end in that sad boat
Wherein the dead men unto Minos float;
There stood the ferryman, who now, seeing her, said:
"O living soul, that thus among the dead
Hast come, on whatso errand, without fear,
Know thou that penniless none passes here;
Of all the coins that rich men have on earth
To buy the dreadful folly they call mirth,
But one they keep when they have passed the grave,
That o'er this stream a passage they may have;
And thou, though living, art but dead to me,
Who here, immortal, see mortality

80

Pass, stripped of this last thing that men desire
Unto the changeless meads or changeless fire."
🌿 Speechless she shewed the money on her lip
Which straight he took, and set her in the ship,
And then the wretched, heavy oars he threw
Into the rowlocks and the flood they drew;
Silent, with eyes that looked beyond her face,
He laboured, and they left the dreary place.
🌿 But midmost of that water did arise
A dead man, pale, with ghastly staring eyes
That somewhat like her father still did seem,
But in such wise as figures in a dream;
Then with a lamentable voice it cried:
"O daughter, I am dead, and in this tide
For ever shall I drift, an unnamed thing,
Who was thy father once, a mighty king,
Unless thou take some pity on me now
And bid the ferryman turn here his prow,

81

Wood-engraving by David Jones (reduced) from *The deluge* (70)

64

SANTA MARIA DELLA SALUTE

A poem by John Sparrow, with illustrations by John Piper, 1975.

200 copies on J. Green mould-made paper, signed by John Piper and John Sparrow.
58×39 cm. *W.*
Hand-set in 24pt Palatino. The wash drawing printed by the Cotswold Collotype Company.
Unsewn sheets.

65

EARTH-MOON

Ted Hughes, illustrated by the author. Rainbow Press [1976].

226 copies on Barcham Green Hayle hand-made paper, signed by Ted Hughes.
12.5×12.5 cm. *S.*
Machine-set in 9pt Century Schoolbook bold, with display in Modern No.20 italic.
The illustrations printed from line blocks in smokey blue.
Bound by Davis and Hodges in dark blue Japanese paper boards, with a large circle of
cork veneer inlaid on the front board.

❡ This was a tiny book, made even tinier by the binders' accidental trimming of the fore-
edge. The cork veneer circle on the front suggested the moon very effectively, and the
blocking and the top edge were both in a ghostly lunar silver. Ted Hughes' drawings are
remarkable, and the first ones that he published.

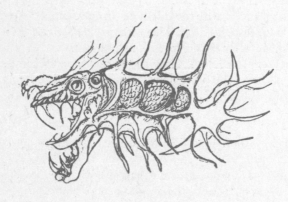

Drawing by Ted Hughes from *Earth-moon* **(65)**

66

THE CAMBRIDGE CHRISTMAS BOOKS
Brooke Crutchley. Brighton, 1976.

220 copies on Barcham Green Tovil hand-made paper, signed by Brooke Crutchley.
19×12 cm.   S.
Machine-set in 11pt Bembo.
Pamphlet-sewn at the Press, in Swedish marbled paper wrappers, with a paper label.

¶ Brooke Crutchley originally gave this as a lecture at the opening of an exhibition of the Cambridge Christmas books at the St Bride Printing Library on 9 December 1975. The thirty-four books produced over forty-three years (from 1930 to 1973, with a gap for the war), given as Christmas presents by Walter Lewis (urged originally by Stanley Morison), and then by his successor as University Printer, Brooke Crutchley, are an outstanding series, produced by one of the leading printing-houses during the great age of letterpress in this country.

67

THE RIME OF THE ANCIENT MARINER
Samuel Taylor Coleridge, with twelve aquatints by Patrick Procktor, published by
Editions Alecto [1976].

110 copies on Barcham Green Crisbrook hand-made paper, bound in quarter black canvas with patterned paper boards; plus 30 copies bound in full morocco, with four loose aquatints; both editions signed by the artist.   35×27 cm.   S.
Hand-set in 20pt Palatino italic, with the side-notes in 9pt Century Schoolbook bold.
Title-page lettering by Sebastian Carter. The plates printed by Charles Newington at Tisiphone Etching (the intaglio division of Editions Alecto).
The ordinary edition bound by John P. Gray, using a patterned paper designed specially by Sebastian Carter, and printed by Megara Screenprinting (also a division of Alecto); the special edition bound by Sangorski and Sutcliffe, with a blocked design by Patrick Procktor.

¶ We were asked by Joe Studholme of Editions Alecto to design this edition and print the letterpress.
    When we came into the project, Procktor had already made one plate, which was too large for a comfortable book and was later editioned as a print on its own; but the only way to accommodate the size of the plates he wanted was to trim them to the plate mark and make that the format of the book. This was a visually impressive way of presenting the

plates, but it meant guarding every one in, and not having plates and text on conjugate leaves as is our usual practice. It also made for difficulties in preventing set-off from the plates, since the tissue protective sheets had to be full format, and the slightest movement exposed part of the plate to rubbing.

The large format used allowed us to place the side notes on the left of the poetry on both rectos and versos without destroying the book's balance: usually they have to go on the right-hand pages, and are difficult to place against the ragged ends of the poetry. The text was printed in grey throughout, so as not to swamp the delicate lines of the engravings.

68

INDIA LOVE POEMS

[Translated by] Tambimuttu, [illustrated by] John Piper. Paradine [1977].

200 copies on Arches mould-made paper, signed by Tambimuttu and John Piper. 56.5×38 cm.   *W.*
Hand-set in 24pt Walbaum. The Piper illustrations, mostly gouache, printed by offset lithography by Adrian Lack at the Senecio Press, Charlbury.
Bound in quarter morocco and pure undyed Tussah silk, with ink printed leather label on the spine. The binding designed and carried out by Alfred Brazier and John Mitchell.

69

PERCEPTIONS OF THE EARTH

Original prints and text by J. G. Lubbock. Bertram Rota, London [1977].

70 copies on Barcham Green Crisbrook hand-made paper, signed by J. G. Lubbock. 32.5×25 cm.   *S.*
Hand-set in 18pt Palatino. The plates printed by the artist. Title-page lettering by Sebastian Carter.
Bound by George Percival in full morocco, blocked with a design by the artist, in a slip-case.
Lent by the Fitzwilliam Museum.

❡ See the note on 35.

70

THE CHESTER PLAY OF THE DELUGE
With ten wood-engravings by David Jones. Clover Hill Editions, London, 1977.

250 copies on J. Green mould-made paper; plus 80 copies on Barcham Green hand-made paper, water-marked 'Clover Hill', with a separate set of the engravings printed on Japanese Hosho paper; plus 7 copies on vellum, with separate sets of the engravings printed on vellum, hand-made paper, and Japanese paper. The prints on vellum printed on a hand-press by Ian Mortimer, of I M Imprimit, London. 33×25 cm. *W.*
Hand-set in 18pt Golden Cockerel roman.
The 250 mould-made paper copies bound by Davis and Hodges in quarter cloth with Swedish marbled paper sides, and a printed jacket; the other 2 editions by Sangorski and Sutcliffe, the 80 hand-made paper copies in quarter morocco, in a slip-case, each containing the separate set of engravings printed on Japanese paper; and the 7 vellum copies in full morocco with separate solander box containing the three sets of engravings, the whole contained in a slip-case.

¶ The ninth Clover Hill Edition. Douglas Cleverdon wrote in his prospectus: 'In 1927 David Jones engraved on wood a series of ten illustrations for the Golden Cockerel Press edition of the Chester Play of *The deluge*. These have long been recognised as his master-piece in the field of wood-engraving. Unfortunately, in order to keep a publication date, the edition was printed in some haste, and the preliminary damping of the hand-made paper was omitted. Consequently, to David Jones' bitter disappointment, much of the delicate detail of the wood-blocks was lost. . . .

'When the wood-blocks of the Golden Cockerel Press came on the market, the generosity of a friend enabled him to secure the blocks of *The deluge*, so that they could not be used again without his approval. Some time before his death, he readily agreed that they should be reprinted by Will Carter at the Rampant Lions Press and published in a Clover Hill Edition. As he was now in a nursing home, he rather reluctantly allowed a couple of friends to search for the wood-blocks in his cluttered bed-sitter. Unhappily, only eight of the ten could be found. As it would have caused him great anguish to learn that two blocks were missing, the project was silently abandoned.'

After his death, and in view of the increasing enthusiasm for his work, it was decided to make the book available with the two missing blocks in reproduction, rather than not to reprint at all.

We were just on the point of going to press when, miraculously, they turned up. And, in order to make doubly sure that they appeared in the best possible light, we decided to print all ten separately from the type, thus giving them the fullest possible attention. We persuaded Ian Mortimer to print the engravings for the vellum copies on a hand-press, for the best result on this difficult material.

The Golden Cockerel roman

Eric Gill designed the type commissioned by Robert Gibbings for the Golden Cockerel Press in 1929. Two sizes were cut, 14pt and 18pt, with associated 24pt and 36pt titlings. The design is clearly related to Monotype Perpetua, which Gill was designing at the same time, but it is superior to Perpetua on several counts: it is more robust, it avoids Perpetua's more annoying idiosyncrasies (such as the lower-case d), and it benefits from having been cut by a sensitive craftsman, J. Collinge of the Caslon foundry. The cutting is remarkable for having been done apparently with an eye firmly on the presswork it would receive and the kind of paper to be used: printed on smooth paper with a 'kiss' impression, it looks not just lighter, but actually distorted. An italic fount, lower-case only, was cut in 14pt; it looks rather like Aries italic, and is equally unsatisfactory.

The first major use of the fine 18pt size was in *The four gospels* of 1931, which has wood-engravings by Gill and is generally considered one of the best productions of the English private press movement, along with the Kelmscott Chaucer and the Doves Bible. The 14pt was used for several books, most notably for the Ravilious *Twelfth night* (1932), and for a number of prospectuses. Then the Depression hit the Press; Gibbings had to close the Waltham St Lawrence workshop and sell the imprint to Christopher Sandford. The type went to the Chiswick Press, who thereafter did the printing of Golden Cockerel books (the *Paradise lost* was the most important book using the 18pt), and thence into storage at Bentall's warehouse at Kingston-on-Thames.

Around 1975 we became interested in using the type for a book of translations from the Greek. We wrote to Christopher Sandford, who had since sold the Golden Cockerel Press to Thomas Yoseloff, a New York publisher, and Sandford referred us to Yoseloff's London office, where we drew a blank. Some years later, when Deighton Bell asked us to consider printing an edition of the Psalms, our interest was revived, and this time we were more fortunate. Through Peter Cowie, then his London representative, we obtained Mr Yoseloff's permission to borrow the type. When we got it out of store (or some of it: there turned out to be a great deal) we found that the 18pt was in remarkably fine condition, and the titlings were fair, but the 14pt was virtually useless, very worn, and mostly standing in pages – or rather sagging, since the wrappings were decaying.

When we had finished *The psalms of David* in the 18pt, we printed *The deluge* in the same type. By this time we were so enamoured of it that we began negotiations with Yoseloff to buy it. He generously agreed, and also asked us to oversee the scrapping of the useless 14pt. We invited the St Bride Printing Library to take sample founts, but aside from these, so far as we know, we have all the Golden Cockerel type in existence. (The matrices are in the type archive at the Cambridge University Press.)

(See next page.)

THE
GOLDEN
COCKEREL
ROMAN

DESIGNED BY ERIC GILL
for use at the Golden Cockerel Press.
This page is printed in the original type,
cast in 1929, now in the collection of
The Rampant Lions Press.
The history of the type is outlined
on the previous page.

71

THE PSALMS OF DAVID

[Miles Coverdale's translation, taken from the Book of Common Prayer. A Deighton Bell Edition, published by Wm. Dawson and Sons, 1977.]

315 copies on J. Green mould-made paper.   34×22.5 cm.   *S.*
Hand-set in 18pt Golden Cockerel roman. Title-page lettering and psalm numbers by Sebastian Carter.
Bound by George Miller of Bryn, Shropshire; 295 copies in quarter vellum with patterned paper sides, plus 20 copies in full vellum.

¶ The lengthy setting of this book was partly shared among helpers, chiefly two visiting Americans, Anne Geer and Kate Emlen. The figures at the head of each psalm were made as line blocks; they were stuck on shoulder-high mounts with quick-drying Araldite, which allowed adjustments to the alignment. Up to about psalm 100 the digits were mounted separately; thereafter, we found it easier to make line blocks of each psalm number as a group.

The patterned paper was designed specially for the edition, using a printers' leaf ornament generally known as the Aldine vine-leaf, although it was earlier used by Ratdolt and is not very like a vine-leaf.

72

THE SOBIESKI HOURS

A manuscript in the Royal Library at Windsor Castle, examined by Eleanor P. Spencer. Academic Press [Roxburghe Club, 1977].

300 copies on machine-made paper specially prepared.   33×22.5 cm.   *W.*
Machine-set in 16pt Bembo. Nine colour plates printed offset and mounted on coloured leaves bound into the book, and the latter half of the book consisting of the illuminated pages of the manuscript printed offset in monochrome, both by the Curwen Press.

¶ Bound in quarter red morocco and red cloth sides in the traditional Roxburghe Club style. The only divergence from this style, at our special request, was that the spine lettering was gold blocked on a black leather label instead of being hand-tooled.

73

TIME IS UNDONE
Twenty-five poems by Lucy M. Boston. Privately printed, 1977.

750 copies on Abbey Mill antique laid.   21.5×13.5 cm.   *S*.
Machine-set in 11pt Ehrhardt with display in Fairbank italic. Title-page lettering by Sebastian Carter.
Pamphlet-sewn at the Press in Aldine vine-leaf patterned paper, with a printed label.

74

EDWARD THOMAS
A centenary celebration, with etchings by Arthur Neal. [Eric and Joan Stevens, 1978].

50 copies on T. H. Saunders mould-made paper, signed by Arthur Neal; plus 25 copies with four loose etchings signed by Arthur Neal.   29×20 cm.   *S*.
Machine-set in 14pt Ehrhardt, with display in Walbaum. The intaglio plates printed by the artist on conjugate leaves.
Bound by John P. Gray in oatmeal linen with a leather label.

75

MOORTOWN ELEGIES
Ted Hughes. The Rainbow Press [1978].

175 copies on hand-made paper specially made for the Rampant Lions Press by Barcham Green, signed by Ted Hughes.   33.5×23.5 cm.   *W*.
Machine-set in 14pt Ehrhardt. Title-page calligraphy by Will Carter. A drawing by Leonard Baskin reproduced at the end.
143 copies bound by W.T. Morrell in full limp white vellum; and 32 copies by Sangorski and Sutcliffe in full morocco, of which 6 presentation copies had the name of the recipient printed below the colophon.
Lent by Olwyn Hughes.

❡ 100 copies of 6 of the poems were individually issued as offprints.

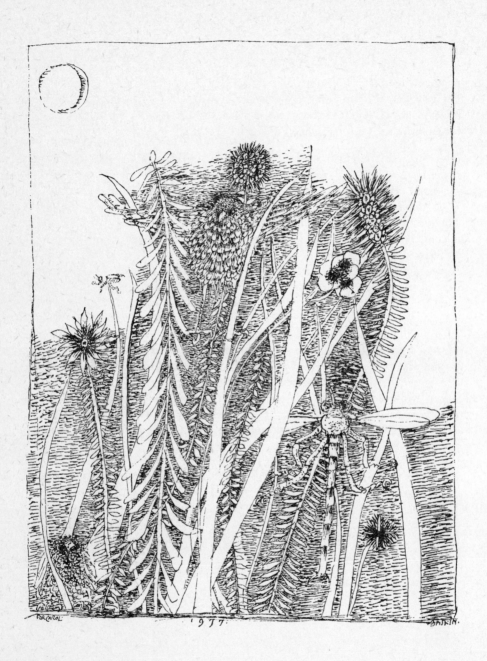

Drawing by Leonard Baskin from *Moortown elegies* (**75**)

76

MR CHESTERTON COMES TO TEA

Or: how the King of England captured Redskin Island; written by Aidan Mackey, to accompany sixteen hitherto unpublished pencil drawings by G. K. Chesterton, with an introductory essay on Chesterton as artist by Richard Ingrams. Printed by the Rampant Lions Press, Cambridge, for Vintage Publications [1978].

370 copies on Zerkall mould-made paper, signed by Aidan Mackey and Richard Ingrams. 19 × 26.5 cm. *S.*
Machine-set in 13pt Bembo. The drawings printed by offset lithography at the Senecio Press by Adrian Lack.
Bound in quarter black buckram with boards covered with patterned paper printed for the edition, copied from *The coloured lands*; also used for the matching slipcase. The binding by Weatherby Woolnough.

¶ Aidan Mackey is a bookseller in Bedford who specialises in Chesterton's works. He had bought some of the drawings reproduced here at a sale at Sotheby's in 1977: they were plainly a group, and appeared to illustrate a story, and his interest was aroused. One of the reasons why Chesterton is less well known as an artist than he should be is that much of his work was done for friends, or friends' children, often illustrating stories he told them. This turned out to be the case here. Through Sotheby's, Aidan Mackey traced the two ladies for whom the drawings had been made. They remembered well how Chesterton would draw while he made up the stories; but though they were able to produce some more drawings, they could not remember more than the bare outlines of the tales. So it fell to Aidan Mackey to write a plausible version of the missing stories to make sense of the drawings.

The Sotheby's drawings, showing the characters of the stories, were upright postcard size; the others, the dramatic incidents, were double-sized. This determined the landscape format of the book, with double columns to allow for the character drawings to be inserted where appropriate.

Laughing Bull

Drawing by G. K. Chesterton from *Mr Chesterton comes to tea* (76)

TED HUGHES

Remains of Elmet

Photographs by Fay Godwin

RAINBOW PRESS · 1979

77

HENRY WILLIAMSON

A tribute by Ted Hughes, given at the Service of Thanksgiving at the Royal Parish Church of St Martin-in-the-Fields, 1 December 1977. Rainbow Press [1979].

200 copies on Zerkall mould-made paper, signed by Ted Hughes.   26 × 18.5 cm.   S.
Hand-set in 18pt Palatino. The frontispiece by Bill Thomson printed by The Stellar Press. Pamphlet-sewn at the Press in printed Fabriano Roma wrappers, in either Moretto (terra cotta) or Guido Reni (brown).

78

REMAINS OF ELMET

Ted Hughes, photographs by Fay Godwin. Rainbow Press, 1979.

110 copies on T. H. Saunders laid mould-made paper, signed by Ted Hughes.
28 × 21.5 cm.   Plus 70 copies on Barcham Green Charing hand-made paper, signed by Ted Hughes and Fay Godwin.   29 × 23 cm.   S.
Machine-set in 14pt Ehrhardt semi-bold, with display in Albertus light. The 4 photographs printed by duotone screenless offset lithography at The Stellar Press.
The ordinary edition bound by Weatherby Woolnough in quarter brown buckram with Aldine vine-leaf patterned paper sides, in a box; the special edition by W. T. Morrell in full treed calf, in a slip-case.

¶ The trade edition which this edition preceded was extensively illustrated with Fay Godwin's magnificent photographs. Ted Hughes and she had collaborated on the writing and picturing of the Calder valley, part of the old Yorkshire kingdom of Elmet. Sometimes poem suggested photograph, sometimes photograph poem. We could print only four photographs but were able to concentrate resources on them.

The Charing hand-made of the specials was some lovely old stock kept by Olwyn Hughes, which still had the strong gelatine-size crackle of the old hand-made papers. The photographs were printed on a matching smooth cartridge.

Treed (or tree) calf is, according to Carter's *ABC for book collectors*, 'a calf binding . . . the sides of which have been stained by the interaction of copperas and pearl-ash to a design resembling the graining of wood (or certain types of veneer on furniture) and then highly polished'. The effect was well suited to Hughes' grainy poetry.

79

THE BOOK OF JONAH

Taken from the Authorised Version of King James I, with engravings on wood by David Jones. Clover Hill Editions, Douglas Cleverdon, 1979.

300 copies on J. Green mould-made paper; plus 100 copies on Barcham Green RWS hand-made paper with an extra set of the engravings on japon; plus 10 copies on vellum with extra sets of the engravings on japon, hand-made paper and vellum. 28 × 19 cm. *W.* 60 sets of the engravings on japon issued separately.
Hand-set in 18pt Golden Cockerel roman. Title-page lettering by Will Carter. The engravings printed separately from the text, and in the case of the vellum copies printed on a hand-press by Ian Mortimer of IM Imprimit, London.
The 300 mould-made paper copies bound by the Scolar Press in quarter cloth, with patterned paper sides specially designed by Sebastian Carter; the two special editions bound by Sangorski and Sutcliffe: the 100 hand-made copies in quarter morocco with the same patterned paper and lettering, and with the separate set of engravings tucked into a pocket inside the back cover, in a slip-case; and the vellum copies bound in full morocco, with the separate sets contained in a matching portfolio, all in a slip-case.

¶ This, the eleventh Clover Hill Edition, was a re-issue of the Golden Cockerel Press edition of 1926 for which David Jones engraved the blocks. The original was set in Caslon, but it seemed logical for us to use the Golden Cockerel types, provided we could achieve the same final line in caps at the foot of page 11 – THE SEA CEASED FROM HER RAGING. By enlarging the format, and doing some tight spacing, we managed to do this, and it all fitted.

Wood-engraving by David Jones (reduced) from *The book of Jonah* (**79**)

80

THE SONG OF SONGS

Which is Solomon's, with prints by Michael Rothenstein. [Rampant Lions Press] 1979.

150 copies on Zerkall mould-made paper, signed by Michael Rothenstein, Shelley Rose and Sebastian Carter.   55×38 cm.   *S*.
Hand-set in 24pt Albertus light. Title-page lettering by Sebastian Carter. The prints on Crisbrook hand-made paper, printed by Shelley Rose at the artist's studio. Each print signed by the artist.
The folders loosely laid in a box made by John P. Gray, in red buckram with a screenprinted paper label.

¶ This edition was sponsored by the Sovereign American Arts Corporation through Eaton House Publishers, so that although technically it is a Rampant Lions publication, in effect it was fully subscribed in advance. It was by chance that Rothenstein's choice of text fitted perfectly the format already established, although he chose it simply as a text to illustrate: *The song* is divided into eight chapters of almost equal length, which we were able to fit neatly on our folders, with room to spare – in fact the type is leaded 24pts.

The prints show Rothenstein's development towards photographic techniques, and are virtuoso examples of screenprinting. They include much popular imagery: the 'eyes looking through the wall', for example, are those of John Travolta.

81

FROM GARDEN TO GALAXY

Original prints and text by J. G. Lubbock. Bertram Rota, London [1980].

80 copies on Barcham Green hand-made paper, signed by J. G. Lubbock.   28.5×20 cm.
W.
Machine-set in 16pt Bembo. Title-page lettering by Will Carter.
Bound by George Percival in full morocco, gold-blocked with a design by the artist on the front, in a slip-case covered in Aldine vine-leaf patterned paper.

¶ See note on 35.

82

THE DESERTED VILLAGE

Oliver Goldsmith, with two wood-engravings by Miriam Macgregor. Privately printed, 1980.

10 copies on Hodgkinson hand-made paper.   24.5 × 15.5 cm.   *S.*
Machine-set in 14pt Octavian.
Each copy to be bound by a different binder, mostly yet to be commissioned.

¶ Nigel Grimwood, who sponsored this book, makes a point of commissioning work from living craftsmen. In line with this policy, he is also asking different binders each to design and bind one of the ten copies.

He gave us a free hand in the choice of text, type, paper and illustrations, an unwonted freedom which proved rather daunting. We had seen Miriam Macgregor's wood-engravings done for the Whittington Press, and liked them: they seemed just the thing for the poem, and we asked her to engrave an opening and a tailpiece.

Wood-engraving by Miriam Macgregor from *The deserted village* (**82**)

74

Bindings

62

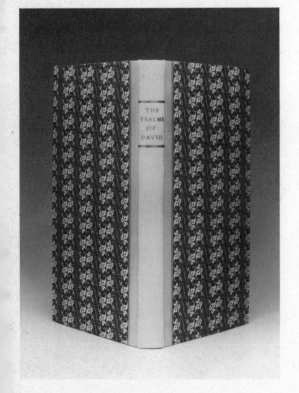

71

78

ANTHONY GROSS · AND THE　　RAMPANT LIONS PRESS · 1980

83　reduced

83

THE VERY RICH HOURS OF LE BOULVÉ

Written and illustrated with twenty-six etchings and engravings on copper by Anthony Gross, with a foreword by David Garnett. Printed and published by the Rampant Lions Press [1980].

120 copies on Arches mould-made paper, signed by Anthony Gross; plus 15 copies with an extra set of the engravings, each signed by Anthony Gross, and an original working drawing.   32.5×25 cm.   *W&S*.
Hand-set in 18pt Palatino. The plates printed by Mary West at the artist's studio.
The ordinary edition bound by John P. Gray in quarter brown morocco with buckram sides; the special edition by Sangorski and Sutcliffe in full brown morocco blocked on the front board with a bull design by Anthony Gross, with the extra material in a separate quarter morocco solander box. Both editions with endpapers of a patterned paper specially designed by Anthony Gross and Will Carter.

¶ Anthony Gross, with whom we had collaborated on the *Sixe idyllia* of Theocritus (45), approached us in 1978 with a view to publishing this celebration of the village in south-west France where he spends his summers, which he had written himself and proposed to illustrate with a large number of intaglio plates. His neighbour David Garnett had offered to write a foreword, which turned out to be the last piece published before his death. Gross' text describes the customs, characters and surroundings of his village, the quality of the local wine and the vendange, the food and the regional history; it is vivid, entertaining and frequently scandalous, so that we regretfully had to cut some parts for fear of legal reprisal.

In order to plan the book in the way demanded by the large number of plates, we retyped the entire manuscript line for line, taking the opportunity to do some tidying up and rearranging. We could then paste up the book page for page in typescript, enabling us to plan the falling of the illustrations in the best way possible. We could also set the first and last pages of a signature and print them together, without having to set all the intervening pages, which we could not do with our relatively meagre stock of type. The burden of this task, and of all the preparation of the book, was greatly eased by a gift from Anthony Gross of some wine from Charlie Verhaeghe's vineyard, which is described in the book.

The title-page presented some difficulties. The sight in Gross' studio of a wide landscape painting of the Le Boulvé countryside (similar to the one which won the Charles Wollaston Award at the Royal Academy Summer Exhibition later that year) suggested to us that we might have a double-page title spread with a landscape engraving on two plates right across it. Gross duly produced a lovely spread, but we spent a long time vainly trying to fit all the verbiage normally put on a title-page underneath it. Nothing looked right. We eventually sidestepped the problem by running the wording over several pages, from the half-title which gives the name of the book, through the double-page spread, which simply states the author, publisher and date, to the edition page following, which recapitulates in more detail. This film credit treatment of the prelims will probably be the despair of bibliographers, but seems to work well enough.

84

THEY FELL IN THE BATTLE

A roll of honour of the Battle of Britain, 10 July-31 October 1940. Royal Air Force
Museum [1980].

80 copies on Arches mould-made paper, signed by Prince Philip, Duke of Edinburgh,
Marshal of the Royal Air Force.   37.5 × 26 cm.   *W.*
Hand-set in 36pt and 24pt Walbaum. Printed in Air Force blue. Title-page blocked in gold.
Bound by W. T. Morrell in full goatskin dyed Air Force blue, with the title hand-tooled
on the spine with tools designed specially at the Press.

¶ This was commissioned to commemorate the 40th anniversary of the Battle of Britain.
From a practical point of view it was ideal for our small workshop. Compositor and press-
man took exactly the same time to set and to print one sheet, so in fact only the two sheets
actually being worked on had to be in type at the same time. There were no proofs.

85

DIALOGUE OVER A OUIJA BOARD

A verse dialogue. Sylvia Plath, with a drawing by Leonard Baskin. Rainbow Press, 1981.

140 copies on Barcham Green Canterbury hand-made paper.   25 × 14.5 cm.   *S.*
Hand-set in 18pt Arrighi-Vicenza. Title-page lettering by Sebastian Carter.
Bound by Alan Winstanley in limp vellum.

¶ The choice of the type, which was made for simple love of it, entailed one difficulty:
parts of the text which are questions put by the characters to the ouija board were underlined, and as Arrighi-Vicenza is an italic type with no true related roman, some other way
of distinguishing these parts had to be devised. We decided to print them in a second
colour, which was a complicated and extravagant solution, but fun to do once in a while.

86

LAPIDARIA OCTAVA

[Edited by John Sparrow, 1981]

200 copies on T. H. Saunders Drawing mould-made paper.   25 × 19 cm.   *S.*
The inscriptions hand-set in 12pt Perpetua titling, the notes in 16pt Bembo.
Bound square-back at the Press, with printed wrappers.

¶ The series of collections of Latin inscriptions edited by John Sparrow, formerly Warden of All Souls and an author and editor of Rampant Lions books of long standing (see 11 and 64), was begun in 1943. The first six had been printed at the Cambridge University Press to Stanley Morison's design. A feature of all of them had been the handsome title-pieces and colophons engraved in wood by Reynolds Stone. We took over number seven in 1975, retaining Morison's design (with reservations: it was clear that the great man had never himself tried to set a text abounding in long proper names in 16pt type on a measure as short as 26 ems) and (with more enthusiasm) Reynolds' two new blocks, and were delighted by Sparrow's rendering of our Press name as 'officina quae a leonibus erectis nomen ducit'.

By 1981, when we came to print this volume, Reynolds Stone had died. We therefore made line-blocks from clean pulls taken from Golden Cockerel titling, which kept the style as closely as possible.

87

THE ENGRAVINGS OF DAVID JONES
A survey by Douglas Cleverdon. Clover Hill Editions, London, 1981.

260 copies on vélin d'Arches mould-made paper; plus 105 copies on Barcham Green hand-made paper watermarked *Clover Hill*, with a portfolio containing an extra set of the plates on japon and prints of 9 copper-engravings and 1 dry-point from the original copper-plates; plus 6 copies on vellum with a solander box containing extra sets of the plates, and prints of 9 copper-engravings and 1 dry-point, on japon, hand-made paper and vellum.   31.5×24.5 cm.   *W&S*.
75 sets of the plates, and prints from the copper-plates, also issued separately, matching the sets issued with the hand-made paper edition.
The text machine-set in 13pt Bembo. The bulk of the 96 plates printed from the original wood-blocks but, where lost, reproduced by offset lithography at the Senecio Press by Adrian Lack. The intaglio subjects reproduced in the plates by half-tones, only 10 being printed from the copper-plates in the extra sets. The intaglio printing by L'Atelier Georges Leblanc in Paris and by Bernard Cook in London.
The ordinary edition: early copies bound by the Scolar Press in buff buckram with morocco labels; later copies by Smith Settle in green buckram; the hand-made paper edition by Sangorski and Sutcliffe in quarter morocco; and the vellum edition also by Sangorski and Sutcliffe in full morocco.

¶ This, the twelfth Clover Hill Edition, marks another high point in Douglas Cleverdon's championship of the work of David Jones, which has ranged from the commissioning of the *Ancient mariner* engravings to his radio adaptations of *In parenthesis* and *The anathemata*. (See also 24, 27, 46, 70, and 79.) Here, as well as the survey, which describes Jones' engraved work in detail, there are lists of engravings and of books and ephemera containing engravings. As for the plates, though not all could be printed from the original blocks

Wood-engraving by David Jones (reduced) from *The engravings of David Jones* (87)

because they had been lost, it is most unlikely that such a collection will ever again be assembled for printing.

David Jones began to engrave on wood in 1921 under the guidance of Eric Gill at the community at Ditchling. He developed quickly, moved with Gill to Capel-y-ffin, and began to engrave on copper in 1925. But in 1933 he suffered a nervous breakdown and made no more prints, turning thereafter to watercolour and to writing. In the short space of time that he was engraving, he produced a remarkable amount of work, of great variety; some witty, some mystical; some boldly cut, some delicately shaded; some simple to print, some virtually impossible. Although he never attained, particularly in wood, the greatest technical mastery in the conventional sense, his prints are nearly always distinguished by their excellence of design, personal commitment and absolute individuality. At their peak, in the *Deluge* and *Ancient mariner* sets, they are major achievements of book illustration.

This was the most massive operation we had undertaken so far. The sheer bulk of paper to be handled tested our resources to the full, and all was done without anything getting lost. Unlike 70 and 79 we printed all the vellum letterpress ourselves. Vellum is very much a two-sided material – one side being next to the flesh of the animal, and therefore smooth, and the other side with the hairs already beginning to grow outwards and with a consequently rougher surface. To overcome this we printed all the engravings on single sheets, on the smooth side of the skin only. The introductory text was printed both sides in the usual way, being run-on from the paper editions.

88

CARTER'S CAPS

An alphabet of capital letters cut by Will Carter and printed from the wood, with commentary. Rampant Lions Press [1982].

Unlimited edition on Abbey Mill autumn brown antique laid paper.   20.5 × 22.5 cm.   *W.*
Machine-set in 14pt Octavian, with Dartmouth display. The letters printed in white, within a sepia border.
Bound square back with printed covers.

¶ The idea for this book dates back to one of the displays in *Portfolio two* (59) which shows the capital letters QU cut on teak veneer chip-board and printed from the wood. The success of this, and the simplicity of its production, encouraged us to create something worthwhile and to complete the alphabet. A technique of this kind has the great advantage of being straight from the creator's tool – in this case his knife – warts and all. A display of the actual blocks is included in the letter-cutting section of the exhibition (94).

89

PORTFOLIO THREE

A further collection of resettings, specimen settings and display settings printed by Will and Sebastian Carter at the Rampant Lions Press, Cambridge, England, 1982.

About 500 copies on various papers.   21.5 × 28 cm.   *W&S.*
25 items, in a wide variety of settings.
Portfolio of green card made at the Press.

¶ See also 31 and 59.

90   Jobbing printing

Although this exhibition is mostly of books, nevertheless, when the Press began its life as a full-time workshop, it earned its living by jobbing printing (letterheadings, business cards, invitations, menus, posters and the like). Jobbing work remains of great importance to us, even if the printing of books has come to take up an increasing amount of our time. Many small presses despise, or resist, this kind of work, which is thought to be mundane, tedious and distracting. Sometimes it is, but the compensating advantages are many. We always design the jobs ourselves, and these daily design problems help to keep our creative muscles in good trim, whereas with bookwork we do the layouts at the start, and for months afterwards we just carry out the designs. There are also the advantages of trying out ideas on a small scale, of seeing the results quickly, and, not least, of satisfying a constant social need.

The conviction of the Press at the outset was that there was a demand for well-designed jobbing printing which was not being met. Small printers, by and large, could not design, and larger ones could not be bothered with small jobs; while to employ a free-lance designer would mean fees out of proportion to the size of the job. What was wanted was a printer who designed his work *as a matter of course* and not, as is too often the case, as a separate service, and it was that need that the Press set out to satisfy.

Events showed the conviction well-founded and the Press has never lacked orders. The small selection shown in the exhibition includes exhibition cards, letterheadings, business cards, menus and invitations.

91   Book design

From time to time we are asked by publishers to design books for other printers to print. We accept these commissions gladly, since it gives us a chance to do something on a larger scale than our small workshop permits.

Nevertheless, the way of working is very different from our own printing. Working by ourselves, we rarely make finished layouts unless it be to persuade a client to accept a design without the trouble of setting it: normally we rely on scrawls so schematic they would be unintelligible to anyone else, or we design straight into type. We can then move the setting around until we are satisfied. But in designing for others, we bear in mind that we could not ask someone else to do on command the amount of correction that we would ourselves do voluntarily to get the job right. There is an ethical distinction as well as a common-sense one. Francis Meynell, the great director of the Nonesuch Press, having had forty revised proofs for a title-page from the Cambridge University Press, suggested to Walter Lewis that it might be amusing to make them into an instructive book. Lewis, who

did not mince his words, replied that it would do Meynell's reputation more harm than good. For our part, we sympathise with both points of view, both the desire for the best, and the dislike of messing around. Particularly in outside design, but also in our own work, we try to get it right, or very nearly right, first time.

These considerations reinforce our preference for simplicity. Simplicity is the chief aim of the typographer, both in the appearance of what he does, and in the means used to get that appearance. When we print for ourselves, the task is easy; but the temptation before the designer working for other printers is to justify his existence by too much activity – in other words, to over-design. We hope that our experience of the practical end of the process helps us to avoid this.

The books shown are:

The Swiss family Robinson, illustrated by David Gentleman, published by the Limited Editions Club, 1963; printed by W. S. Cowell Ltd, designed by Will Carter.

Saint Thomas Aquinas, illustrated by Reynolds Stone, published by the Limited Editions Club, 1969; printed by W. & J. Mackay Ltd, designed by Will Carter.

The riddle of the sands, illustrated by John O'Connor, published by the Imprint Society, 1971; printed by W. S. Cowell Ltd, designed by Will Carter.

The stained glass of William Morris and his circle, published by Yale University Press, 1974-5; printed by the Curwen Press (Vol.1) and Aberdeen University Press (Vol.2), designed by Sebastian Carter.

The Officina Bodoni, published by The British Library, 1978; printed by the Curwen Press, designed by Sebastian Carter.

The Rothschild family tree, 1981; printed by The Stellar Press, designed by Sebastian Carter. (The standard version was folded like a map between cloth covers; the framed version shown on the wall was kindly lent by Lord Rothschild.)

In addition to books we also design a considerable number of book-jackets; some of them are are shown in frames on the wall.

For some of the books we have printed (see 67, 71, 79, and 83) we have designed patterned papers for the bindings. These were printed by other printers lithographically or by silk-screen to get an adequate sheet size. In 1977 we decided to issue four designs in three colours each, for other binders as well as for our own use. One of these was Morris' Willow design which we had used for *Cupid and Psyche*, one was the Aldine vine-leaf designed by Sebastian Carter for *The psalms*, and the other two, Ripple and Kelmscott flower from the same designer, were new.

92 Calligraphy

Early days at Cambridge, from 1934 onwards, were very much taken up with calligraphy. Close contact with the Edward Johnston school was a most powerful influence, and with Sydney Cockerell in charge at the Fitzwilliam Museum, the glamour and excitement of it all seemed very close. Constant practice was the order of the day. A few weeks spent in Cologne during school holidays in about 1928 with a Frau Hermanny, who had been a close friend of Rudolf Koch when she had lived at Offenbach, led to contact being made with Koch's son Paul in 1938. His letters were written in a fluent uncial hand. During my annual holiday that year I went over to Frankfurt and worked in the Haus zum Fürsteneck, in the old part of the city (obliterated during the last war), where Paul Koch had his work-shop and where printing, punch-cutting and calligraphy were apparently everybody's business. Hermann Zapf was one of the young men working there, and I have a copy of the book of songs he was working on at that time. He has been for me one of the most formative influences. Berthold Wolpe and Fritz Kredel had also been deeply involved in the Koch circle before having to flee the country – Wolpe to England and Kredel to America.

This experience gave great impetus to my enthusiasm for calligraphy, with now a strong emphasis on black-letter. In due course I came to make practical use of all this, in the design of book-jackets, title-page lettering, book labels and type-design (see 93). Title-page lettering is shown in the books themselves, and several frames in this exhibition contain examples of jackets and book labels, using straight untouched pen calligraphy and also built-up lettering. It must be obvious that the built-up forms go straight back to the pen letter, and in fact I often trace over and elaborate on basic pen forms.   WC

93 Type design

In the note on 'Calligraphy', above, the influence of the Koch school, with its heavy emphasis on 'gotisch' or black-letter, is sharply underlined, and during my short stay in the workshop at Frankfurt I learned the rudiments of punch-cutting.

One of the results of this was a letter-form written with a broad pen which was excellent for things like book-jackets (A) and proved adaptable for both weight and width. Tentative approaches were made to Monotype in the person of Stanley Morison, and the result was Klang, series 593, which appeared in time for IPEX in 1955 (B). Second thoughts made me feel that the design could have been slightly bolder and would benefit from a closer fit, so Stephenson Blake were approached with the idea of a companion bold, and a trial drawing was made (C). For some reason the result was a failure and was nothing like what was intended (D).

84

The quick

Adam's Bearded Creator Designed Eve For Getting Him

brown fox

Imparadised, Judging Knowledge Less Motivational.

jumps over

Nonetheless, Our Parents Quickly Relished Sin, Though

the lazy dog

Unusually Vestured When eXpecting Yahveh's Zetetic.

36pt Klang and 14pt Octavian; Monotype leaf border No. 1271-3; all designed by Will Carter
(Octavian with David Kindersley).

Shortly after this, the University Press at Cambridge suggested that I worked on a Greek type in collaboration with the then Professor of Greek, Denys Page, and a good deal of work was done on this. A workable lower case was evolved (E), and capitals with a strong Klang flavour (F). But unfortunately somewhere along the line the project foundered.

During this period my friendship with David Kindersley led to many discussions about the roman alphabet, and the shortcomings of some printers' types. By 1955 we had decided that we could design a new roman with a completely fresh approach, but within the established framework. Monotype were encouraging. The University Press was also encouraging because it was at that time seeking, and failing to find, a suitable type for a Folio Bible, on the lines of the great Bruce Rogers Bible from Oxford. The economy, and the weight, of our design might be the answer. The type, at my brother's suggestion, was called Octavian, and was initially cut as series 603 in 14pt only (G). Because of this limitation the trade was unwilling to take it up and the Rampant Lions Press has on the whole been its main user, a number of our books having been set in it. Unfortunately, for economic reasons, the Folio Bible project had to be abandoned. But it is pleasant to record that the type was re-issued in Monophoto in 1979, incorporating a number of design afterthoughts, and it is now generally available (H).

Shortly after this, a commission from Dartmouth College, at Hanover, in New Hampshire, for a series of dedicatory plaques carved on teak for the new arts complex, Hopkins Center, led to the development of another alphabet. This had to be suitable not only for incised carving but for all the public notices around the building. Not surprisingly it became known as Dartmouth and was taken up by Letraset (I). It has proved to be the backbone of most of the letter-cutting done in this workshop – a strong and highly adaptable letter form (see also 88). It also, and quite obviously, comes from the same stable as Octavian, which is not surprising since it was David Kindersley who was the strongest influence on my early letter-cutting.   WC

In the exhibition are shown:

A. A selection of book-jackets showing early versions of Klang.

B. Working drawings and the design principles of Klang.

C. Enlarged trials of Klang bold.

D. Stephenson Blake's type-specimen of Klang bold.

E. Enlarged trials of Greek lower-case.

F. Enlarged trials of Greek capitals.

G. Working drawings of Octavian.

H. Monotype specimen of Monophoto Octavian.

I. Sheets of Letraset Dartmouth.

86

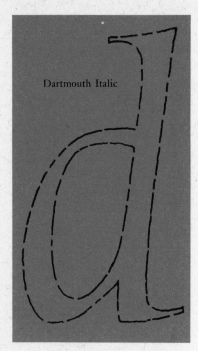
Dartmouth Italic

ABCDEF GHIJKLM NOPQURS TVWXYZ

Dartmouth Titling

ΑΒΓΔΕΖΗΘΙΚ
αβγδεζηθικλ
ΛΝΜΞΟΠΡΣ
μνξοπρσϛϛτυ
ΤΥΦΧΨΩ
φχψωϝ

Greek

ABCDEFGHIJ
abcdefghijkl
KLMNOPQRST
mnopqrst
UVWXY&Z
uvwxyz
1234567890

Klang Bold

Λίγξε βιὸς νευρὴ δὲ μέγ᾽ ἴαχεν ἆλτο δ᾽ὀιστός
ὀιστός Αἶψα Πανομφαίωι Ζηνὶ ῥέζεϲκε θυηλάς.

93 Type design

IN LOVING MEMORY OF
MARY ELIZABETH·
COUNTESS OF STRAFFORD

21 MAY 1863 – 2 OCTOBER 1951

SIR ALLEN LANE
COMPANION OF HONOUR
Publisher
1902   1970

94 A selection of carvings, and opposite

THE EDINBURGH BUILDING
opened by
Her Majesty The Queen
on the 29th May 1981, and named in honour of
The Chancellor of the University of Cambridge
His Royal Highness
The Prince Philip, Duke of Edinburgh

DAVID ROBINSON
who founded this College and inspired the building of this Chapel
was born in Cambridge 13 April 1904, the third of nine children.
On leaving school at fifteen, he worked in his father's bicycle business
later moving into the motor trade, and later still to the television industry.
In 1922 he married Mabel Alice Baccus who had been born into a family of
stonemasons long established in the Cambridgeshire village of Histon.

In memory of
Herbrand Edward Dundonald
Brassey Sackville
9th Earl De La Warr PC GBE

1900-1976

WWWS
SSWW
SWSS
WW
SWWS

94   Letter-cutting

From a fascination for letters of all kinds – calligraphic and engraved, and printed from metal types – it is a short step to one of the most basic of all methods of recording letters, by cutting them on stone. No one young during the great years of Eric Gill's prominence could help being caught up in the excitement of his incised lettering, and I was encouraged by my brother to try my hand at lettering on wood. The first job I ever did, in 1936, was a round breadboard for Brooke Crutchley, made of beech wood and a very amateur job. But I am glad to report that it is still in daily use after forty-six years, and can be seen in this exhibition alongside another board done for this occasion to show the improvement.

As a point of purely technical interest, the usual method for incising letters on wood is to use a series of chisels of various shapes and curves. For some reason I found that it suited my hand better to use a knife, a short-bladed tool with the cutting edge at an angle to give it a slicing action. In Frankfurt in 1938 I bought a Solingen steel knife, made for making wood-cuts on the plank, and I use it to this day. Since then I have discovered that this way of cutting letters and decoration on wood is extensively used in the Bavarian Alps and in Switzerland. The method gives one great freedom of movement and very fine lines can be cut. It is also extremely fast.

When I met David Kindersley in 1948 I felt that here was the opportunity to learn how to do the same work on stone, for he had been a pupil of Gill's and was at that time teaching a class one evening a week at what was then the Cambridge School of Art. I blush to recall that, with the careless abandon of the beginner, I undertook my first job only a few months after cutting my first letters on slate. This was the war memorial at Magdalene College, Cambridge, carried out to Reynolds Stone's overall design.

All sorts of work came into the workshop, and it is interesting to note how much the handling of type and the setting out of carved inscriptions came to influence each other. The letter-spacing of printer's caps in particular has reached a fine point of sensitivity as a result of this cross-fertilisation. There is endless scope for experiment in the preparation of surfaces and the colouring of letters. One experiment we carried out recently has resulted in the Siena lady which is featured in the exhibition. This was a copy of the Hellespontine Sybil in the floor of Siena Cathedral, which is the work of Neroccio di Landi and dates from 1483.   WC

In the exhibition are shown:

Crutchley breadboard: untreated beech. 31 cm. diameter. Lent by Brooke and Diana Crutchley.

'This gallery...': mahogany, lettering coloured with ink. For Eton College, unused because the date was changed.   33 × 167.5 cm.

'The Rampant Lions Press': parana pine, coloured with gouache.   21 × 163.5 cm.

Arabic inscription: lime coloured with gouache.   45.5 × 112 cm.   Lent by Colin Franklin.

Hebrew grace: plain wood with lettering stained.   10 × 213 cm.

Alphabet: lime coloured with gouache.   30 × 38 cm.

'Colin and Shamsi' breadboard: walnut.   35.5 cm. diameter.

'Carter's caps': the blocks from which 88 was printed.

'Siena': black granite sandblasted and filled.   58.5 × 33 cm.

The inscriptions at each end of the Adeane Gallery in which this exhibition is shown:
lime coloured with gouache.

Checklist of books printed at The Rampant Lions Press

For the purposes of this checklist, a book is anything of more than four pages, sewn, stapled, glued, or loose. The short titles are listed alphabetically under years; the semi-bold figures in parentheses after books refer to entries in the catalogue.

Abbreviations: RLP – Rampant Lions Press; PP – privately printed; nd – no date.

1934
A preface, John Baskerville, RLP (1).

1936
A Spanish triptych, Robert Nichols, RLP (2).

1937
A prayer, RLP (3).
Memorandoms by James Martin, RLP (4).
The song of Solomon, illus. Harry Hicken, RLP (5).

1938
Clerihews, RLP (6).
Irish bulls, P. Grierson, RLP.

1939
Sonnets from the Portuguese, Elizabeth Barrett Browning, RLP (7).

1941
Ecclesiastes, RLP (8).

1946
Clerihews (2nd edition), RLP (6).
The last chapter of Urne buriall, Thomas Browne, illus. John Piper, RLP (9).

1947
Youth, Arnold Moon, RLP.

1951
Emblems of experience, Siegfried Sassoon, RLP (10).
Lucretilis, William Cory, RLP (11).

1953
Collects and prayers in wartime, Barrett Parker, PP.
Floreat bibliomania, A. N. L. Munby, PP.

1954
Garland of flower verses, Elliott Howes, PP (nd: approx date).
Italic handwriting, ed. Blunt and Carter, Newman Neame (12).
The Shakespearian touch, T. S. Carter, RLP.

1955
Hymnus in nativitate Christi, RLP (nd: approx date).
Seven poems in pattern, John Farrow, RLP (13).
William Belmont Parker, Barrett Parker, PP.
Wood engravings past and present, RLP.

1956
The poet, C. Day Lewis, RLP.
The song of Deborah and Barak, RLP (14).

1957
Memorial day address, August Heckscher, PP.
The pilgrimage, Walter Raleigh, RLP.
Three tributes to Sir Geoffrey Keynes, PP.

1958
The food of love, Stephen Bedford, RLP.

1959
Read between the lines, J.P., PP.
The first ten, RLP (15).
William Johnson Cory, [John Carter], PP.

1960
A song to David, Christopher Smart, RLP (16).
Poems from Panmure House, Ninth of May.
Two ballads of the muse, Robin Skelton, PP.

1961
A letter to John Fairfax-Ross, [Christopher Stone], PP.
Kubla Khan, Samuel Taylor Coleridge, RLP (17).
Lobsters, Alexis Lykiard, RLP (18).
Poems, Sir William Jones, RLP.
Poems and songs of Sir Robert Ayton, Ninth of May.
Poems and verses, Russell Brain, PP.
The bright cloud, Christopher Lee, PP.
The ceremony of the lilies and roses, PP.
The hospital of St John in Jerusalem, Ruby Cromer, PP.
The pen of my aunt, Glyn Daniel, PP (19).

1962

Double Crown Club roll of members, PP (20).
Tact in typographical design, Stanley Morison, Monotype Corporation (21).
The Thailand refinery, Shell Petroleum.
The Thrissil, the rois and the flour-de-lys, Ninth of May (22).

1963

Institute of Petroleum, Jubilee dinner, PP.
Visions of element, Eric Schroeder, PP.

1964

Cory's 'Lucretilis', F. J. Lelièvre, RLP (23).
The rime of the ancient mariner, Samuel Taylor Coleridge, illus. David Jones, Clover Hill Editions (24).
Versions and diversions, D. S. Macnutt, PP.
Wood-engravings by Humphry Trevelyan, PP.

1965

Sarah, PP (25).
Oxford chicken pie, Glyn Daniel, PP (26).
The fatigue, David Jones, PP (27).
The paper makers craft, Oliver Bayldon, Twelve by Eight Press (28).
Translations from the Greek anthology, David M. Mitchell, RLP.
Weeds and wild flowers, Armida Maria-Theresa Colt, Two-Horse Press (29).

1966

Antoinette Esher, PP.
Holy communion, PP (two edns, for Trinity College and Churchill College; nd: approx date).
The marsh picnic, Iris Tree, RLP.

1967

Geoffrey Langdon Keynes/Margaret Elizabeth Darwin, PP.
Henry James in Cambridge, Geoffrey Keynes, Heffers (30).
Portfolio one, RLP (31).
Stephen versus Gladstone, Virginia Woolf, PP.
The elegies of a glass Adonis, C. A. Trypanis, Clover Hill Editions (32).

1968

Engraved in the wood, George Mackley, Two-Horse Press (33).
Sir Alan Barlow, Lady Sharp, PP.
The mountains, R. S. Thomas, illus. John Piper and Reynolds Stone, Clover Hill Editions (34).
The narrow ledge, Kate Playfair, PP.

1969

Aspects of art and science, J. G. Lubbock, Twelve by Eight Press (35).
Directives aux présidents et comités nationaux, Congrès mondiaux du pétrole, PP (English edn also printed).

Making of the far-eastern agreement at Yalta, J. A. Siracusa, PP.
Por los caminos del dia, Manuel Joglar Cacho, illus. J. A. Torres Martino, PP.
The Agamemnon of Aeschylus, Raymond Postgate, RLP (36).

1970

Catalogue of books and manuscripts by Rupert Brooke, John Schroder, RLP (37).
Lessons of the war, Henry Reed, Clover Hill Editions (38).
Old Rectory : the prologue, Martyn Skinner, RLP (39).
Shades, David Piper, Clover Hill Editions (40).
Tributes to Allen Lane, PP (41).
With love and eighty candles for M.E.K., PP (42).

1971

A list of the writings of H. M. Chadwick and N. K. Chadwick, Isabel Henderson, PP.
Discretionary settlement, PP.
Do you know your way through the Whitehall maze?, D. A. Wilson, PP.
Lyonnesse, Sylvia Plath, Rainbow Press (43).
Mark Pryor, PP.
Reflections from the sea, J. G. Lubbock, Twelve by Eight Press (44).
Sixe idyllia, Theocritus, illus. Anthony Gross, Clover Hill Editions (45).
The adversaries, Mary Lascelles, RLP.

1972

An introduction to 'The rime of the ancient mariner', David Jones, Clover Hill Editions (46).
In fair Verona, Nicolas Barker, PP (designed by Hans Schmoller) (47).
Kerdruc notebook, Michael Collie, RLP (48).
King Henry VI and the royal foundations, John Saltmarsh, PP.
Poems 1972, Barrett Parker, PP.
Seed leaves, Richard Wilbur, illus. Charles Wadsworth, Godine (49).
Suns and moons, Michael Rothenstein, RLP (50).
The north, Samuel Beckett, illus. Avigdor Arikha, Enitharmon Press (51).
The quest of Gilgamesh, D. G. Bridson, illus. Michael Ayrton, RLP (52).
Verses, Jasper Rootham, PP.

1973

Areopagitica, John Milton, Deighton, Bell (53).
Book-collecting in the 1930s, A. N. L. Munby, PP (54).
Directives et instructions générales pour le 9è congrès, Congrés mondiaux du pétrole, PP (English edn also printed).
First principles of typography in the 1970s, Sebastian Carter, Bowaters (55).
Freedom medals, American Express.
King Orphius and Sir Colling, Ninth of May.

Mandrakes, Thom Gunn, Rainbow Press (56).
Old Rectory : the session, Martyn Skinner, RLP (39).
Pursuit, Sylvia Plath, Rainbow Press (designed by Leonard Baskin).
Spring summer autumn winter, Ted Hughes, Rainbow Press (57).

1974
Charles II to Lord Taaffe, ed. Timothy Crist, RLP.
Light and the mind's eye, J. G. Lubbock, Rota (58).
Portfolio two, RLP (59).
Seven colours, Edward Lucie-Smith, illus. Michael Rothenstein, RLP (60).
Specimen printed on the original Kelmscott Press watermarked paper, RLP (61).
The story of Cupid and Psyche, William Morris, illus. Edward Burne-Jones and Morris, Clover Hill Editions (62).

1975
Eine kleine Nachtmusik in Miami, Vadim Hammer, PP.
John Waynflete Carter, PP.
Lapidaria septima, John Sparrow, PP.
Poems, John Hancock, PP.
Root and sky, Christopher Fry, illus. Charles Wadsworth, RLP (63).
Santa Maria della Salute, John Sparrow, illus. John Piper, RLP (64).
Tibullus : elegies, Guy Lee, PP.

1976
Earth-moon, Ted Hughes, Rainbow Press (65).
The bristle cone pine, Sheila Cudahy, Harcourt Brace Jovanovitch/Harvill Press.
The Cambridge Christmas books, Brooke Crutchley, PP (66).
The rime of the ancient mariner, Samuel Taylor Coleridge, illus. Patrick Procktor, Editions Alecto (67).

1977
A song of the Great Eastern Railway, T. H. Cobb, PP.
Emmanuel College chapel, Frank Stubbings, PP.
India love poems, Tambimuttu, Paradine (68).
Now comes the light, Robert Brittain, PP.
Perceptions of the earth, J. G. Lubbock, Rota (69).
The Chester play of the deluge, illus. David Jones, Clover Hill Editions (70).
The Crafts Study Centre, PP.
The history of the horn-book, Leslie Shepard, Broad-sheet King.
The principal benefactors of Emmanuel College, PP.
The psalms of David, Deighton, Bell (71).
The Sobieski hours, Eleanor Spencer, Roxburghe Club (72).
Time is undone, Lucy M. Boston, PP (73).

1978
Adam and the sacred nine, Ted Hughes, Rainbow Press.
A questionnaire for God, W. A. Rathkey, PP.
Edward Thomas, illus. Arthur Neal, Stevens (74).
Moortown elegies, Ted Hughes, Rainbow Press (75).
Mr Chesterton comes to tea, Aidan Mackey, Vintage Publications (76).
Old Rectory : the epilogue, Martyn Skinner, RLP (39).
The owl window, Rosemary Lyttleton, PP.
Washington winter [Armida Colt], PP.

1979
Henry Williamson, Ted Hughes, Rainbow Press (77).
Little Things, Pamela Bruce, PP.
Remains of Elmet, Ted Hughes, Rainbow Press (78).
Robert Hill, PP.
Terminal rhyme, Ralph Grant, illus. Zelda Nolte, Hobson Gallery.
The book of Jonah, illus. David Jones, Clover Hill Editions (79).
The red raku tea bowl, Vadim Hammer, PP.
The song of songs, illus. Michael Rothenstein, RLP (80).

1980
A single man, Christopher Isherwood, Land Press.
Collected poems, J. M. de Navarro, PP.
Four Latin poems, Peter Davidson, illus. Alan Powers, PP.
From garden to galaxy, J. G. Lubbock, Rota (81).
The deserted village, Oliver Goldsmith, illus Miriam Macgregor, PP (82).
The very rich hours of Le Boulvé, Anthony Gross, RLP (83).
They fell in the battle, Royal Air Force (84).

1981
Dialogue over a ouija board, Sylvia Plath, illus. Leonard Baskin, Rainbow Press (85).
Edward Malins, Walter Kaiser, PP.
For Stanley William Hayter, Oxford Gallery, PP.
Lapidaria octava, John Sparrow, PP (86).
The English language, G. M. Trevelyan, PP (designed by Abe Lerner).
The engravings of David Jones, Douglas Cleverdon, Clover Hill Editions (87).

1982
Carter's caps, Will Carter, RLP (88).
Portfolio three, RLP (89).

Rampant Lions Press device drawn by John Buckland Wright

Catalogue of an exhibition at
the Fitzwilliam Museum, Cambridge   11 May - 27 June 1982

With a foreword by the Director of the Fitzwilliam Museum
and an introduction by Brooke Crutchley

The device on the cover was drawn specially for the exhibition by Berthold Wolpe.

ISBN 0 902591 12 6